THE DEVIL

KNOWS

WHAT YOU LIKE

For information contact:

Front Porch Press
4621 Foreland Place
Orlando, FLA 32812

FIRST EDITION
ISBN: **978-0-9790725-1-2**

Printed in the USA

Contact Porter at eric@finallyfit.net

A BITE of THE BAIT

AIN'T WORTH THE PAIN OF THE HOOK.

GOING THE DISTANCE WITH ADDICTION

G. PORTER FREEMAN

To Linda
Chapter 1 page 33 —
We agree!

Arthur Sherman

Dedication

To every woman I have ever known, I'm sorry…… probably!

G. Porter Freeman III

"Since 1949"

The Real Dedication

I try to read as much as I can. Often there are two or three books waiting and on occasion, I might try and read two at the same time. There are just too many good books and not enough time. That's probably true about a lot of things. I remember a girl telling me, "The spirit is willing, but the timetable is a tad weak." She's been gone a long time now, but I still have my books.

One thing I always read is the Dedication. This is the part of the book where the author gets to thank or, at the very least, recognize someone or a group of people who have had an impact on their life. It can be funny or sad or whatever the writer wants it to be. You will better understand when you write your book. I look forward to reading it.

None of the following candidates asked me to be included in this list of dedications. Something tells me NOT all of them would agree with me on several subjects, nor the way I think. Nobody would expect that. Some of them might even disagree with me on a few points. That's just fine, I expect it. Still, I worked hard on this book and spent a lot of time (62 years) getting it together and because I have so much respect for all of them, I give them the credit... not the blame, and there is going to be plenty of that! Remember, these are my ideas, not theirs.

Here are some candidates in no particular order. They each have touched my life and in some way helped me grow, or at least stay out of jail. Some passed through quickly and others seem to have been here forever.

My pal Eric Shrieves has been here since 1974. He is a part of everything positive I do and most of what I have accomplished. Thank you, Eric; I couldn't have made it without you. If the good reader is real unhealthy and honestly wants to improve his or her health and Life, look Eric up. He isn't hard to find; he's in the phonebook in Orlando, and he's on the Web. He has the answers; all you have to do is be willing to do the work.

To my pal Joey Vincent, the guy on the cover of this book; in my darkest hour, he very calmly explained the situation, diagnosed the problem, and we discovered it was me! What a wakeup call that was; I was addicted and it was me causing the addiction.... WOW! I owe Joey a debt I can never repay.

I don't get to talk to these ladies as often as I would like to but knowing they are there is priceless. I would not trade their friendship for all the gold in Ft. Knox. Lisa Cashi has been as dear a friend as Eric and Joey. I was honored to perform her marriage a long time ago, and years later, I flew back to America from South Africa to bury her husband. They had a long and loving marriage, but he got sick and unfortunately passed away. Something tells me she would have flown to South Africa to help me. I know she would have. Thank you, Lisa; it is a one-of-a-kind friendship. Let's talk again soon.

Couldn't write this book without thanking Julie Whitt, but I have to do it in a prayer. Julie is in heaven with Jesus and nothing I write about her will do her justice. I hope to see her again some bright and shining day. When I get to heaven, I hope to write her a speeding ticket and she will bat her eyes at me and talk her way out of it and we will laugh and laugh and laugh. You ought to look her up on the Internet and while you're at it, look up Jared Horomona from New Zealand. They changed my Life.

Maybe I will dedicate it to Suzanne Klein, Bill Phillips mother... I moved to Golden, Colorado, and her and I developed a great friendship. I bet she is laughing right this minute reading this. Thank you, Mrs. Klein... you made me feel at home.

Let me publicly ask every teacher I had in public school to forgive me. I am so sorry they got stuck with me for nine months out of the year. I am very sorry I was so lost and such an airhead back then. They tried to set me straight, and I am sure I drove some of them to drink. So, from Mrs. Bergeron in the first grade at Houghton Elementary in 1955 to Coach Williams at Richmond Academy in 1968, I promise to do better when we meet at the big chalkboard in the sky.

The more I write the more people who come to mind. There are two fellows in Louisville, Kentucky, whom I immediately think of: Maj. Kelly Jones from the Metro Police and Capt. Matt Keith from the Jeffersontown Fire Department. If there is a picture of "Class" in the dictionary, it should be of them. It's so much more about what they do behind the scenes than what they do in public. Yes, they have both dedicated 20-plus years of their lives to the service of the citizens of Louisville, and that alone stands pretty high… but, the hours without end that they dedicate to the children's hospital and the fundraisers they do each year, asking nothing in return, it's beyond belief. I have to tell you that to say they are friends of mine is an honor. Thank you both seems so little compared to what you give. If the readers ever get to Kentucky, look them up, you will see what I mean.

Did I mention Ken Young and Nick Boswell? I don't think I did. Here are two young men cut from the same cloth. Ken is a Gunnery Sergeant (just got the news, he has been selected for First Sergeant) in the Marine Corps, and Nick is on the Papillion, Nebraska, Police Department. Both of them absolutely turned their lives around 100 percent as far as their health and fitness is concerned. They were doing well, but they both admitted to themselves, they could be doing great and they did. After knocking out a couple of pizzas for supper more often than not, Ken went on to win the Body-*for*-LIFE Challenge and then went on to be named Marine Athlete of the year… not a bad improvement. Nick was overweight and getting by when he decided to change the entire Department. And he did. He has excelled in every division of his Department and went on to place in several Nebraska Bodybuilding and fitness contests. By the way, he and his Department won the Group category Body-*for*-LIFE Challenge. Both of you guys inspire me when I don't think I have another rep in me; I know you guys think I do. And like Kelly Jones and Matt Keith, these two young men have dedicated their lives to helping and protecting others… am I seeing a pattern here?

Maybe I should dedicate this book to Nelson Reyes (Ret.) from the North Miami Beach Florida Police Department. I won't name his new Department because there is no telling what division or role Nelson is playing at this time. He has done it all.

I have known Nelson for about 13 or 14 years, and his story would make a good book. When I don't feel like getting up or going to the gym or trying to shave a little time off my best mile, all I have to do is ask, what did Nelson do this morning? It helps me get off my fat rear end. Quite a few years ago, on a routine annual physical, the doctor told Nelson his blood test was a little off whack and probably a few more tests should be done and he should get his lymph nodes looked at and on and on and on… well, Nelson was in great shape and on the SWAT team and tough as nails and busy training other cops and he put it off. The next year she asked him if he had it looked at, and he explained how busy he was and she said, "OK, no exam, no going back to work. Get this blood work and lymph node looked at. End of subject!"

Long story short, in a few months Nelson found himself at a Cancer Center getting some very bad news. A few short weeks after that, Nelson found himself in ICU. A few short days later, Nelson found himself in a sterile room. He was so sick and so contagious that the nurses wanted to shove the liquid food under the door instead of walking around in his room... but they did come in because they are nurses! His lymph nodes had been removed from his throat and he lay there cut wide open from his chin to his breastbone.

Nelson went on to fight like a World Champion, and for the last few years, he continues to improve. He got back on SWAT and has set records on his Department since the cancer. He has raised thousands of dollars for research and asks nothing in return. I mean, this man was so close to death, he could smell its breath, but Nelson did not die. He was meant to live and get better. He did, and I know him, and that makes me a better person. Thank you, Nelson. One other thing about Nelson Reyes: If I had to go down a dark alley or into a sterile operating room with my life on the line either time, I would want Nelson with me. He's been both places and has come out alive both times. He would be a good man to have with you regardless.

Let me add Linda Roberts and Denise Bianchini to the list. I spent years with these two ladies when I worked for Abbott and EAS. We went all over the world helping people and companies get a Health Program in place. I don't think I have known better people who believed in what they were doing more than Linda and Denise. They practice what they preach and they know their subject! Abbott is fortunate to have them on board. I believe the new program is "Changes that Last a Lifetime." That is an appropriate name. A lady named Leila Russell was in charge of all the technical support. There were blood draws and weigh-ins and blood pressure checks and records of improvement and on and on and on. What a team we were. It was a privilege to work with these champions. They dedicated their lives to helping other people; I should dedicate this book to them.

Can't forget Paul and Niamh McMahon in Ireland. Now there is a story for all time. Paul has an interesting background… what part of it you can get out of him! This guy was with the London Police and The Royal Military Police, taught martial arts, was the lead singer and accomplished guitarist in a rock band, and was blown to smithereens in Iraq back in 2004. Wait, what was that last thing? Yes, he was working as a Security Specialist for British and American Diplomats in the Green Zone and while driving to the Bagdad Airport, a car from the opposing team pulled up and ran head first into Paul's car. Both cars were destroyed. Needless to say, Paul was in bad, bad trouble. That's where his beautiful wife, Niamh, comes in. Thank the Lord, she is a nurse. She immediately flew to Germany to meet Paul's medical emergency flight. She never left his side until he was well. She is still by his side, and I am happy to report he is in great health.

The pictures of Paul, what parts are left of the car and the whole story are like Nelson's; it is worth a book someday. I'm not sure what Paul is up to these days. I visited him in England, and I visited him in Ireland a few years ago. He does some sort of cloak-and-dagger security work; just not exactly sure what. He and Niamh and their daughters, Jade and Hannah, opened their home and hearts to me. (P.S., good thing Paul knows a lot of Karate; these girls are absolutely beautiful.) It was one of the best trips of my life. I hope I see them again someday.

Maybe my buddy Jerry Braam would be a good candidate for a dedication. He was a two-fisted, hard-drinking (off work) pipefitter on the Alaska pipeline. He worked up in Dead Horse and went out on fishing boats like you see on that television program "Deadliest Catch." I've been up there with my pal Denty B Moore, and it was about 10 degrees (with a high of 14) while I was there. It gets down to 20 and 30 below and Jerry lived there. That's a little too cool for a boy like me from Georgia! Anyway, Jerry is a pretty tough guy and the old waistline was creeping up year after year until one day Jerry made that life-changing decision to turn things around! He gets in shape and goes back to school and gets his degree, and if you can guess what he is today, you should go play the lotto. He is a nurse in the prenatal inhalation therapy ward of a hospital! Babies scare me to death and Jerry does whatever it is he does so a little innocent baby can breathe and has a chance at life. Thank God for the Jerry's of this world.

I can't forget Mac Roberts… this guy is a USMC Vietnam Veteran and has endured more hardship and unfair life than any human should have to. I don't know how he has such a positive attitude and outlook when he gets up in the morning? Maybe it's for his two children who love him dearly. Maybe he lives for the child that didn't. I just don't know where people get the focus and will to put one foot in front of the other when life has been, at times, so cruel. I know this, if I am ever mentioned in the same sentence with Mac, I will have reached a level of class and character unknown to me before then. Thank You, Sir… Semper Fi.

OK, this can't go on… there are far too many people to thank and show my appreciation. But stay with me, only one or two more. One night a long time ago, I shook hands with a guy named Jim Schneeberger in London. Little did I know what lay in store? If you get a copy of "Finally Fit at 50," you will read a chapter about Jim Schneeberger and my pal Duke Dearing. I don't have the time or space to rewrite it here, but let's just say Jim introduced me to the Selous Scouts. I will never be the same. Here is the short explanation: The Selous Scouts were the "Special Forces" in Rhodesia in Africa. It is a real shame they (without our help and the help of half the world) lost the war in what is now Zimbabwe. Don't get me started on that, I didn't have a dog in that fight, but America did voice an opinion and now Mr. Mugabe is in charge and 93 percent of that country is starving and white settlers are being driven out and people are starving in the streets, but the Zimbabwe President has a new multimillion dollar home in France… if you think the white farmers should have to give their land back to the Rhodesian "War Veterans," then please get up and go sign the deed to your home over to the American Indians. Same difference… exactly the same difference. OK, I need to calm down… this is a dedication.

One night a few years back, I walked down a very dark, and I mean *very* dark, trail somewhere in South Africa. There were a lot of other people there and none of them seemed to be bothered by the pitch-black darkness, but I was a nervous wreck. I walked down the side of a mountain or hill or whatever it was and there in the side of some rocks or cave or whatever it was, there was a party going on. The only light was from torches and a big bonfire. It smelled good and they were cooking something (I will never know what the hell I was eating, or drinking, but it was pretty good). I was extremely fortunate to be invited to a Selous Scout reunion. Men I had read about were there and yes, they had gotten a

12

little older but were still dangerous, nonetheless. You really should read about them to get the drift of who they were and still are. At the end of that night, one of the Scouts stood alone and sang an African Funeral song that was always sang before going into battle. It was like our Taps. It was the saddest and most haunting song I ever heard. No one said a word and a cool calm settled over all the Scouts sitting by the fire. I will never forget it. (Remember, they sang it before going into battle, so if a Scout didn't come back, he had already heard his funeral song... whoa!)

Then one night we were in a hotel and I am at the bar and it's time for a sit-down meal with plates and silverware this time. Keep in mind, I am NOT a Selous Scout and never could be, but I am their guest and I go sit alone at a table and wait for some food I might recognize. An elderly gentleman and a young man come up and asked if they could join me for dinner. It turns out to be Lt. Col. Ron Reid-Daly and his son, David. That is one of a very few dinners that I count as a blessing in my life. I rate it up there with having dinner with Bill Phillips and the other nine Champions at Ruth Chris Steakhouse in Denver in 1997. One morning, Ken Young and I had breakfast at the White House and Karl Rove was at the table next to us... that was pretty sweet. So in my life, getting to have dinner with Col. Reid-Daly and his son is right up there. I walked away knowing so much more history about Africa and so much more about the world in general. I would not trade that night and that dinner and the ability to say I shared a meal with "Uncle Ron" for anything. He truly is a legend. We lost him last year to cancer. He put up a good fight but it was his time and all the SAS training and the entire Scout training can't come between us and eternity when it is our time. Thank God I got to talk with him before one of us passed away. Thank you to Jim, Tom, Wingnut, Pat, David, Johne, and "Uncle Ron"... if I may and with your permission: "PAMWE CHETE."

OK, that's it... now I have to choose the person or people to dedicate this book to. It isn't what's in this book as much as it is the days and weeks and months and years (62) that I spent learning to write it. So much has happened to stall finishing it. Life will send all sorts of roadblocks and detours in our travels... you are going to read about a few of mine in here somewhere. It has taken almost two years more than I anticipated being finished. That's why I think it is so important to get busy living because "we run out, time don't."

As always, when I write something, David Kennedy comes in at the last dot and corrects most of it. He doesn't change the thought; he fixes it so the good reader has some idea of what the hell I am trying to say… good luck David. I appreciate you more then you know.

I, Porter Freeman, being exhausted and on the verge of a nervous breakdown do hereby dedicate this book and all my efforts to:

Lt. Steve Grossi PAPD and Det. Miguel Rivera of the NYPD. There is nothing I can write or say that hasn't been written and said a thousand times. Everyone reported to work or to the Twin Towers immediately on September … Steve was sent to the airport to evacuate the buildings and be prepared for whatever was coming next. No one knew anything except for days and days and day's police officers and firefighters and first responders stood their post. I don't think we realize how many days and nights these officers went without a change of underclothes and with wet socks and no toothbrushes and little to no food those first few weeks. Yet, they reported for duty (what a strong word… DUTY) and stood ready to defend the rest of us. Thank you, Lt. Steve Grossi, and thank you to the men and women of the Port Authority Police Department.

Det. Miguel Rivera, NYPD, was at work in Washington Heights when the call came in on September . I am unable to tell anybody the level of fear or anger or sadness Miguel felt in the days and weeks to come, but I do not think I could have done his job. For the first 24 hours, he and his team couldn't get near what had been the Towers. When they could get there, what awaited them was pure Horror. Miguel is HazMat trained and part of his job for weeks on end was to sift through the debris looking for anything for identification… a finger, a toe, a tooth, anything… a fingernail, a lip, a clump of hair, a bone. Think about that, if he found a nose, it was success… somebody's loved one could be notified that part of their son or daughter or wife or whomever had been found. It took several years before Miguel would talk about any of this and he still hasn't said it all. What I can do is tell him Thank You more then he will ever know… both he and Steve are quite unassuming, humble Real World Champions, and neither one want you to know it.

Again, I do not expect Steve or Jim or Linda or Lisa or Eric or anyone listed above to agree with me on any of the content… that's up to them. I just want them all to know how much I love and respect them and how much influence they have had on my life. Sometimes when my addiction calls my name late at night and I want so very badly to go to it or have it come to me, I try and think of what these people have been through and have emerged True Champions. There is a True Champion in you... let it shine, let it shine, let it shine.

Table of Contents

My Definition of Addiction

"It's like Pavlov's Dog, but the bell never quits ringing."

G. Porter Freeman III

Preface

If you are addicted to something, anything, in your life, no matter what else comes into your life, it's coming in at second place.

Addiction is the merry-go-round that rides you.

It's a problem when it creates a problem.

Killing time is murdering opportunity.

The biggest fish gets caught on the smallest of hooks.

Keep banging your head on the wall because it feels so good when you quit.

There is a story about a fellow who keeps going to a crooked poker game and always lost his money. One night his wife asks him as he was going out the door, "Why do you keep going there, you can't win?" He looks at her and says, "I know, but, it's the only game in town!"

Never take a bologna sandwich to a barbeque.

You know why a sponge doesn't sink? It adjusts to the height of the water.

(The above one will make a lot of sense when we start talking about chasing that drug high. It always stays as high as you, and you never quite get as high as it.)

Keep feeding the alligator, hoping it eats you last.

Addiction: The gift that keeps on taking.

Addiction is loving something that is killing you, more then you love living.

You're not in trouble until you are in trouble and then it's too late.

When you change your address on the Addictions credit card, the bill collector can always find you. You are your own forwarding address.

We can fall into addiction, but we have to work our way out.

Everything is temporary with enough time. (I think whoever said this was talking about the pain associated with giving up our addictions.)

When they sing the song of our life, will it be an opera or the same three notes over and over and nothing else but blank empty paper? When you write your book, what will it say? Nobody owns words, they belong to everybody. If you put them in some order or set them to music, they become a poem or story or song.

You can own a story or poem or song, but we do not now, nor will we ever, own a word, no more than you can own a letter in the alphabet. This book and all the books in the world are nothing more or less than words put in order by the writer. If you write your story tonight, what will it say? The words belong to all of us, the story is yours.

Addiction is the anchor that keeps you in the grave while you are still alive.

If you are in addiction, you might live your life on your own terms, but you won't die on your own terms; addiction demands and gets that privilege.

Did you enjoy the way you woke up this morning? Did you enjoy where you were? Did you enjoy who you were with? Yes? Great, keep doing exactly what you are doing. If not, CHANGE SOMETHING!

Habits start as cobwebs, and then they become cables.

In the battle with addiction, you keep giving your enemy all the bullets.

Addiction is voluntary slavery.

In Addiction, it doesn't matter your income, just your outcome.

As Surely As We Are Living

As surely as we are living, we are dying. Our heart like a muffled drum is beating a funeral march to the grave.

Henry Wadsworth Longfellow

"Repent therefore and be converted that your sins may be blotted out. And as it is appointed unto men, once to die, but after this, the Judgment."

Acts 3:19

Hebrews 9:27

Death's frozen fingers, quickly severs life's dearest ties...

From Cradle to Grave

From the cradle to the grave, very little stays the same. Most things in our life can and will change. Let's name some of them: We can change the color of our hair, the color of our eyes, teeth, address, and skin if we are willing to bake in the sun all day. I'd be real careful of that last one.

We can change our children, our husband or wife, job, sweetheart, religion, address, our political party, our school, our major, our minds; we can change our clothes, our hair, our everything, the list is endless. I hear you can change your sex if you have the money and the wardrobe!

Here are a couple of things you can't change: your biological parents. It is what it is; you cannot change your family tree regardless of the strong roots or the rotten fruit. And in my 61 years of watching and sometimes living it, I am convinced you cannot change addiction. You go in and out of it, but addiction is rock steady. If you have an addiction or if you interact with someone who is addicted, you know what I am talking about. I'm not saying you can't walk away; you sure can. But, addiction doesn't walk away from you, it waits. Like that famous hotel chain, addiction keeps the light on.

My friend Joey Vincent (that's him on the front cover) told me "Addiction is a patient lover; it will wait on you forever."

A few of us have danced with addiction and gone home, and a few others, have danced with addiction and are still sitting at the bar... waiting on the next slow song. The bar didn't close, I did. Maybe the worst addiction is loving somebody that is an addict, and you're not, and it's killing both of you. But, you just keep on dancing.

In this pitiful attempt at what I hope will help someone, I want to share a few experiences. Most of them I either witnessed or participated in. Whichever way, they are the truth. I quit lying back in 97 (19, not 18) when I sobered up. Mostly I quit lying to myself. That was probably the hardest thing to do. If I've got a date or time wrong, I'm sorry; I was probably drunk and had given my watch to some girl so you can understand my confusion.

This would be a good time to admit I wrote this book for me. It is part of my recovery. I just don't have the money to attend a three-month addictions program, nor do I have the time. I will go on record that I think any kind of HELP is beneficial. There are 12-step programs and 10-step programs and 90-day retreats and addiction hospitals and on and on. I think the best one is the one-step program. It's also known as the First Step... take it. Ask for help. It's out there. We simply have to stay with what we can afford. So, to come home and sit in front of this computer and write (instead of going and doing what I really want to) helps me achieve my goals. I am here writing tonight instead of being out at some Juke Joint trying to chat up some poor woman who has lowered her standards to the point that she would sit at a bar and talk to me... Dear God! It doesn't really matter which bar, and it doesn't really matter which woman, I have been all over the world and there are bars everywhere, with women and guys like me.

The people I wrote about who didn't make it leaves me so sad and so sorry that I couldn't say or do anything to help or comfort them. They saw and heard the freight train coming, yet they chose to stay on track and take their chances. They lost. There are others you will read about who completely turned their life around, have overcome unbelievable odds. That keeps me going. Their success stories and their lifestyles, not the ones who lost. What could I have said to help the lost? What can you tell them tonight that will save their life? Maybe nothing. I found out just in the nick of time, and the hard way, that some people do NOT want to be changed or improved. Maybe that's the key... to know, as soon as possible, who wants to be helped and who doesn't. Sort of like trying to teach a pig to sing; it's a waste of your time and it annoys the pig. Learn the difference.

Let's hurry up and make that change in ourselves or the people we love or at the very least give up soon so we don't keep torturing us and them. If you honestly believe that someone you love isn't going to get off the dope or booze or smokes or porn or gambling or credit cards or lovers or whatever it is that is wrecking both your lives, start distancing yourself from them today. If they really want you to stay around, they will change. If they don't change, and you are still there at the end of this book, then shut the hell up and live with it! Good Lord, if nothing else, have a little peace and quiet there at the old homestead.

As a final thought and as a defense, please know I absolutely do not care if you agree with any of this book or think it is a candidate for the Pulitzer Prize for Science Fiction... it matters not one twit to me. Here is why it doesn't matter: I was, for a long time, addicted to what other people thought. That is no longer the case. I have tried to get my Father and my Step-Father's approval all my life... if they are OK with the man I have become, what other person's opinion could possibly matter? There are none. You are who you are and if Mrs. Spreading-Lottabottom at the Church Auxiliary didn't like your hat last Sunday, who the hell cares? She doesn't have to wear it. If the man or woman you love is a "rounder" and it's OK with you, then it's none of anybody's business. You didn't love and accept them for anyone's approval. If you are as sick as I was and this book or the people in it can give you a sliver of hope, if something in this book, or if one of the stories offers you a helping hand, then I thank God tonight that I stayed home and stayed sober and worked on it... and the Lord probably saved me and that unknown woman at the bar a lifetime (or at least one night) of heartache.

All that said, I hope it does you, or somebody you love, some little good. But, if it doesn't, throw it in the garbage and try a different book. There are thousands of good books out there. Remember what Janis Joplin said, "I'm just trying to find a little peace." I hope you go and find yours.

I want to take full responsibility for all the misspelled words in this book. I accept responsibility for all the wrong or nonexistent punctuation. I accept complete responsibility for the content on these pages. I purposely wrote the word "ain't about 50 times. Hell it's even in the title....

Now, if you want to go get a red pen (better make it 4 or 5 red pens) and correct all the things wrong with my writing; I suggest you become an English teacher. But......if you or someone you love and care about is dying in Addiction, read it for the message, not the misspelled words. Enjoy!

Magnolia Cemetery

October 4, 2008.

This morning I am sitting in the Magnolia Cemetery in Augusta, Georgia. I came down here today with a purpose in mind. I am well aware there is a day coming when I will be down here and not have another purpose in this life, whatsoever.

There are a lot of people in this cemetery; some have been here a long time, and others just a little while. As a matter of fact, about 200 yards south of me, a new member is moving in today. They all have several things in common, but the most obvious is this: At the exact day of the exact hour of the exact minute, death came calling and could not be turned away.

Mark my words: This is a club everybody gets to join. It won't matter how much money you had or how poor you were, your I.Q. won't get scored and race, religion, gender, nor the number of teeth you had will make any difference. The day you were born, your application to this place (or one like it) was stamped "Accepted." I believe there are only two things that will count when (not if) you activate your membership: Your will to live and the relationship you had with the Lord. Nothing else is much going to matter.

That day, hour, and minute is coming to all of us, no getting out of it. Maybe somewhere in this book I can convince myself and one or two good readers to take whatever time we have remaining and do something good with it. I hope so.

Looking around this place, I wonder how many gallons of liquor these people drank. I wonder how many cartons of cigarettes they smoked, how many hours did they spend glued to the screen on a television or computer? That number might be a tad low because some of the residents were here long before the light bulb was in invented. How many of them spent half their life worrying about somebody or something they had very little or no control of? I wonder how many of them got shot to death because they were messing with somebody else's husband or wife... wonder how many of them gave their life defending this country? There are some good ones and some bad ones; a new member is moving in today and some have been here for 200 years. Nonetheless, they are all here getting their grave on.

I've had friends who led wonderful, loving, productive lives. I'm sure you have friends like that. I have also had a few friends who drank themselves to death. I've known two or three people that died of an overdose of illegal drugs and several who came real close. You know anybody like that? I thought so. Do you know a few folks throwing their life away, who you love and care for and maybe gave life to, but no matter what you say or do, they refuse to change? Do you think it is because they believe they can't live another minute without whatever it is they are addicted to? I understand how they feel; when I was an addict, my addiction was the only thing that mattered. Let me offer a quick example: I swear to God this is true. I've watched people walk away from a graveside funeral in progress to have a smoke. Buddy, that's addiction!

Maybe that's what this book is about: The things that control us and will eventually (or sooner) kill us. I am nowhere near smart enough to tell anyone how to beat addiction. Far be it from me to advise anyone about anything. I know NOTHING about addiction, but I damn sure recognize it when I see it.

What I did do for the past 10 years and 10 months was stay fairly sober, keep about 50 pounds of fat off me, and for the most part, I am now able to say "no" when some cross-town lady calls me in the middle of the night. That last one is tough. None of the above gives me the authority or license to advise council or direct anyone concerning addiction. I just know how I did it, and trust me on this one: They ain't quit making liquor, they ain't quit frying chicken, and every day, thousands of ladies turn 21. Lord help me! I was smart enough to consult two people who do know a lot about addiction. They gave me words and stories I knew nothing about. These two people pulled the hooks of addiction out long before I realized I was hooked. You will meet one of them and the other will remain anonymous.

I listened to them and wrote what they had to say. I watched how they lived their lives and how they maintained control. Remember, you are going to be one of two places every minute of every day; you are either "in control" or "out of control." There ain't any grey area. There are a lot of people who contributed to this book. Some of them you will know and others you won't. Some of them you can meet, and for others it's too late. Some of the people will seem like friends of yours and you might think I am writing about them. Some of us might think I am writing about us. I am.

Let's wrap this up with a few thoughts. I shouldn't have to write this but some smart ass will point out that all people in cemeteries didn't die of addiction. No kidding. That's all I am talking about here, are addicts. There are wonderful people and innocent children and Veterans and scores of good men and women here. I'm not writing a book about them. I want to prevent someone from driving drunk into a tree and killing themselves or killing some innocent family because they couldn't put the bottle down. They could put it down; they chose not to. I want to interview the person who was loved and adored by their family and friends but hacked up both of their lungs because they had to "smoke, smoke, smoke that cigarette" and the one who will die with a needle in their arm. I hope to prevent another me from eating until his or her heart burst like a racehorse's. I wonder if police could run into an all-you-can-eat buffet and, with guns drawn, yell, "drop that fork, drop that fork"... no, probably not. It doesn't HAVE to be any of us, but only if we stop and turn our lives around.

All the liquor and all the smokes and all the dope and all the different sex partners and parties and excess cookies and pies and cakes and speeding and senseless risk, don't amount to anything. All the cheating and lies and stealing does not amount to a single blade of grass on one plot. All the hate and jealousy and rage does not generate enough energy to shoo a single spider off a headstone. All the arguing and tears and fights with people that loved you means nothing now. You either did or didn't prove your point.

It took me a while to come around to it, but I do believe that fine cars and beautiful houses and rich food and dollars can create a level of comfort on this earth. I wish I had more of all of them. The level of comfort for everybody in the ground is built on good deeds and kindness and control of themselves, an honest heart and for us old Southern Baptists, their walk with the Lord. Everybody here is sleeping at the same address: 702 Third Street. There is no First Class or Business Class or Economy... there is no cashing in of airplane miles to upgrade to anything. Getting here ain't a round-trip ticket. Once you arrive, it's all she wrote and all she mailed.

Two more thoughts on the subject; here's the first: If you look hard enough, I bet you can find a headstone somewhere that has your birthday on it.

You probably won't know the person laying there but the truth is, they died on the very same day and year you were born. Think about that for a minute. You came into this world on whatever date, they left this world on the exact same day. If you care to do it, I bet you can find that grave. I believe unless Jesus comes back in your lifetime, you will die on the same day a baby is being born and maybe in the same hospital. I've worked in two hospitals and assure you, it happens. Somewhere, someday, someone will walk past your grave and say, "Oh my goodness, he (or she) died on my birthday." One comes, one goes. Off with the old, on with the new.

My last thought on this: Magnolia Cemetery was here before you were born and it is here now. It will be here when you and I are dead and gone. Why hurry? It isn't going anywhere; we are. I am convinced every addiction shaves a little time off the clock. Like a number two pencil that has been sharpened over and over and over again, it's finally used up. What the hell was I thinking at 265 pounds and drinking for a living? Why was I in such a big fat hurry to get down here? Why are you? The Magnolia Cemetery isn't going to shut down; there isn't a "Going Out of Business Sale" anytime soon. Let's wait as long as possible to get here. One way to postpone that meeting is bringing to a close those bad habits dragging us down here.

There is a small post office box in the Magnolia Cemetery office, but they don't get many letters. Nobody here has ever left a forwarding address!

If you ever make it to Augusta, Georgia, I urge you to drop by and visit the Magnolia Cemetery. In my opinion, it rates up there with the National Golf Course where they have the Masters. The difference is, I doubt we can play the National, but we can absolutely play this course. Be sure and leave your clubs at home… you ain't going to need them.

My friend Jane Cox (author and Body-*for*-LIFE Champion) read this introduction and told me it was "all over the place." I respect her and appreciate her advice and counsel. So… let's get this down to the real nitty gritty: One day we are going to die, one way or the other. I am absolutely sure of that. Why rush it by staying addicted to something that is going to kill us or, at the very least, ruin our life? Why stay addicted to anything or any person that brings that day closer? Why did I? Why would you? It doesn't make sense. I am convinced that day is coming soon enough without our own or someone else's help.

Proverbs 27:1. Do not boast about tomorrow, for you know not what a day may bring forth

I Want to Go Back

I want to go back. I want to be 6 years old again and spend the summer on Pop and Grandmother's farm in Asheville, North Carolina. I want to spend the day helping feed the chickens and hoe weeds out of the garden and help Grandmother pick strawberries and raspberries. Usually after lunch, I would have to strap on my cap guns and cowboy hat and me and Roy Rogers would pretty much clean up the territory of rustlers and bad guys in general.

As the day wore on, it was time to feed the chickens again. It was a huge responsibility and to be honest, I didn't know how Pop and the chickens got along without me when I went off to Georgia for the first grade. They managed somehow until summer rolled around again and I was there on the farm to set things straight.

Maybe the best time of the year on a farm is Christmas. Maybe as I look back, the farm was all the best time of my life. Maybe I want to go back to those innocent days and the excitement of riding on Pop's tractor and damming up the creek so we could water the garden. I was a very important part of Grandmother's canning the vegetables and once again, I just don't know how they managed without me being there the whole year round. I guess they just made do. Oh yes, I do remember some cousins that lived nearby in Fairview, NC, but I'm sure they didn't clean up as many bad guys after lunch as I did. Well, maybe they did. I wasn't there, I don't know.

But, I can't go back. That window is closed forever. End of the show. That's all she wrote and all she mailed. My Grandmother and Grandfather are long dead and buried. The farm was sold off and has been divided into several sections and the new owners tore the house down and I hear tell the chicken coop is gone. Maybe that's how it should be, off with the old, on with the new.

Something else I know is this: The only addiction I had back then was sitting on Pop's knee and listening to Gunsmoke on the radio. For a half-hour after dinner every night, me and Pop and Matt Dillon helped keep Dodge City and the Longbranch Saloon on the straight and narrow. I remember every day

30

when it was time for lunch; Pop would find Paul Harvey on the radio. I cannot hear Paul say "Stand by for News" that I am not right back on the farm. Now, even Paul is gone.

In 1955, in Asheville, North Carolina, I did not know about liquor or dope or sultry women that magically appear in the night. I didn't know about porn on the Internet or needles or credit cards or cigarettes. I didn't know what lazy was. I had no idea how much money you could make on welfare. I didn't know about arguing or stealing or eating my own body weight at an all-you-can-eat buffet. Funny, growing up don't always mean getting smarter, does it?

As we march through this little book, do me and yourself a favor... think back to the best time of your life. When was it? What was going on that made it so good? When were you the healthiest? When were you the happiest? When were you free? Mine was Granddaddy's farm a long time ago. I am well aware that time can't come again... we all understand that. What I know is this: About 75 percent of the B*&&%$#^ I have dealt with since about 1960, I brought on myself. I know most of the misery that sunk its hooks in me was invited. Not one time has a box of cookies jumped in my shopping cart without my help. I have never walked in a bar or liquor store and had someone come up and say, "Take whatever you want, there's no charge, and it's all free." I paid for every drink. I've never had a pork rib roast, side of bacon, or ham, come flying off a pig's ass and barbeque itself then slide on my plate. I ordered it with extra sauce. And I am still waiting on that gorgeous babe with trouble written all over her to walk up to me and say, "Hi Porter, I have been sitting here waiting for you to show up so I can get started wrecking your life... let's get going." I had a great hand in welcoming about 90 percent of it to come home with me either in my stomach or on my arm.

I need to remind myself that the things that hurt me the most are still out there. I have overcome most of my addictions, but they didn't lose the fight, they just sat down and waited to see if I would pick them up again. Every day that you beat addiction, you win the day, not the fight. The fight never ends; controlling addiction by itself only wins you a 24-hour round. I have done pretty well since 1997, but I was doing perfect in 1955. Let's see if we can both work on living today and being our age, but getting back to where we were before we just couldn't go another day, hour, or minute without whatever it is that's been killing us.

Just like I needed Roy Rogers and Matt Dillon and Miss Kitty to clean up the bad guys on the farm in '55, we might need some help handling these addictions in 2012. There is nothing wrong with asking for and getting some help. In all honesty, it makes the task at hand easier. When I was at my wits end, I sat down and had a long honest chat with Joey Vincent. That started the ball rolling and the more I listened and worked on myself, the better I got. Somewhere along in that time period, Bill Phillips came up with a Transformation Challenge, a 12-week contest of sorts for folks who wanted to change and improve their life. Then I got the help of Eric Shrieves. Guess what, just like Roy Rogers and Matt Dillon, Joey Vincent and Eric Shrieves stepped in and helped. When I see myself slipping I call on them again and again because I am human and I do slip.

Writing this book and meeting some of the heroes in this book has helped me stay on the straight and narrow. They helped me, and if I can, I am more than willing to help you. Let's get started soon because every day it gets further and further away from 1955.

Chapter 1
If There Is a Reason

If there is a reason for this book, this story might be it. I want you to know about one of my mentors and best friends. He was my boss for about 10 years and taught me a lot about the bar business and life in general. His name was Jack, and I think of him often.

As I understand his history, he was quite an athlete. He played several high school sports and made pretty good grades. He was good enough in basketball to go to college and play four years on the starting squad. He went to class, made good grades, lettered in basketball, and worked a part-time job all the way through school. That's a pretty good accomplishment. Jack was quite a guy.

If you had to sum it up, he was an all-American boy. He loved his family and his friends and especially his mom. He always spoke fondly of her and a week didn't go by in the years I knew him that he didn't call and talk to her. He also loved his country. Immediately after college he volunteered for the U.S. Navy. If you have seen "An Officer and A Gentleman," according to Jack, that was pretty close to how it was. He did a lot of running, push-ups, chin-ups, sit-ups, marching, standing at attention, and a lot of intense training. He of course completed Officers Candidate School and was commissioned an Ensign in the Navy and shipped out for Vietnam. He told me upon graduating from OCS, he was in the best physical shape of his life.

After a year in Vietnam he returned to the states, finished his military commitment, and was Honorably Discharged. Jack went back to college and began working on his Master's degree. He graduated with an MBA and started a career in the restaurant and hospitality business. He moved up the corporate ladder and was a huge success with a major restaurant chain. There was only one slight variation in his post-Navy life; he never played sports anymore. He watched them in front of the television with a cold beer and a cigarette… two little habits he picked up somewhere along the way. The beer and cigarette, not the watching TV.

Since he and I worked in the same office, we usually went to dinner three or four nights a week. I can distinctly remember him telling me he had run enough between high school and college and the Navy to last him a lifetime. He was through with working out and gyms and exercise. How wrong he was. He hadn't done enough to last him a lifetime.

There were more late-night dinners, more parties, more cigarettes, more cold beers, and no exercise of any kind... well, you know what I mean. He gained financial success, a beautiful home, beautiful new cars, beautiful girlfriends, worldwide vacations, and still no exercise or nutrition program at all. As the business grew, the hours increased and the sodas (not diet) and cigarettes (unfiltered) increased and the pressure increased, but, no exercise.

By the end of the fourth or fifth year that I knew him, he was buying three packs of smokes on the way to the office every day. There was a convenience store at the end of the block where we worked, and he would shop there every morning like clockwork. On the way home or to dinner, he would pick up one or two packs for the night. That's 60 to 80 cigarettes every day, day in and day out. I don't know what he did on Sundays; the office was closed. I do know that on several occasions he would be yelling or screaming about some employee or a new law or something and have two smokes burning in the same ashtray, at the same time. I have seen that more than once.

Granted, there were some 10- and 12- and 14-hour days, but regardless, three packs in the morning, and one or two packs at night is a little much, even if you are working a 24-hour day. The hook was in. He was addicted. The first sign of anything being wrong was the increase in soda consumption. Remember, these were full-fuel sodas, not diet. He complained his throat was always dry and the syrup or sugar or whatever it is in soda soothed it. He was up to eight a day by the time I left the company.

Because I want to make an important point in a minute, let's follow a normal work day in his life: Get up about 8 a.m., have a smoke first thing. Put on the coffee, quick shower, couple of more smokes on the way to work, stop and pick up three packs at the store. Arrive at office a little before 10 a.m. Read the paper, have a smoke, and then start the daily grind from behind a desk. Maybe drink one soda an hour until 3 or 4 p.m. There was a fast-food restaurant between us and the cigarette store. Sometimes we would walk the 50 yards to the restaurant and get the two for $2 cheeseburgers. We would have four of them and fries and a soda. This happened over and over and over. It was easy, it was close, and it was on sale. You know you just can't miss a sale! By 9 p.m. we would go by and check on the bars we managed. If all was well, about 10 p.m. we would go to one of our favorite five or six restaurants and have a "one-a-day" gut-bombing, fat-laden, heart-clogging, grease-dripping dinner. We did this over and over and over.

I, and everybody else, began noticing Jack clear his throat more and more. He began eating cough drops like candy. He coughed a lot more often. Finally he made an appointment specifically to have his throat examined.

Here comes the bad news; 10 black spots on his vocal cords. The appointment was made to have them removed and a biopsy done. Here comes the good news; they were NOT malignant! Thank God. He did have to spend the night in the hospital and then was sent home and out of commission for a FEW DAYS. He couldn't talk for about a week, so I would go by each night with all the paper work and he would write me notes and questions about the business, and we managed to communicate enough to keep him up to speed on what was going on. I noticed on my first visit (and each one after that) he reached over some papers on the cocktail table and lit a cigarette. He couldn't talk and he had had his throat scraped and we were all scared to death it was going to be bad news and he still lit another smoke. Not talking had nothing to do with his being able to inhale. He kept right on smoking.

WHY? Why in the world would an intelligent man with a great education and lots of money and lots of friends and family and a thriving business smoke three or four packs of cigarettes the same week he had 10 spots cut out of his throat? WHY? It wasn't that he didn't care; he cared about everybody. It wasn't that he was alone in this world; he had more friends and family and people who loved him and Lord only knows how many girlfriends. It wasn't that he couldn't quit; he could and he later did. It was because he was addicted, plain and simple. His addiction was bigger and a greater priority than breathing. Smoking wasn't a problem until it became a problem and then instead of correcting it, he lived and eventually died, with it. One time I heard a lady say, "You ain't in trouble until you are in trouble and then it's too late."

One night we went to buy him some boots and he gave out of breath and got so red in the face trying on the boots that he said to hell with it, forget about it. Can you imagine having to sit down and catch your breath from trying on boots? Can you imagine having to walk out of the store and have a cigarette and sit down just to catch your breath from trying on shoes? HELLO!

A couple of years later, I changed jobs and would occasionally stop by and have a soda or maybe even dinner with him, but like most boss/employee friendships, we sort of drifted away. One night at my new job, I had a phone call from Jack. He said he wanted to tell me goodbye and thank me and all in all, I had been a pretty good guy to work with. He told me he hoped he had never done anything mean or unfair and if so, he was sorry. Sometimes in the heat of business and with almost 600 employees, things can get intense. It was never personal. I asked him what in the hell he was talking about? He told me he just wanted me to know how he felt. I said he had been more than fair with me and more than fair to all the people and friends he worked with. We talked for a little while and laughed about a couple of old war stories, and I couldn't help but ask if he was moving back home to be with his mom or what?

No, he said, I've got cancer. I am going back home and check into the hospital and see if there is any hope. I told him I would come see him on my next day off and he said no, just wait, he would come see me when he got back.

He didn't get back. First a lung came out, then part of the other one. Then the all-American boy, Vietnam veteran, Naval officer, son, college athlete, mentor, and friend, died. He never saw 50. He had done so much good in this world; he had set up college scholarships for children of his employees and supported orphanages back in Vietnam for 20 years after he had left. He gave honest sincere counsel to anyone who came to his office door, and now he was gone.

Julie Whitt, the 2002 Body-*for*-LIFE Champion, never lived to see 40. She died from lung cancer after fighting like Mike Tyson to stay alive. Julie never smoked a cigarette in her life. My friend Jack was addicted to dying, and my friend Julie was addicted to living, but they both died all the same. I miss them both.

Look, I don't hate smoking, so don't think this is about not smoking because it isn't. Hell, I might have a cigarette before the day is over. Remember what Joey said, it ain't a problem until it becomes a problem. In the bar business, we used to say, "It ain't late till 2, and then it's too late." Sort of the same thing.

We have known employees in the bar business that smoked at work and left their smokes in the locker until they came back the next day. That isn't addiction, it's a poor choice to smoke for 10 hours at work for four days straight, but it isn't addiction. They didn't smoke on vacation. Go figure. I've never had an employee miss work from over smoking. I've had them miss work from over eating, over partying, over drinking, and over sleeping, but never over smoking.

If we have to put a warning label on every pack of smokes, then why isn't there a cop standing at a turn style in front of all the fast-food joints? He could be there with a tape measure and a pair of calipers and as you enter, you would have to have a measurement and body-fat composition done. If you fell into the fat-ass or obese category, you couldn't eat there.

Maybe for the people who were borderline, there could be a treadmill and stationary bike where the playground used to be. See, that way you could do 30 minutes of cardio and then buy a double bacon cheeseburger and a strawberry shake to wash it down. If we have to put a warning label on a pack of smokes, why not on a bucket of deep-fried chicken? Are you going to tell me 20 cigarettes are worse than 20 pieces of fried chicken for someone who is at 33 percent body fat? I don't think so! How about this... once in a while, a smoke isn't going to kill you, and once in a while, a piece of fried chicken isn't going to kill you. It's the constant day-in, day-out abuse of this stuff that is going to put us in the ground!

I saw a label on a bottle of wine that said, "Warning: The consumption of alcoholic beverages may be harmful to pregnant women." In my opinion, the warning was a tad late. The wine may have contributed to them getting pregnant in the first place! Since the #*&! government is so far up our @%$ already, why don't they demand that cars can only go 50 or 60 MPH top speed? If you have to put a picture on a pack of smokes, why not put a dismembered body from a wreck on a car's windshield that has been speeding? Don't get me started.

Am I making any sense? One cigarette isn't going to kill you. One glass of wine isn't going to kill you. One cheeseburger, one doughnut, one beer, or one piece of chicken isn't going to kill you. Probably anything legal in moderation isn't going to be the end of you. Now, one bullet, one razor blade, or one bomb can kill you. One unprotected sex with the wrong person can damn sure kill you, but that's not what we're talking about. We are talking about the stupidity of both the person doing it and the "people who make the rules" about what is good for us.

I am in the airport today, writing this. Directly in front of me is an ice cream and donut shop. Next door is a "Bar and Grill" where you can buy hard liquor or beer or wine and plenty of it. Swear to God, if you buy a draft beer, they will knock a dollar off a straight shot of liquor to go with it. (The waitress encouraged me to buy one.) You can get the nachos, loaded nachos, or smothered nachos... not sure what that is. You can get pizzas, burgers, loaded baked potatoes, and a large selection of other high-fat, low-protein unhealthy food. And, you can drink booze until somebody has the sense to cut you off. But, God forbid, you can't smoke. You could honestly buy four or five shots of 100-proof booze before you stagger on an airplane, but if you light up, you will be arrested. Want to eat 10 chocolate bars before you board the plane, go ahead. Want to eat two gallons of ice cream, no problem. Want to have six donuts and two scoops of ice cream, let me suggest the maple-covered, powdered donuts and the walnut, marshmallow, coconut, macaroon ice cream chocolate bomb, again no one will say a thing. But, one more time... don't you even think of being fit, fairly healthy, and lighting a cigarette... the TSA will haul you out of the airport and then off to jail.

P.S. Did I mention you can ask them to dip the ice cream in syrup and put it in a sugar cone? They will be happy to. P.P.S. I am spelling donuts that way on purpose. Get it... do-nuts!

Addiction is addiction is addiction... it doesn't matter if it is food or smokes or liquor or the wrong person or porn or shopping or plastic surgery or sex or church or hate or jealousy. It can be gambling or credit cards or lies or money or whatever it is that controls you. What is it that is controlling you today this minute?

I hate so much that my friend died of his addiction, and I hate that some of my other friends didn't learn one single thing from his passing. They must think it can't happen to them. That's what he thought and he was (and they are) wrong.

Surely you know people like this... good people who are in the clutches of some addiction that is going to take the ultimate toll someday. What do we say to them? What do we plead? How do we explain to them that they will live without it? How do we explain that their life will be better? How do we tell them that their love affair with this crutch isn't holding them up, in truth, it's fighting tooth and nail to drag them down. It ain't easy to give up what takes the pain away even if the pain of comfort is greater than being miserable. (You might want to read that sentence again.) My friend Laird Boles always said, "The Devil you know is better than the Devil you don't know," and my pal Eric Shrives says, "It's the comfort of your misery." They are both right.

Death is just another form of freedom. It's not the last freedom, but it is the final one. Your last freedom is giving up! You can give up the addiction or you can take it to the grave... your choice.

Please, please, please don't have as much to offer to the world as my friend Jack did and then leave it so soon by your own hand. He had so much to tell and so much to teach and he was a good, good man and he made his choices... make yours, stay here, we need you.

This morning I am in a hotel outside of Washington, D.C., sort of toward Virginia. I couldn't get a flight out last night and had to stay over an extra day. That happens a lot more often these days. Commercial flying in America has gone to (or dropped to) a whole new level. I wonder if the CEOs and stock holders took the same cut in pay and service that us passengers and employees have. If ever in my life the old expression, "When you overload the wagon, you don't buy another mule, you get a bigger whip" applies, it's to the airlines today. It makes me wonder what other cuts are going on that we can't see. Are there some cuts in maintenance? I don't know. Are there some cuts in pilot training? I don't know. Are tires staying on the plane longer before being changed? I don't know. Do you know? Like Jack's health, sooner or later, something has to give. Something will and is going to give. My complete and total concern is arriving the same time the plane does and, if possible, landing safely. So far that has happened, and I am thankful for it each and every time. I bring this up to prove a point. It wasn't the loss of peanuts that has anything to do with a safe flight. It wasn't the added cost (usually $25) if you call for a ticket. It wasn't the $25 or $50 or $100 fee for extra bags. It wasn't half a soda instead of the whole can. It wasn't a dollar for a drink of water. It wasn't the flight attendant asking for the plastic cup back so it could be rinsed out and reused! It wasn't the loss of ticket holders at the counter. Now there is an idea for a million-dollar business: leather ticket holders by some French designer... please send me my cut for the wonderful idea! What it is, is the sum total of all the losses. That is what makes flying less appealing.

Let me give you another great example. I'm looking at my hotel bill and there are some strange Chinese Algebra mathematics going on here. I checked in last night at 10. I came to my room and never left until I went down for breakfast. I am here only one night, but I was charged $2 for a safe in my room that I never saw. It was on the top shelf of the closet. Who the hell was I going to hide anything from, myself? Then I was charged a tax for three different things that I will never see. I do not live here and will not enjoy the new baseball field, so why am I paying for it? I won't play one inning, I won't hit one home run there, and I don't even think this town has a baseball team! What the hell is a water impact fee? Here's an idea: I don't know what these hotel chains are thinking but I am available for a small consulting fee. Why not take a $10 deposit for excess water use, depending on how many flushes you take. Now there's an idea! If you stay within the allotted number of flushes, you get your $8 back. (There will naturally be a $2 handling fee.) Have you seen the signs in almost every hotel that says "Help us save the world: If you are not going to need new towels, please hang them up"? And, "If you do need new towels, throw the soiled ones on the floor! Do your part to keep the planet healthy." SOILED towels, throw them on the floor... there is no guilt trip there! I wish I could mess up the sheets, but at my age, there is very little chance of that happening. They are safe there.

Here's my idea for the new signs: "Help us cut costs: Our owners need a new Bentley and our bonus depends on what we can save. Use your towels over and over so we don't have to spend money on cheap detergent and labor at minimum wage to wash your nasty towels and sheets. You know you use them over and over at your house, why not here?"

And here's another sign they can use: "Enjoy this cup of God-awful free coffee, 'cause in the very near future, you ain't getting it anymore. Get off your wallet and go buy some in the lobby. Have a nice day."

Here is my point: You lose one thing, you might not notice it. You lose two things, you still might not notice it. At three or four, you begin to notice it and then when you have lost five or six, you do notice it, but you go right on hoping it will get better and go back to what it used to be. At seven, eight, or nine, it's too late. You have lost so much, you are no longer in control. Now they are completely in control, and you will accept it how they dish it out or not at all.

That's what happened in one of the best books ever written: "Animal Farm" by George Orwell. I urge you to read it. That is sadly what happened to my friend Jack. He developed a slight cough. That was number one. He was out of breath, number two. He didn't smoke one cigarette and wake up the next morning with cancer… he lost one defense and then another defense and then another. And then he really started losing a freedom here and a freedom there and slowly, over several years, it took him. Abuse it and it will take you. Control it and you can use it when you want. I would love to talk to Jack again and tell him how much I did appreciate him. That won't happen until eternity. I wonder if he could come back, would he go visit our mutual friends and beg them to quit smoking, or at least slow down. I wonder… I wonder if they would listen. Would you?

As I wrote this, I thought back to one of my grammar school teachers. I think it was the or grade. It's been so many years ago, I have a hard time remembering. I do remember this… she was out for about a week and, of course, all us little harebrained troublemakers went wild with the substitute teacher. I stayed in trouble that entire week. On a Monday morning, our regular teacher returned. Funny as a child what you remember, but I remember this vividly. She told us to write a Thank You note to the substitute teacher and she would collect them and send them to her. Then out of nowhere, she started crying. The crying advanced to sobbing and we all sat there in total silence. We had never seen a teacher cry. We didn't think they could or did. This was about 1958 or '59, and we thought teachers were Gods. They could actually spank you back then. This lady sat at her desk and cried her eyes out. Nobody said a word or moved.

After a few minutes she got her breath and wiped her eyes and said she was sorry. She then reported that she had been out because her husband had surgery to remove part of his lower lip and part of his chin and teeth and bottom gum. She had been there with him when the doctors cut away his lower mouth and disfigured his face. The worst part was he lost the tip of his tongue. Then she got real angry and said she hated his pipe and for years he had clenched it in his teeth and on that side of his mouth where they cut him. I remember her telling us not to smoke those nasty old pipes. I remember thinking, "Santa does!"

41

I don't know if smoking a pipe for 20 years caused that man's cancer. I don't know if he lived or died because of it. I do know he was horribly disfigured and I know he could not eat normal food anymore. According to her, he had to eat soft food and mush the rest of his life. It's hard to chew with half your bottom jaw missing. I also know this: He quit using a pipe. It becomes real difficult to hold it in your mouth and draw on it when part of your mouth is missing.

Again, I do believe that if either of these gentlemen could come back from eternity, they would say that it wasn't a wound received in battle, it wasn't an automobile accident or an unfortunate illness or injury: It wasn't nature and old age that got us; it was the choice we made. We chose to die a painful hard death, every time we abused tobacco. We knew what we were doing; we knew the damage being done. But, when the brain cells and the blood cells and the addiction cells demanded a dose of tar and nicotine, we fed them and in appreciation, they ate us.

Are you reading this? Is someone you love reading this? Be real quiet and see if you can hear a voice from the grave telling you, "Please, please at least cut back on your addiction with tobacco. Don't be like me and end your life far too soon. There were places I wanted to visit and things I wanted to do and people I loved and miss and if I can just have another chance, I'll change, I promise I can, I promise I will, I... never mind, the night is too far spent! It's much too late. You will see me soon enough, don't hurry. I loved you."

This would be a good place to stop but I can't. I want the good reader to read real close; I have nothing against having a smoke. There are some fat-ass politicians who want to force people in the military to not smoke. They want it to be against the law. Brilliant. They get the same "government" insurance and the same tax dollars go to pay their six-figure salary, but if you are 12,000 miles away from home and being shot at day and night while they are in Washington at big dinners, it is in your best interest and for your good NOT TO SMOKE!

That has got to be the stupidest thing I have ever heard. I've got an idea, why don't some of these politicians make it a rule that if you are an active duty soldier and you masturbate, you will be sent to Leavenworth for life! It is OK for them to have affairs and they can be drunk and they can be up to their necks in scandal, but you better not touch your pee-pee while bullets and missiles are flying all around you all day. It's bad for you. They know what's best and they have your best interest at heart.

They are going to say it cost so much for cigarette-related illnesses at the VA. How much does it cost for politicians and their wives and children to be on the payroll and how about their retirement? Is that free? No double standard there. Don't get me started... you want to have a smoke, have one. You want to smoke on a regular basis, that's your decision. They are not good for you, and they are getting more and more expensive. You decide. Want to have a drink every day, OK. Want to drink a half-gallon... not a good idea. You see and know the difference. Have some control and some moderation. Smoke if you want to; just don't smoke yourself to ashes!

I get so aggravated talking about this... I think I will go have a cigarette and a beer!

Chapter 2
Joey Vincent

The picture on the front of this book is of my pal Joey Vincent. We have known each other for about 30 years. I knew who he was long before he ever heard of me. He was pretty famous down south, especially around Orlando, Florida. I wasn't. He didn't know me from Adam's house cat.

Joey was a pro boxer and at one time was ranked in the top 10 of his weight class by Ring magazine. He held a pretty good amateur record of about 80 wins and 20 losses. He always ranked in the top of Golden Gloves and was fairly well known around Pittsburg as an outstanding AAU athlete. After high school, Joey joined the Air Force and continued boxing for the Armed Forces on the 1968 Air Force team. After four years and an Honorable discharge, he began fighting as a pro. During his career he won the Southern Middleweight Championship and held the Florida State Welterweight belt until he retired. When he finally hung up his gloves, he had a 44-10-2 record with 39 knockouts. One other title he earned was "Mr. Excitement." The local paper wrote that it would be exciting to watch Joey fight Little Bo Peep! He always put on a show.

Like so many pro athletes I have known, Joey was absolutely violent in the ring and a perfect gentleman outside of it. That rule applies to a lot of walks of life. I have met pro football players who created a lot of mayhem on the field, but were marshmallows when they spent Christmas Eve wrapping presents for very sick children in hospitals. I have known a few police officers who you really wouldn't want to argue with, but they were the same officers that on their own time would go to hospitals and homes, to check on victims of a brutal crime. I remember one particular K-9 that would let first-graders climb all over it and pull its ears and the dog would just sit there with his tongue hanging out and take it. The dog looked around like, "When in the world is this going to end?" and accepted it as part of his life. That is, right up until the handler put the work collar on and then it was all business.

It's kinda funny, put that work collar on and everything changed, no more Mr. Nice Doggie... at that point, he was all tooth and muscle and growl. I make this point because it works both ways; when the work collar came off, he was a big old clumsy dog again that liked his stomach rubbed. Maybe that's the way it is with addiction. When the addiction comes off, we might be able to go back to being half-way normal again. More about that later…

Back to Joey: It's an unwritten rule that celebrities have people who like to hang around them. Some of these fans are honest friends who love the sport or art and it doesn't really matter who the Champion is. Others are just plain old leeches… the leeches want to be big shots and throw your name around, see what it can get them. There were and always will be people who admire and respect Joey for his accomplishments and others who were there simply for the free drinks. They didn't know a right hook from a fishing hook.

I have often wondered how rich, successful movie stars or athletes, who have everything, can screw up so badly, they risk losing it all. When you have fame and fortune and success, how can you deliberately throw it away? I found out.

I think that's sorta what happened to Joey. When he was training for a fight, he lived like a monk. Nothing got in his way. He was up early and put in a 5-mile run, ate clean, never any junk food, was in the gym religiously, no smoking, no drinking, no nothing. He wanted to fight like a Champion, so he trained and lived like one. He never missed a workout, never missed a sit-up, never quit one minute early. He took focus to a whole other level. And like you hang up your winter coat when the spring comes, Joey would take off his healthy lifestyle and hang it in the closet with his winter coat at the end of each fight. Win or lose, the fight was over and it was time to party.

I hope you get to meet him someday. Maybe he will tell you his story. It's a good one and well worth hearing, but this isn't the time or place. There is a much more important story here. I want the good reader to know that at my lowest point, when my addiction was on me like a duck on a June bug, Joey (and one or two others) helped me through it. I don't know if I would be here without him

Here is some of Joey's story. He gave me permission to share it in the hope of it helping someone else. Maybe if you see a little of you or someone you know and love in it, it will help. It's free; there is no charge… Joey already paid the price.

One afternoon about 30 years ago, Joey has the day off and runs his errands, takes care of all the normal stuff folks do on their day off, and just happens to stop by his favorite neighborhood bar in Orlando. He was married and had a beautiful wife and daughter and gorgeous home, but they were at work and school and the house was clean and he was only going in to have "one," chat with his pals, then head home to start dinner, etc. As he recalls, one and then two and then a few more of his pals and fans showed up. He had a couple more, and some other people wanted to meet him and then somebody bought the house a round and on and on and on. Sound familiar? (I remember back in 1997 when I was one of the Body-*for*-LIFE winners, I had lost about 70 pounds and been sober for six months. When I won, all my friends showed up at the bar where I worked and bought me a drink! To celebrate my winning and being sober, they bought me a drink. Think about it.)

So anyway, Joey is laughing and telling jokes and having a grand old time. He is reliving fights and is the center of attention and the clock is standing still. To hear Joey tell it, he took a drink, the drink took a drink, the bar took a drink, everybody took a drink, and then the drinks began to take him. Let's fast forward to the next morning.

Joey's wife has to be at work at 8 a.m., so she's up and dressed and ready to go out the by 7:25. Joey works evenings, so he is sleeping like a baby, until... and the conversation goes something like this:

"Wake up, Vince"... a name she used when she meant business.

"Hey, Vince, WAKE UP!"

Groan, mumble, cough, cough... "What, what do you want, I'm sleeping."

"Where's my car?"

"Huh?"

"Where's my car, I have to go to work!"

At this point, Joey thinks he said something like, "Don't ask me those hard questions, I'm not awake yet."

His wife found his keys, took his car, and left him to get wherever he was going the best way he could. Later that day, Joey began looking for her car. He was sure he left it in the driveway, but it most certainly wasn't there. Her keys were on the table where they always were but no car. He had to bring it home, he thought, because the house keys were on the same ring and he made it home last night. It was all very confusing.

To be on the safe side (and before he called the Sheriff), he called the bar. Of course they weren't open at 10 in the morning; no answer there. He called a few other places and a few other bars and friends, but nobody knew anything. Where could it be?

On mornings like these, he always felt better if he got in a few miles of road work just to clear his pounding head. Also, if he reported it stolen, he wanted to be a little less hung-over when the cops showed up. He grabbed the house keys and out the door he went. About a mile and a half from his home he noticed a car sitting on the side of the road that looked a lot like his wife's. Hmmm? Joey jogs over to take a look. There are no scratches, no dents, and no damage whatsoever. He looks at the tag and sure enough, it's her car. What the hell is it doing here on the side of the road? Wonder why she left it here last night?

Joey gets in and everything is there, nothing missing until he tries to start it. There is not a drop of gas in the tank. It won't budge. He also noticed a 24 hour gas station a few blocks back. I guess the 24-hour gas station was closed last night when he drove past it, right?

That evening when his wife got home, it was short and sweet: "Get some help, or I'm gone." End of subject.

Here was a hell of a tough guy who didn't run from anybody or anything, inside or outside of the ring. He wasn't scared of anything, and now the family he loved with all his heart was leaving. He was going to lose his marriage, his daughter his home. It wasn't another woman; it was two ice cubes in a glass of horrible-tasting brown liquid that was giving him the beating of his life. All his friends drank, and all his fans drank, and he loved them and they loved him and even the hangers on liked to be around him. The one thing he loved more than them was slipping quickly out of his life. That night he made a choice: his family or the scotch, either one, plain and simple, but not both. He made a choice that night in April of 1980 and has been clean and sober for over 30 years.

Joey's was single malt scotch; mine was bourbon and a lazy, partying lifestyle. What's yours? Is it booze? Is it porn? Is it smokes? Is it drugs of any kind, prescription or street level? They are all the same. Is it food, lack of food, welfare, or maybe your addiction is trying to save the wrong person? Is it sex, politics, or religion? Oh hell yes, you can be addicted to religion, you just don't know it and the dealer keeps you hooked because they are personal friends with God. I am convinced it can be anything that controls you. One of my definitions of addiction is, it's like the fog; it takes whatever shape you are, walking into it. I wrote another book called "Finally Fit at 50." In it I said, "The difference between a rut and a grave is the depth. We can get out of a rut, but we ain't getting out of the grave." Do you see the difference? You, Joey, and I can walk out of that fog and find our way out of that rut. Start walking...

Not only did Joey quit throwing his life away, he went back to school and became an Addictions Counselor. I will never know how many people he has helped, but I sure know one of them. Me. Cleaning up your life has a couple of steps. The first one for me was to stop and ask myself did I really want to get well? How easy was that? Pretty easy. If the answer is yes, then you are on your way. You're not there yet, but on your way. There are ways and people and groups and doctors and hospitals and churches and former addicts who are willing and able to help you. All you have to do is ask.

If the answer is no, then don't waste your time. Could you at least have enough character left before you completely ruin your life to tell the people who love you and care about you that you are not going to get well? Would you please tell them that you are going to continue to steal from them and hurt them and lie to them and no matter how much rehab they pay for, there is a God somewhere that picked you out of thousands of people and cursed you with addiction and there is no cure. Please tell them that you are broken and either don't want to be fixed or can't be fixed. You are the exception to all the success stories in this world. I mean, it's just bad luck that they love you and care about you and you're not only hurting yourself but you're killing them at the same time. If the answer is No, I don't want to get well, then please save them the trouble of burying you twice, once a day while they watch you throw your life away and once when you finally get it done. Joey and I think you can beat addiction; we just don't know

48

how to make you want to. By the way, I have had a drink since April of 1997, but I had the drink, it didn't have me. I don't want to be held hostage to anything, not a job or a person or alcohol or anything. Fourteen years of not buying the bar a round, of not calling cabs to get home (which was a great idea at the time), of not making alcohol the binding element between my girlfriend and I, of not breaking my car key off in the front door of my house. That next morning I couldn't get in the house or the car... hmm!

I'm telling you, if Joey Vincent and I can sober up and turn our lives around, SO CAN YOU! YOU CAN, YOU CAN, and YOU CAN... I remember Joey telling me he stopped hanging out with people who continued to want to buy him drinks. He began lifelong friendships with people who were trying to live and improve their lives, not drown. Is drinking a beer wrong? Is having two beers wrong? I don't think so. If you can stop after one or two or three and you are not driving then OK. The problem is can you stop at one? With addicts the answer is no. Regardless of the addiction, addicts cannot control the number... there is never going to be enough of any fix because the problem is never going to be fixed until they fix it. Eternal problem... equals an eternal fix or eternal pain... which one?

If you know you can't stop at one, don't do the one. How do you stop? Don't do the first one. What forces us to do that first one is it tells you it will take away the pain. About my third beer used to tell me that. Guess what? When the bottle is empty or the cocaine is all snorted up or the person is dressed and gone or the plate is empty or the wallet is empty... the pain comes right back. Gotta find out what is causing the pain... then we fix the addiction.

Here is one of Joey's stories: If you have a horrible throbbing toothache and someone hands you a needle and a vile of Novocain. You could give yourself a dose but the pain WON'T permanently go away. Of course, the nerves will be blocked and you will have some wonderful relief for a while... happy days! Now suppose the next day the pain is the same and right back where you left it, you have three choices: more Novocain or extract the tooth or fix it.

Now suppose the pain is in your heart. Suppose the pain is a large gaping hole in your chest. You can't remove your heart, you know what I mean, and I'm talking about the pain being inside you. You have to walk around all day with this empty gap in your chest where your heart should be. It might be so bad that you feel the wind blow through it even if you have all your clothes on. Let's suppose that nothing, and I mean nothing, in this world fills that hole except ice cream and cookies and candy. What are you going to do? Like the tooth and the Novocain, you are going to give yourself a dose. If you don't fix the hole and if sugar and sweets and ice cream are all that makes you feel better, then pretty soon not only will you weigh 300 pounds, you really will have rotten teeth and have to get some Novocain! That's called self-medicating, and sooner or later, you should realize it's no way to live. It's just a slow death by spoons.

In this book, you are going to read about a few examples of people who just kept on filling up the addiction hole with self-medication. Unfortunately they never got well. They just kept getting worse. It's simply a matter of time. You will read about a couple of people who surrendered and finally, for whatever reason, said, "OK, I need help, I can't do this by myself, and I want to get well" and you will read about one or two who, I am sorry to say, extracted the problem. Those people took the pain away with an overdose or a gun or an automobile or in one case a belt. I won't forget any of them; I knew them all. I will especially remember the one who took away the pain with a belt and a shower nozzle; he had been my roommate.

Joey isn't the only one who contributed to this book. There is a lady who is a doctor and an addictions specialist who answered about a thousand questions. Real names were never used, and I got information from her in general conversations. We have to remember and abide by HIPPA rules and we did. Her and I made a deal, she isn't going to write any books and I am not going to practice medicine (other than a little voodoo now and then). Keep in mind, I barely have a GED education. I have told everybody that I liked the and grade so much I stayed twice for both of them. If I remember, I graduated 503 out of 505 in high school. Therefore, I urge you not to act on any information in this book. I wouldn't. What I want you to do is, if you see yourself or maybe someone you love, a light might go off in your head and you might say OK, OK... that's me or that's him or her. That's just exactly how I feel. I want to get well or, at the very least, have them read this... they are not alone.

If I had not done something about my throwaway life in 1997, 265 pounds, 33 percent fat lard ass body, drinking every night and God only knows, running around with a couple of the wrong ladies... I would be dead. I like being in control a lot more... I went and got some help. I urge you to find an addiction group, a support group, a church, a doctor, get into a rehab hospital, it's your life we are talking about. Don't go off to some "celebrity" rehab where all the news media will be waiting at the front door. I think some people go into rehab because it's the latest fad in L.A. and everybody who is anybody is doing it. I can't say who is doing it because they honestly want help and who is doing it because they think their roommate will be a big star... Lord help us. Go for the right reason. Look, you wouldn't throw away a perfectly good car because it had a dead battery. Don't waste a good life because of a bump in the road. You can fix them both.

If you are old enough to remember, you know exactly where you were on September 11, 2001. I certainly remember I was getting on a plane to fly from Detroit to Denver. The crew stopped us and asked us to return to the terminal. I thought it was a mechanical problem. On the way up the concourse, I stopped at a television and watched the second plane fly into the second tower. Why would I bring this up? Because I bet all I have, and all I will ever have, that any of those innocent people who died that day would be happy to trade places with us today. I bet if any of them could come back and live in our shoes, they would not waste one second trying to kill or harm themselves with addiction. None of those people were perfect and neither are you or I... but there is a difference. They don't get another chance; we do. If you are reading this, you get to feed the addiction when you are through reading or you get to start getting well. Our second chance can start today, right this second, if we want it.

So off we go, on a sad journey but with light at the end of the tunnel, or straw, or bottle, or hotel room, or buffet, or needle, or wrong person, or whatever. There is hope and relief and rescue... but you have to want it.

Joey: In order to get well, you have to surrender to a higher power. There is a God out there somewhere, and it isn't you. I am clean and sober for over 30 years because I want to be clean and sober. My way didn't work, so I had to find a way that did work, and then I had to do the work. I admitted I had a problem, and I accepted help. ACCEPTING is a verb, not a noun. You can't think yourself into good acting; you have to act yourself into good thinking".

So much of this book are my words and Joey's information. He answered so many "what ifs" and "what about" and off-the-wall questions, and he sent me in the right direction to not only find answers but to find the truth. Maybe I am on

51

to something here. Sobriety and control is truth; addiction is false. The results of addiction are true, but the avenue is false. What Joey finally got through my thick head was, if you are in addiction, nothing around you is real. You are changing what is really happening into what you want to happen. That seldom works.

I spent several years trying to get my girlfriend to stop using drugs. It drove me and her crazy, and we fought about it most of the time. One afternoon over our cup of coffee, Joey put it to me pretty simple where I could not help but understand it. He said, "Porter, she's not going to quit using drugs, and she doesn't want to quit using drugs. Here's the real problem, you're not going to stop trying to change her, and you don't want to stop trying to change her. You're the problem, not her!"

What? That's crazy… there is nothing wrong with me. I'm trying to do what's right! We ordered our cup of coffee, and he tried to explain it again. Then one day I finally got it. Joey must have felt like Anne Sullivan when she got through to Helen Keller. I FINALLY GOT IT! Down south we have an expression that goes, "Don't try to teach a pig to sing; it's a waste of your time and annoys the pig." I was addicted to changing someone who didn't want to and wasn't going to change.

The end of the long story is this: I changed my phone number. I changed the locks on the doors. I got an answering machine at work and in the clubs, had someone screen all my calls. I got well. Trust me, there were some long, lonesome nights and some broken-hearted days, but I was getting well. All the other pains were gone. There was no more missing money, no more missing credit cards, and no more loss of character. There were no more lies, no more 3 a.m. phone calls, no more police buddies calling me to come get her, and no more trouble. I picked up my bruised and battered life and began to recover. About 14 years ago I was at my new job and got a phone call. It was her. She had seen my picture or read about me somewhere and found out where I worked and called me. It was great to hear from her… with one small exception, she was drunk. There was a two or three-hour time difference between where we lived, and it must have been "Happy or Unhappy Hour" where she was. I was sober. In seven years she had still not gotten well. Joey was right on the money! He had been right all along. It just took me quite a while to come around to it. He's still right.

That conversation was about five or six years ago, and I haven't talked to her since. She is probably still drunk, and I am very, very sorry about that. There is help available if she wants it. There is help available to the thousands of people in pain, if they want it. What I am very happy about is this... I am still getting well. Thank you, Joey!

Chapter 3
July 19, 2000

On July 19, 2000, life as Dianne Weeks knew it took a little unexpected detour. Sometimes these things happen, and if it hasn't happened to you yet, just wait, it's possible. Oh, it might be a flat tire when you are already late for an important meeting, or it could be a chipped tooth the day you are leaving for vacation. It might be the unexpected death of a loved one. It can be as bad as the World Trade Center on 9-11 or just a little inconvenience, but sooner or later, an unexpected, unwelcomed "bump in the road" is going to come your way, regardless.

That July day, Dianne was bringing her 30-plus-year employment with the state of Georgia to a close. She was in Atlanta with the new lady who would eventually replace her. They were attending an Information Systems Training session. This was going to be Dianne's last trip to Atlanta as an employee. Retirement was just over the horizon... life was looking good.

Growing up in the South, Mrs. Weeks had lived the Steel Magnolia Lifestyle. She had found the job she loved and the man she loved (Dianne married her high school sweetheart) and had given birth to two beautiful healthy baby boys. Dianne and her husband, Carl, had built a lovely home and the American dream was so very close at hand. Everything people work for was within her grasp.

Dianne is a healthy, fit woman with blond hair and soft blue eyes. She has an easy, almost slow, way about her. Her most redeeming feature is her warm and friendly smile. It lights up a room when she does it. In all, she is a beautiful Southern lady... never any real health issues and, as a matter of fact, the whole family is healthy.

There is one small problem that you probably wouldn't notice. Dianne notices it every morning when she wakes up. Her little problem is always there and will always be there. And that brings us back to July 19, 2000.

Dianne and her group were going to be in Atlanta from Wednesday until Friday. Let me remind you, this was her last business trip from Augusta to Atlanta. She had been there numerous times over the last 30 years on training and seminar trips but all that would be over on Friday. As it turned out, it was far from the last trip.

The first day events ended a little early and everyone headed for the level parking lot. People were milling around and chatting and trying to figure out what restaurant they would meet at, etc. It was a very normal end-of-the-day atmosphere. As luck would have it, Dianne's car wouldn't start and she had to get it pushed back to a safe area for a jumpstart. A couple of guys gave it a shove, the cables were connected, and it fired right up. So far, so good, the car was completely out of the way and others were driving past Dianne waving good-bye. There were a few people standing at Dianne's car making final dinner arrangements while other attendees had begun to pull out and vacate the parking lot. Everything was just fine, and then…

Dianne reports she heard some sort of a squeal or loud noise. She couldn't really identify it, just something very loud and out of the ordinary, like maybe a huge fan being turned on or maybe a large canister of $Co2$ was being opened. It was just some noise and it just wasn't exactly right.

Dianne was standing by the left-front fender of her car when another car came directly head first at her and crashed into the right-front fender of her car.

The impact picked Dianne up and drove her and the car into a third car parked behind her. In a split second, Dianne Weeks, one month from retirement, found herself wedged, pinned, stuck, caught and vice-gripped between two cars. Picture a pair of pliers, except the handles are two automobiles and Dianne is caught between them. Her right leg is severed but she can't move. She is pinned between the parked car behind her and her own car.

Now people are screaming and yelling and trying to get the first car to back up. More screaming and more yelling for help and complete and total chaos, except for Dianne. Dianne tells me she was fairly calm, until a man jumped in her car and started to back it up. She knew her car was not only crushing her, the bumper/ headlight was embedded in her leg, if they backed the car up, it would continue ripping her leg completely apart. She went ballistic screaming to pick

up the car, don't back it up. Pick it up, pick it up, pick it up! Pick up the
*&^%$#@ car! A couple of guys did just that; they picked the car up and she had
been right, the twisted metal came up and out of her leg. Now here comes the
blood, lots and lots of blood.

A nurse happened to be in the parking lot and immediately responded.
(Thank God for nurses.) She applied a belt to Dianne's thigh to stem the flow of
blood. As Dianne was lying on the concrete, the nurse reassured her she would be
all right. "Help is on the way, you are going to be OK, stay still, I'm here with
you, and help is on the way." There was just one more, small problem: Help was
on the way but the ambulance was too high to enter the parking garage. The ramp
was too steep for the fire truck to enter the driveway and clear the roof. The
paramedics (or angels, as Dianne calls them) had to run up five floors of the
parking garage. They got to her, carried her on the stretcher down five flights of
stairs and into the ambulance.

There was a lot more "you will be OK now" and a lot more "try to stay
calm" and a lot more PAIN! Dianne says she realized the trouble she was in
when they cut her tan linen pants leg open and she saw what had been her leg for
the first time. That's when she began fading in and out. The call was made to
Grady Memorial Hospital and by the time she got there, the emergency staff was
ready and waiting. She didn't have to wait in the lobby or fill out a ton of papers,
there was no 45 minutes of questions, i.e., where do you work, how do you
intend to pay for our services, none of that. She was shot-put through emergency
and prepped for surgery, as luck would have it, she was wheeled on the elevator
with two resident surgeons who would assist. The last thing Dianne remembers is
someone saying, "This looks like an amputation" and she replied, "No you
won't, don't cut my leg off."

Just to prove a point, I asked Dianne if she wanted a cigarette at that
time. Did she ask for a drink of liquor or was she jealous of some new fashion
one of the other ladies was wearing? Did she want to go buy a dozen donuts and
sit in front of the TV and wash them down with a half-gallon of double-goo,
walnut, cherry ice cream bomb? I asked her if at that time she wanted to argue
with her sons or maybe listen to the latest gossip about one of her neighbors? I
asked her what was really important as she was being wheeled into the operating
room. She looked at me like I was an idiot and very calmly said, "No, saving my
life and my leg was the only thing I wanted." Get my drift here? All of that other

stuff is crap when it gets down to how and if you are going to spend the rest of your life on this earth and in this world.

At this point of the interview, Dianne insists we thank the nurse in the parking lot. I think we should thank all nurses everywhere. She wants to thank the Atlanta Firemen and Paramedics who carried her from the floor to Grady Memorial Hospital. Thank you to the emergency room staff and the two Resident Fellow Doctors on the elevator who listened to her beg not to take her leg. Without question, she wants to thank and sing the praises of Dr. David V. Feliciano, M.D. More about him later. That's a lot of people to thank and think about every time she takes a step but, if any one of them was out of the equation, Dianne most likely wouldn't be here. They were there and she is here and they saved her leg and a day doesn't go by that she doesn't think of them.

Oh it's not the same leg, nowhere near, but it is the same Dianne. She didn't give up, she didn't quit. She survived 13 (or 14, who's counting) major operations, a total-body blood transfusion, countless liters of blood; she has seen more blood then Dracula, thousands of hours of therapy, days on end lying in ICU and CCU. She has become very familiar with bed pans and needles and wheelchairs and crutches and walking canes and wheelchairs and pain! But, she kept her leg. It is her leg and she wasn't ready or willing to give it up. She credits Jeff Dowling and Dr. Michael Tucker at the Medical College of Georgia with the second half of her story. Without them and the years of therapy, she would not have regained the level of use in that leg. She calls them two more of her "angels." To maintain her level of recovery, she is in the capable hands of Claude Thompson at Health Central in Augusta, Georgia. They have contributed as much to the use of her leg as the first group of "angels" did to saving it.

I didn't know she had ever been in an accident until six months after I met her. Incidentally, I met her in the gym, where she is a devout attendee. She doesn't miss her workouts. When I learned about the accident, I couldn't believe this lady has one-and-a-half legs. You couldn't tell by the way she exercises. She hits it! She trains with a purpose and is focused and is determined and has a goal in each workout. She certainly has earned the right to sit on the couch and eat buckets of Bon Bon's all day, but that ain't Dianne. She could cry and moan the blues and say "ouch, that hurt" but no, she pushes through the pain and discomfort. She fought to keep her leg and she means to use it. She reports, her only addiction is her workouts. If you are going to be an addict, that's not a bad one to have.

Now, if you or someone you know wants to smoke three packs of cigarettes today, fire 'em up! You want to drink a fifth of liquor after work today? I've tried it, it doesn't work, but you go ahead. Want to do a bag of heroin with a dirty needle? You might as well stick your hand in a cage holding a rabid dog. I can't stop you. Want to throw your life and health in the commode, flush away! You already know how I feel about an occasional drink or even a smoke once in a while. I am going to buy another lottery ticket and even bet on a horse one day. I don't want to do anything illegal, but a legal bet once in a while… fine by me. Want to eat a donut, eat one once in a while. It won't kill you. Please remember Dianne and how hard she worked to walk again and how hard she continues to exercise and eat healthy. She told me she did not want to carry one extra pound to put unnecessary weight on what is left of her leg. Smart idea.

Are you putting unnecessary weight on your heart? Are you intentionally putting unnecessary stress on your blood pressure? Why? Why was I? It doesn't make any sense. Look, neither Dianne nor I are perfect. She is light years ahead of me, but, nonetheless, neither of us are claiming to be little angels. What she is, is so thankful to be alive and have a second chance at life and walking that she isn't going to, with purpose and forethought, try to kill herself one spoonful at a time. She is not going to see how many cigarettes she can smoke when her body is still fighting to keep her leg and foot alive. She is not going to get drunk and fall down a flight of steps or wreck her car and undo all the great work Dr. Feliciano did. She has already stayed in one (of many) hospital for six weeks, had an external fixator in her leg, slept for years with pillows under her leg, had electric stimuli attached to her leg all night, slept on her back without being able to roll over, made her husband sleep on a sliver of the bed so she would not hit him if she moved her bad leg, given up things she used to do and will probably never do again. That's OK, she's alive. SHE IS ALIVE, AND SHE IS NOT GOING TO GIVE UP HER LEG!

As I wrapped up the interview, I asked, "What would you take for your ability to walk?"

"Nothing, it's priceless."

She has a beautiful home and family and children and grandchildren, and she has so many wonderful things and people in her life, and she loves and appreciates all of them. So, I asked her, "How important is your health?"

Dianne replied, "More than anything."

I asked, what was the most exciting thing she has done since the accident? Of course I meant skiing or some exciting vacation experience. She thought about it and said, "Driving my car." When you lose complete use of your right leg and foot, you have a hard time driving. That leaves you stranded, and Dianne refused to be stranded. She was hell-bent to regain use of that leg and foot so she could drive again. If you don't think that's important, don't drive, or walk, for a full week and see how precious it becomes.

I asked what the worst moment was, and she said, "I looked down and saw one tendon still attached, a little skin and tissue, the rest was just a dark, empty hole where my leg used to be."

Mrs. Weeks wants you to know an accident like hers can happen to anyone at any time. This happened to her before the World Trade Center attack on Sept 11 happened to our country, but they both did happen and they were both unexpected. There were consequences from both events. We all suffered on September 11, 2001, but on July 19, 2000, only Dianne and her family suffered. Ask yourself this: Are you waiting to suffer like Dianne did? Are you or someone in your family inching closer and closer every day to the unexpected heart attack or auto wreck or arrest or having to sell your house to pay a gambling debt? We were not prepared for 9-11, and Dianne and her family were not prepared for 7-19-00. Are you ready for what is coming? Because if you don't change or get the person you love to change, I guarantee one of life's little detours is in the future. Is it you, are you dying and a little bit of them is dying with you, every time you light up or shoot up or hook up or throw up or ante up or belly up?

All the support and love of her husband, Carl, and sons Chris and Brian and her co-workers and friends and in-laws and trust in the Lord helped Dianne survive the first year and the nine years since. Endless nights in different hospitals and sleepless nights and worried days on end... still, Dianne, and Dianne alone, was the owner of the pain. She had to want to live, and Dr. Feliciano had to give her his best shot. By the way, you ought to look up this guy on the Web; he's done some pretty amazing surgeries. It was a winning combination, and she lived. Do you have all these people lined up ready to save you? I don't. So I better take good care of myself just in case a nurse isn't right there and Dr. Feliciano might be on vacation and I might be off in some strange country, driving on the wrong side of the road. We never know, we just never know.

If you want to meet or talk to Dianne and you find yourself in Augusta, Georgia, I suggest trying Health Central or the Family Y or one of the gyms in the afternoon… more than likely she will be there.

There is one more little "P.S." to this story: Dianne started out after the initial operation on a big dose of morphine. She wanted off of it as soon as possible. She never did any drugs in her previous life and because of the accident, she started her relationship with drugs, beginning with morphine. She reports it made her sick, she didn't like the feeling of being out of control, and she would have rather dealt with the pain. Then came, Oxycontin. She really didn't like that. The sooner she was off that the better. Here is a lady who today could "without question" get a dose of pain medicine but, she would rather "suck it up" and deal with the pain and discomfort. She would rather NOT use something to deaden the reality of life. Don't misunderstand, there was and is a time and place to block the pain, or you can't take it and you will die. That isn't every day. It's not because life is unfair and you got dumped on. If you just had your leg cut off at the knee and you are bleeding to death, then I urge you to get medical help and take some pain medication. If not, then don't just block out life's everyday ups and downs with legal or illegal medication, if you can help it.

I honestly don't know if I am as strong as Dianne Weeks. I hope I am and I hope and pray I never have to find out. I do know this: She agreed to this interview because I convinced her it might help one person turn their life around. If you think your problems are greater than hers, I should be writing about you. If you haven't gotten your life in order but reading her story helps you make the change, then I was right. She is a Champion and a Winner and a Survivor and so are you. Stop what is killing you and walk away from it. You can, you can, and you will. Dianne's counting on you.

Can't help but think about and remember some people (a few you will read about) who had not lost their leg, who had the world on a string and traded it all for some of those drugs that Dianne refused. I guess the thing about Dianne is she fights every day to get well. She wouldn't miss a workout for anything. If she can't get to the gym, she exercises at home. What's different about her? What does she and so many other survivors have that a lot of us don't? I don't know... maybe that's why I am writing this book. Where do you find that determination to live as full and as healthy a life as possible? I don't know where you find it... maybe you dig up a bucket of worms and go fishing for it, but I know it's there. Dianne proves it every day.

Chapter 4
Dope

Don't be acting dopey. She was such a dope. Let's dope that tooth up before we pull it. When we pulled the car over, there was a strong smell of burning dope. What's the dope on that? There must be a whole lot of ways to use dope in a sentence. It looks like it can be a noun or a verb or an adverb or an adjective or even a way of life.

Here's a rough version of what the dictionary says about dope: a kind of liquid preparation added to produce desired properties. (I guess that's like adding something to your motor oil to get different results.) It also says: a narcotic, especially one that is addictive. (Key word there is addictive.) It goes on to say: A stupid person. The last explanation is: facts and information, details.

Doping: to administer a drug, usually in secret.

Doped: in a sluggish or dazed state, as if drugged, as if stupid or foolish. I believe there is a Walt Disney character named Dopey. He is portrayed as a goofy magic dwarf. There is a Walt Disney dog character named Goofy that acts dopey. All this brings us to the conclusion that Dope is a narcotic, it can certainly be addictive and it makes you act like a goofy cartoon character... that's the best I can come up with.

From research I found thousands of pages and hundreds of books on drugs and drug addiction. Far be it from me to ever attempt writing about drugs on that level. I don't know how to do it. The papers I read about drug addiction were often over my head with medical terms and mental disorders and complex explanations. There was an excellent article in Time magazine a year or two ago about what happens when we take a dose of narcotics. I believe it was Time, might have been Newsweek, I can't remember. Regardless, I urge you to read about drug addiction if you are in it or someone you love is an addict.

On my end I can only give you a couple of examples of hard core drug addiction. These are real people and real stories and real sad. Maybe I can explain it right or maybe not, either way I am going try. I guess it's like trying to describe an orgasm; if you ain't had one, it's hard to explain!

A long time ago I was closing a bar about 2:00am one morning and while moving some chairs, I saw 2 small brown bottles (about the size of model car paint) under a chair. I ask one of the bartenders what in the hell is this and he says "Damn, where did you that, it's cocaine". Oh really I say and told everybody to stop what they were doing and lets have a quick staff meeting.

Naturally nobody knew anything about it so I moved the meeting into the Ladies room. I gave a quick speech about our liquor license and our business license and how many people would be out of work if we were caught with drugs on the property. Nobody said a word, so I proceeded to dump both vial down a toilet. Half the people there looked like lions watching a lamb sleep! There were a couple of Oh no, he didn't and No way and I don't believe it, and as far as I was concerned that was the end of it. Not so fast.....

One of the waitresses later told me that a couple of the other girls had gone back in there and wiped their fingers around the toilet seat to see if any of the cocaine was still on there. IT WAS A TOILET SEAT! God help us....

Just like this book or any other book, the author puts it out there and has to be ready and hopefully able to take the praise and criticism. There were mixed reviews about one of the best true stories I read in my life....it is "Out of Control" by NFL linebacker Thomas "Hollywood" Henderson. I urge you to read it. He did not hold back on anything. I will let him tell his story because he lived it. Thank the Lord he has turned his Life around and wrote a sequel called "In Control"....

Remember, in control or out of control.....there is no grey area.

Chapter 5

Carl

There seems to be as many drugs, legal and illegal, as there are people who abuse them. There are the drugs and there are the people who become addicted. It's a dangerous combination. Sometimes the drugs are legal but being in possession of them is illegal. There are all kinds of combinations here, and the next couple of stories are about a real drug, an illegal drug, and some wasted, ruined lives. I hate telling these stories. I have changed the names but, so help me, they are the truth.

Carl was your above-average, good ol' boy. He made it through high school and never got in trouble. He played football and lettered three years in a row. He was a pretty good player but not interested enough in college to pursue it. He wanted to get out and go to work and make some money. Vietnam was over and there was no chance of him getting drafted. He got a job doing construction work. I believe he told me he joined the union and got a pretty good-paying job for his skilled labor. He had some school buddies that opened a bar and restaurant and they hired him on holidays to barback and check IDs and help out sometimes on Friday and Saturday night. Guess what? He met a girl at the bar and cupid shot them both in the butt and they fell in love. How wonderful.

A couple of months go by and sure enough, wedding bells! These were two pretty smart people who had never been married and were going to wait a year or so to have children. They both kept working and saved enough money for a down payment on a small house and about two acres of land. It was the American dream come true. In order to save the money for the house, my friend Carl (not really his name) didn't give up his two nights at the bar. The wife spent Friday nights with her family, but Saturday night she was alone. Maybe that wasn't such a good idea, we'll see.

A year or so later, Carl shows up where I was working and reports he is getting a divorce. It came out of nowhere and we were all sort of shocked. He said it had been coming for a while and there were no hard feelings and no children and no real debt. She could keep the house or sell it; either way was fine with him. Yes, he was sad and he wished it had worked out but it was inevitable. I remember him getting a little misty eyed and saying marriage was hard and just wasn't for everybody. He was sure he would be fine. Next thing I hear is Carl has quit his day job and is working full time at the bar and only part time doing construction; no more mention of his wife. Life goes on. He would drop in and see me and have a beer three or four times a month. It looked like he had moved on with his life.

Here we go! One evening a friend of ours comes in and quietly tells me that Carl has been arrested. I hadn't seen him in months and I figured he went back to his wife's house and maybe knocked the door down or was arguing with her or something like that. No, my pal said, Carl had got in a fist fight with a couple of cops when they arrested him as he left a crack house in the worst part of town. WHAT? Yep, it's pretty bad. It looks like he wrecked his car and wrecked a police car and then put up a pretty good fight. WHAT? Yep, they found a crack pipe on him. I did believe it, but I couldn't believe it. It was a long time ago but I remember the bond was about $20,000. They had him on a couple of felonies and several misdemeanors. He also had a weapon in the car. Big mistake!

He didn't make bond. I didn't go to court but understand he pleaded guilty and threw himself on the mercy of the court. With no previous record, he ended up with almost two years. It just doesn't pay to wreck police cars, run from them, and try to beat them up with dope pipes in your pocket and a weapon in your wrecked car. What was that boy thinking?

When he finally got out, he eventually came by to have a cold beer with me. It was great to see him, and I had to ask him what in the hell happened? He said it was a long story. I told him to hang around after we closed and he and I would sit and have a couple of cold beers. That night he gave me the best, most complete explanation of cocaine addiction I have ever heard.

Maybe you have experienced this, or maybe your daughter or son has been through this, or maybe someone you love is going through it right now. I hope not. Maybe it's your mom or dad or brother or sister or sweetheart who is sliding down the white-line highway. Maybe they will hit a stop sign before it's too late. Maybe the local Sheriff or some law-enforcement agency will stop them before it's too late. Maybe the drug dealer will put an end to them because they can't come up with the money, or maybe their heart will just come to a screeching halt after a big dose of the drugs. Any way you look at it, they are going to stop one day, one way or the other. They are either going to quit the drug, or it is going to kill them.

I have heard so many users say, "They didn't want to be where they were, and they couldn't leave." Cocaine was the vehicle that transported them mentally and physically from where they were. Remember what Joey said, "Addiction is a big hole in your chest and you pick something to fill it." Does that sound about right to you? It does to me. The addicts we are talking about are in some sort of pain. They wake up hurting and they hurt all day even if they do function in society, and they go to bed at night still hurting. It reminds me of that sad, sad blues song "Good Morning Heartache." You just hurt all the time. To the addicts, this cocaine takes that pain away while they are still here where they don't want to be, but have to be. Doesn't really take it away, it covers it up. Like putting makeup on a bruise that keeps reappearing… it doesn't solve the problem.

So this one night, Carl has come by to see me and I invited him to stay after we closed and finally tell me what in the world really happened. We started off by me asking how in the world a smart, bill-paying, hard-working guy like Carl could end up involved with crack cocaine. These are his words exactly as I remember them:

Carl: I didn't give a shit about dope, never did. You know that. I bounced guys out of bars for talking about dope. It was never my thing. I puffed a marijuana joint about twice in high school but that was it. My wife would hardly take an aspirin. She wouldn't have used dope if you held a gun to her head. I always thought those idiots were nuts to pay so much for something that made your nose itch.

Beer was my thing; I drank about a six pack at night and a case on the weekend but that was it. Didn't like hard liquor. I like my beer.

One night after I got divorced, me and a couple of my buddies were out bar hopping and chasing girls and somebody in the car pulled out some coke. There were two or three guys in the back seat, and I was riding up front and honestly don't remember who had it. Anyway, they all passed it around and you were supposed to squeeze this little tube-like thing and they all did and I kept saying no thanks. I was drinking beer and loaded to the gills (he wasn't driving) and didn't care nothing about no cocaine. I couldn't have gotten higher if I had snorted a pound of it.

It came around again and to me last, and I finally took a snort, more to shut everybody up than any other reason. (STOP RIGHT THERE!) Did the reader hear that? He did it to shut other people up… how many times have we been pressured to do the wrong thing and done it because our "FRIENDS" keep on and keep on… they tell you, come on… try it! Just one, it won't hurt you. It doesn't matter if it's a donut or a crime or another drink. If you can't control it and it leads to your demise, they aren't your friend! Don't do it… It's horse$#!%! It will KILL you. On with the story…

Carl continued: I went on drinking and they eventually took me home and that was that. I got absolutely nothing out of the coke. What a waste of time and money… I didn't care if I ever saw another line of cocaine or not.

By now it was about 3 a.m. and I asked Carl if he wanted to go or stay and drink a few more beers? I remember him saying he wanted to stay and talk about it. He said he had never talked to anyone about it and wanted to get it off his chest. I got us two more beers. (Twenty years later it dawns on me, I was still sitting there at the bar drinking at 3 a.m. His problem was cocaine, mine was alcohol.)

Carl: A few days later we all go out again and are doing the bar crawl when sure enough, the cocaine comes out again. I still thought they were all idiots and I still liked my beer but to shut them up again, I took a dose and like before, same ol' same ol'… nothing. A few more bars and a few more beers and we were headed to the last bar of the night when my pal who was driving offered me one more hit. OK I'll do one more. They were doing the driving and they picked me up and I didn't want to sit home alone so to make them happy, I did my second hit (third in my life) that night. Nothing happened. Then all of a sudden…

It might have been five seconds later or five minutes later but so help me God, I saw notes coming out of the dashboard speakers. All at once my favorite song in the world was being played in that car's dashboard and the music was coming out of those speakers and I could see and feel each and every note. I felt the strings bend on the guitar, and I knew what note was coming next. I went from liking a song, to world-class music appreciation in a millionth of a second. So the song ends and I am speechless until the next song comes on and lo and behold, I can see this song. I know every lick and every note and I feel what people have been talking about for the first time in my life. I ain't never held a guitar and don't know the words to Happy Birthday, but that night in the front seat, I was Chet Atkins and Jimmy Page and Elvis rolled into one. I was the air guitar champion of the world.

I had to laugh at this because this guy has hands the size of Virginia hams and would have a hard time fingering any instrument much less a guitar.

On with the story: Carl described the notes coming out of the speakers and floating into his chest. He not only felt the note, he was the note. He knew if it was flat or sharp or natural. I asked him what song it was and he said, Hell I don't know... whatever was playing was my favorite song! I sort of know what he meant because back then, whichever drink I was having, was my favorite drink!

When they dropped him off, he was not ready to go home. As soon as his pals left, he jumped in his car and became Richard Petty. Carl told me it was the first time in his life he watched the tachometer in his car. He felt every RPM and he gripped the wheel with both hands and for the first time, felt the road and the car's response to his commands. He felt the horsepower and the gears and the windows were down and the wind was whipping through his face and hair... he was driving for the first time in his life. Except, he had had his driver's license for about 15 years and had been driving all 15 of them.

As I recall, he drove a 20-year-old car with six cylinders. It was so beat up, he kept jumper cables in the floorboard. That night it was a Shelby Cobra. He gets to a bar, goes in and buys one beer. He reports sitting there and watching all the lights he has never noticed. He actually watched the blinking lights on the cigarette machine for the first time in his life... and he doesn't smoke. He thought all the girls had had makeovers because they looked like the stars from Baywatch, and he really felt the music coming out of the wall speakers. He is more alive than ever before and now sees the beauty in everything. The bar soon closed and for the first time he enjoyed the drive home. What a night! He felt as if he had possibly reached Zen.

I ask if he wants another beer and would he please tell me if this high is like smoking a joint? Yes on the beer and no, absolutely not. It's not like smoking anything. It's completely different and completely better. I ask him if he was sure it was the cocaine, and he said he didn't know what the hell it was, it just was. Carl reports he got up the next day with no hangover, no headache, and no ill effects at all. The only thing he didn't know and couldn't remember was what song was playing when it hit him in the chest. It really didn't matter but he sure liked that song.

A few days go by and Carl is ready to go out with his pals and have a few beers. He gives a world-class report on how wonderful the last outing was and they are all laughing and saying: I told you so. Deep down inside Carl is secretly hoping they hurry up and breakout the coke and offer him a snort. He wanted to see another song. He wanted to see the notes fly out of the speaker and go through his shirt and bounce off his backbone and float around in his lungs and come back out his mouth… that's what happens when you have perfect pitch! They did and he did and it was another world-class night! More laughs and more pretty girls and more songs and life was wonderful. One other thing, he drank a lot less beer that night.

By now you and I both see where this story is going. I had seen it too many times in the bar business but never from this close of a friend. People kept drugs away from me. I didn't approve of it or allow it in my house or where I worked. Most folks respected my rule about it and either did it before they saw me or outside in their car. There were no exceptions. I might smoke a truckload full, if it ever becomes legal, but until then, the answer is NO. My problems were legal… booze and the wrong women. Somebody ought to outlaw them.

Carl's explanation continues: Somewhere along the line about the third or fourth time, Carl's buddies dropped the bomb on him. They wanted to do a little cocaine and they knew where there was some great dope but, they just didn't have enough cash to score it. They had to have cash because it's not a credit card business. To be a little rude, it's cash or ass… depending on who's buying it. With this bunch of rough guys, it was most definitely cash. They needed about 50 bucks. No problem, Carl had a couple hundred in the bank and would stop by an ATM machine and get the money. Carl gets the money, they come by and pick it up and return with the dope and the merry-go-round starts again, except this is the merry-go-round that rides you.

Carl was sitting there with me in that bar at 3:30 a.m. staring at his beer and said, "That time it was about 95 percent the high I had been having. It was great and I loved it but, it was just a shade lighter than the first few times. So, I did a little more that night and everything was fine.

The next time, it was the same thing, about 90 percent of the original high. It was still wonderful. It didn't take long, and I was doing a couple of lines about twice a week. It began costing me $300 to $400 a month, and I was glad to pay for it. It didn't happen all at once but it did dawn on me one night that I was buying coke and doing it alone (didn't want to share it) trying to chase that first high. The truth was, the more coke I did the further away that first high got. It reminded me of what Joey said, "The highs quickly get lower and the lows immediately get lower; it's the nature of the addiction."

He finally admitted it got to be an everyday thing. He would get enough dope to get him through the day and get to work and then spend the night looking for enough for the next day. He admitted to smoking crack, still looking for that first high. He found it for a few minutes but it went away as fast as it came. He told me he sold his wedding band and a pocket knife his dad gave him. He sold everything and then he started stealing. When he couldn't get the dope he would drink anything with alcohol, in order to pass out and get away from the cravings.

This is real important: Carl reported that pretty quick, all his friends were drug users. He still knew a lot of people but after he started using, he didn't hang out with drinking buddies, he hung out 90 percent of the time with drug pals. It reminds me of an old expression, "Water seeks its own level." We won't even start the discussion about girls, especially coke whores. Females that are into drugs will come out of the woodwork for it. I think some of them come out of the ground for it. They look dead and act dead and are willing to do anything (I mean anything) to get some "Queen" or "white lady" or "Party" or whatever you want to call it. We will talk about that in a little while. Back to Carl.

Here was a good guy who started out with two jobs and a pretty wife who loved him and a good credit history and because of some "friends" wanting him to take a bite of the bait, his life was being ruined.

Let's stop here for a minute and talk about some other friends I've had. I had a doorman who was one of the best employees ever in 20 years in the bar business. He was 100 percent at work, never a problem. I could have used a dozen like him. He would work a couple of extra shifts a month and take a scheduled day off, go buy an eight ball (1/ ounce of coke) and do it at his house that night. He did it every month he worked for me. One day a month and that was it. He told me he was doing it and for me not to call him, because he wouldn't come in. Then the next shift he would be at work and do an outstanding job the rest of the month… go figure? The thing was he didn't have a problem with the dope. It was wrong and illegal, but I guess as intelligent as you can be and use cocaine, he did it. Unfortunately, Carl just didn't have that small of a hole in his chest.

Are you going to be the one in a hundred who can do a line of cocaine at a party and not do it again for months? Are you going to try it and want more the second it gets in your system? If you don't know the answer to that question, you better not take a bite of the bait… there is no cure, there is only recovery for the rest of your life. I have had smart, healthy people tell me they quit cocaine and haven't used in years but, if they did one line, they would spend the rest of the night looking for enough to take them back to the level where they quit. It's like racing in NASCAR and then quitting, to race go-carts. It just doesn't quite measure up.

Will you spend all your money and all your family's money and chance going to jail for a long time? Look, if you don't know which side of the question you are going to land on, you better not jump.

It's no secret that for years I managed nightclubs. When it comes to drugs, they are everywhere but especially in the bars and restaurants. I told somebody that coke is to the nightlife what Kudzu is to a brick wall; it starts and grows and grows and grows… you can trim it and cut it back and pull it off the wall but it won't matter. You have three choices with Kudzu: put up with it, kill the roots, or knock down the wall. I trust you won't choose the latter.

As I said, I have managed almost every kind of bar and restaurant there is. I managed a place called Church Street Station in Orlando that had 600 employees and entertained three presidents and hundreds of movie stars and politicians. It brought in "world-class acts" in the Cheyenne Saloon and Opera House. I have also managed a 2 a.m. till daylight "bottle" club on Orange Blossom Trail. I stayed five years at Church Street and about five days at the bottle club. That bottle club was probably the roughest place I have ever worked in my life. I wasn't mean enough for that scene. The company I worked for at that time owned the bottle club and how I ended up there was the manager got beat to death in a robbery one morning when he was closing. Think about what kind of clientele you are probably going to have, out looking for a drink at 3 or 4 or 5 o'clock in the morning? I've also worked at some private resorts in Miami that were beyond exclusive. Somebody had to pass away and will their membership to get a new member. I remember one bartender there who was a complete screw-up. He was late and out of uniform and when the manager finally had enough, he got fired. That's not the end of the story; I heard through the grapevine that "several" of the members of this particular country club went to the manager and told him to rehire the bartender or they would fire him... must have been the bartender's cologne that made him so popular. Regardless of where I worked, anywhere there is alcohol and the possibility of some wait staff getting drugs, there can be trouble. Addiction and the results of it are equal-opportunity employers.

Here's my point: They all equally sold and dispensed liquor, and they all had guys with drugs willing to sell the dope or trade it for sex. My mother told me a long time ago that "everyone is equal under the sheets." She was right. I have watched millionaire businessmen try their dead level best with money (or I later found out drugs) to buy a waitress for the night. It's funny how when people hit rock bottom, they will confess everything. So many girls have told me the same story about how a guy or girlfriend got them hooked on dope, got all their money, got all the sex they wanted, and when the person telling the story was used up and broke, the dealers gave them to some other lower-level dealer. Women were just as guilty as the men. I found out that often part of the girlfriend's responsibility in order to keep the dope coming is to recruit other girls. We are going to talk more about this later. Carl got caught up in this from his "FRIENDS," not some dope dealer who walked up to him on the street.

My buddy Carl was out buying dope one night and he bought it from the wrong (for him) person. Carl wasn't thinking about who he was getting it from or where he was getting it. Like a song that gets stuck in your head and you hum it over and over and can't quit thinking about it, all he was thinking about was the dope. Turns out it was a set up sting by the Police Department. Carl ran and made it to his car. He sped away and crashed into a patrol car and then into a tree. He jumped out and tried to run through some shrubs and trees then, he got tackled. He put up a struggle but was overpowered. I asked him why he was trying to get away; they knew who he was and had his car. They were going to find him. "Yeah, I know, he said, but I hadn't scored any dope back at that house and I was trying to get away so I could go find some."

Last time I saw Carl he was pulling in the parking lot of a bar in an old broken-down car. He stuck a small pipe in his mouth and had the windows rolled up. He looked bad. I didn't get to talk to him because I was leaving as he pulled in. All I can do is hope and pray it was Prince Albert tobacco in the pipe he was lighting… but, I doubt it. I have no idea what ever happened to him. I didn't see him for a few years after that and he never came back around. I have no idea where he is. Maybe he moved, and if moving out of Orlando and maybe out of Florida helped Carl gets straight, then I hope he is living in China!

Back in 1982 and '83, I had the privilege of working with the U.S. Marshal Service in Orlando. I got hired as a prison guard and did courtroom security. The men and ladies of the Marshal's Service do an amazing job with the first and oldest law-enforcement agency in the USA. It was an honor to work with them. Part of my job was to make sure the "guest" in the holding cells didn't need medical attention, got a phone call, and got a drink of water or whatever before they went to jail. Kind of a "are you OK, do you want me to call anybody, do you need to tell anyone where your car is, are your children in a day care?" Questions like that.

So one afternoon a couple of guys are brought in and they just happen to have 2 kilos of cocaine in their possession. I think the DEA got them off a boat that the Coast Guard caught over in Cocoa Beach, Florida. I can't remember the details (it was a busy office), but I think that was correct. Anyway, I ask the first guy if he needs anything, he says no, there was no one to call. He would wait till he got to the Seminole County Jail. OK, fine, no problem. So, I ask the next guy if he needed anything. He was dead serious and said he was going away for a long time. He had evidentially been down this road a time or two and he knew he was looking at a serious stretch this go-round. Could I just one last time get him a "taste" of the cocaine they were caught with? Just one last taste that was going to have to last him for years and years. Think about that. He didn't want to call his mother or his lawyer or his family, and he didn't want a cup of coffee or a priest or a women. He wanted more cocaine. I told him I was sorry, but I couldn't help him and I meant it more than one way. He was lost and I don't know if he ever found his way. I hope so.

These stories don't end. If anything they get worse. You might read one or two more before the book ends, but the message stays the same. You can't beat the dope. It wins every time. If you are not afraid of jail and you have no sense of right or wrong and self or family value, then just know it will ruin your life (and the people who love you) one way or the other. Are you killing your parents with the addiction? Are your children doing without because you are smoking up your paycheck? Every time you score, you should say, "This drug is more important than anything else in my life, my family's life, my freedom or my job." I cannot for the life of me think of one person, not even the dealers I have known, whose life improved with drug addiction... not one. Somehow, one way or the other, they all either got out of it, or crashed. Like a traffic accident, not all of them walked away from the crash. Some were fatal. Why take the chance?

If you haven't done it, don't do it. If you have been caught up in that merry- go-round, get as far away from the people still caught as you can get. Getting involved with drugs and trying to stop is like trying to untangle a thousand wire coat-hangers... it's really hard to do. Step one is don't add anymore hangers!

No matter if it is money, character, family, or life itself, when it comes to drugs, the price you are going to pay is the only thing that "Stays High."

I can't close without the absolutely true story of a lady we will call Ms. X. We will call her that because I don't remember her name. I remember her face and her story, but I probably blocked her name out because I never wanted to see or hear from her again... never.

She came to work with me in about 1985 or '86, somewhere along in there. I can't remember because I was probably drunk! I do remember this: She was drop-dead gorgeous. Ms. X was about 5'8" and about 130. She had blond thick hair and the most beautiful eyes I think I have seen in my life. They were some sort of blue. They looked like the sky and water in Key West. Perfect white teeth and a smile that would melt you. I was real glad to have her selling our liquor.

She was so good looking that everybody assumed she was waiting to go to work at Disney or maybe to star in some show around Orlando or something like that. A lot of young people go in and out of the bar business because it is fast money and you can work a day job or go to school. I do remember on her application she didn't have much experience back where she came from. (This is important… she was from a LARGE city up north, a very LARGE city up north.)

When I asked what she had been doing, she reported she had been involved for the past two or three years with beauty pageants. Really? I thought she meant putting them on. She said, No… winning them. She had been a model and beauty queen back in her home state. She had the newspaper clippings to prove it… WOW! The next question was why are you waiting tables in a bar? Well, she had broken up with her boyfriend, and he moved out and she was getting a little behind on the rent and didn't want to have to call home and borrow money and the same story I had heard all my life. I got her a uniform and put her to work that night!

It took about six to eight weeks and I (along with everybody else) began to notice the bad complexion appear. Then the dirty fingernails instead of the polished ones. One or two of the employees began to drop hints to me that there was going to be a problem with this one.

You could just see her falling apart in front of your eyes. What was going on? Was she having a breakdown because the boyfriend left? Was she getting evicted? Was the schedule till 2 a.m. four nights a week too much? I finally sat her down one night and simply ask, "What's wrong?"

You already know the answer. Here come the tears and the dry heaves and the uncontrolled sobs and the beautiful blue eyes are blood red and the circles under them look like G14 radial tires. She told me she had been up for

75

about two weeks, getting a nap here and a nap there and she knew she couldn't hang on much longer. She lost her boyfriend over her drug use and now she had to sleep with several people she couldn't remember their names because they were supplying her with a ton of dope and the whole time she is telling me this she is shaking like she was sitting on a block of ice! It was Orlando; it was 89 degrees outside, and it wasn't cold. And, she damn sure didn't smell good.

I am not the hero in this story, or any other story. But, I did play a part in this one. We called her parents and woke them up. They agreed to come get her in a day or two. There was a business to close and dogs to take to the kennel and they would make the thousand-mile drive, day after tomorrow. OK, we got that settled. Now, just go home and pack your bags and cancel your rent and lights and get your stuff together and I will get you a final check by tomorrow and you can be out of here.

"No, Porter, I can't go home."

Why not?

"Because people will be coming by all night and all day tomorrow and want to bring by dope and party till time for work tomorrow. I just can't go home."

I had to do it, I had to take her to her apartment and told her I would stay the night and make *&^% sure nobody came in and "partied" all night. She cried some more and sat in the office till I got off work and drove her to her apartment.

Now, here comes the payoff. The apartment was a dump! Here was Miss So and So a finalist in her state beauty contest to go on to a major title and she is living (or dying) in filth. Garbage piled up all over the house. Not dirty dishes in the sink, dirty carry out bags from fast food places. Clothes all over the place. It looked like a girl's locker room in grade gym. I could go on and on but you get the idea. She had not cleaned the place since he left or she moved in.

All the above isn't the point of the story. Here is the first: The walls were white and the front door and blinds were white except for three places that were absolute black. Two equally filthy places on the door where she stood and looked out the peephole to see who was hiding outside coming in to attack her. And a place on the trim about the same height as the door marks where she

76

peeped out the window looking for people who were coming to get her. Can you say "PARANOID"? These places were black, not brown, not smudged, but black where she had not bathed or washed her hands and would go there hundreds of times day and night looking for ghosts in the front yard. Great way to spend your youth in beautiful Orlando, Florida!

The second amazing thing was who came by and knocked on the door and went into shock when I answered and said "Ms. X isn't playing anymore." About 80 percent of them were my employees. Some of them ran, some of them asked what in the hell I was doing there, and some just stood there in shock. But nobody came in. After a couple of hours of this, I couldn't find Ms. X. I thought she might have gone out the bathroom window, but it was still locked from the inside. The bed was covered in cloths; she wasn't there. The closets were bare, she wasn't in the shower. I couldn't find her. I went in the kitchen and looked in the refrigerator, no Ms. X. Then I opened a cabinet and looked under the sink, bingo! There she was in a knot hiding from the people at the door or me or from herself or that cocaine ghost… I will never know which. There she was, 25 years old waiting on mother and father to come get her and hiding in a filthy apartment, under the sink with the bugs. I went to sleep on the couch… no way I was getting in (or on) that bed… and stayed as long as I could the next day. She hadn't done any drugs in 10 to 12 hours and when I left, she seemed a fraction better than she did the night before. I told her I would call and check and see if they arrived. I did make it a point to call them when I got home and they had already left. Later that night she and her parents called me at work and said thank you and they were here and leaving the next day to get her home. I never saw or heard from her again.

Do you think it can't happen to you? It can. Do you think because she was beautiful that it made a bit of difference? Do you think she didn't have a hole as big as Texas in her chest? She didn't want to be where she was and she couldn't leave… there was nothing she knew to do to relieve the pain and cocaine was the only way out. When she couldn't pay for the cocaine, the delivery boy made a personal withdrawal from her private bank. She may have been pregnant, I don't have any idea. She may have known who the father was; she didn't have any idea. Being pretty or being rich or being educated DOES NOT HAVE ANYTHING to do with the hurt and pain that comes with addiction.

It's like the fog... people from all walks and levels and looks of life drift in and out of it. Some stay.

I beg you to listen to the best song written about addiction... it's wonderful. Elvis Pressley sang it and I think Hoyt Axton's mom wrote it. It's called Heartbreak Hotel. "The door is always crowded, but you still can find some room... for broken-hearted lovers to lie there in their gloom... let me tell you this, the lobby to addiction stays crowded but like that song, you can always get in. Addiction will never have a NO OCCUPANCY sign... it won't happen.

It can be a world-class athlete on his way to a world title and a steady diet of Scotch puts an end to a career. Remember what we said about Joey? It wasn't the opponent that stopped him, it was the celebration after the fight that knocked him out. Happy to report Joey has won that fight every day and night for the last 30-plus years.

No idea what happened to the two guys in jail... I guess they did their time and stayed out or went back. One or the other.

Never heard from the beautiful girl again. All I can do is hope and pray that the love and devotion from her parents was enough to get her started back on the road to sobriety. Twenty five years later, I am still shocked at how pretty she was to have fallen that far that quick. It was like she was waiting to fall and cocaine showed her where the edge was. Maybe cocaine was the edge. Again, it only goes to prove that looks, position, who you are, money, nothing has anything to do with addiction. It's like Christianity, you have it or you don't and with addiction, it has you or it doesn't. No grey area either place.

On a trip back to Orlando recently, one of my pals told me he saw Carl (not the guy's real name) and thank God, Carl was working and reported he was doing good. He has stayed out of trouble and goes to his job five or six days a week. My pal told me Carl looked healthy and wasn't a nervous wreck or sniffing or talking about or asking about dope. He is doing construction work for a big outfit and pretty much lives and works out of town. Maybe that's what it took after he got out of jail... to get away from his "friends" who still live there and got him started on cocaine. Maybe you and I should think about that. Is it where we live that is causing us to be out of control? Maybe. I don't think so. I am convinced there is cocaine and meth and marijuana and dope and alcohol and porn and gambling and the wrong person and shopping and whatever our addiction, no matter where we are if we go out looking for it and want to find it. Maybe it's us, or the people we associate with that are either using or selling our addiction.

Isn't that a funny thought? How addicted would we become to anything, if no one else was involved? For the life of me I can't remember anyone telling me that one day out of the blue they got up, went and bought a needle, got a belt, tied off their arm, and drove around until they found a heroin dealer, and for the first time bought a dose and shot it up. It always involved one of their friends doing the introduction. Same with alcohol, same with any addiction we put in our bodies... someone was there to help us share the exciting experience. How many of those fair-weather friends are around when you are freezing or sweating to death and trying to kick the habit? The worst addiction I know might be food. From experience I can hear people saying, "Now don't lose too much weight, you don't want to look sickly." Why in the hell weren't they saying, "Well, Porter, if you gain about 30 more pounds, you will hit the magic 300 number you pig," when I was weighing 264? Friends fall into two categories: They want to help you succeed or they want you to crash and burn with them... you have to let their actions help you decide which.

As with almost every chapter in this book, there are more stories. As I write and remember, more and more people come to mind. It wasn't drugs for all the folks who were addicted, and it wasn't illegal some of the time but it was addiction nonetheless. Read the chapter about "puppies." It was razor-sharp addiction and had nothing to do with dope or alcohol or food.

I am going to close this for now but want your permission to write about some other examples of people who were involved in drugs but had an even bigger addiction to something else. The drugs only gave them relief from what was really eating them alive. The dope and booze was sort of a sidebar to the real problem. It's like the lady I know who paid thousands to have her stomach stapled in order to lose some weight. All that happened was, she takes one bite of candy at a time now and she does it all day long. It's the same amount of fat and the same amount of sugar, it's just going in slower and in smaller amounts but it's all getting in there just the same. She didn't solve the problem; all she did was try to empty the pool with a teaspoon.

Chapter 6
Roy

Let me give you a quick background. I was absolutely blessed to get to go to work at EAS in 1998. Who would have ever thought it? I sure didn't. It was such an honor to be included in the first group of 10 Champions, I really could not have ever asked for anything else. My trainer, Eric Shrieves, and I got to go out to Denver that weekend in '97, and Bill Phillips gave all 10 Champions a new Corvette and $50,000, and I came home and walked around in a daze for a few weeks.

I still worked for Gene DuPont (one of the best men I have ever known), and I continued working in the night club business... but, something was wrong. I had quit drinking and I was 48 years old and I was done with bars and that life-style. I knew if I stayed in the bar business, I would go right back to my old "used to be." Something had to give. On a trip to Denver to do a Make-A-Wish fundraiser, I got offered the job of Manager of the Body-*for*-LIFE. The rest is history.

After a couple of years, Bill sold EAS, and it ended up being owned by Abbott. Abbott is a huge pharmaceutical company based in Chicago. There is a lady named Jane K. Smith who handles Abbott's EAS Military business, and I occasionally work with her. She has a story that is far greater than mine and I hope one day to write about her. She is an amazing woman. So here is the whole point of all this background. Abbott cares a lot about the military men and woman, who serve and protect our country, and Jane sends me, on occasion, to ports and bases all over the world to meet and greet and appreciate what the troops are doing. We are in a lot of Navy Exchanges and PX's and Air Force bases, and Abbott has always been willing to support our troops, and always willing to send me to visit with the troops. I have been places that aren't on the map! That's OK, I felt real safe around all those armed soldiers, sailors, and Marines.

I tell you all of this because I want you to know how we come to this part of the book. On one trip to the Navy base in Guam, I met two of the most wonderful people I know: Rick and Jan Wynn. She is a Captain in the Navy and is (I think) the in command of the base. They opened their home and heart to me and made me feel welcomed the entire time I was on Guam. Both of them have done the Body-*for*-LIFE program and both of them are in excellent health. As we became friends and as they gave me a priceless tour of the island, I mentioned I was a big battlefield and history fan. At that point, Jan asked if I would be interested in a tour of Iwo Jima later that year. I was floored, Iwo Jima? Are you serious? Yes, she was. I booked my flights, I told everybody I knew I was going to sacred ground, I cancelled all other appointments for that week, I was on fire! Then my flight out of Columbia, South Carolina, got cancelled... I sat on the runway for three hours while they tried to fix a fuse... no luck. I missed my connection in Chicago and San Francisco. I lost my deposit, I lost my trip to Iwo... woe is me! Jan went on the one-day visit to Iwo with the vets of that assault (both Japanese and American), and she was kind enough to send me a bag of the black volcanic sand. Guests are allowed to scrape up a little sand from the beach. There are no words to thank Jan and Rick for their friendship and efforts to get me to Iwo Jima. They will forever be in my thoughts and prayers no matter where she is on duty.

One reason I wanted to go was to interview a survivor of that week or two in 1945. It had to be absolute hell, and I really wanted to talk to some of the men who lived through it. It wasn't meant to be. What was I to do? I wanted (for this book) to interview a few people who lived through unbearable circumstances and share with the reader what they had, that you can have, to see you through the toughest of times. What to do, what to do? Then it dawned on me, I would like to introduce you to my step-father, Roy L. Broussard. I wrote a little bit about him in my first book, but now I hope to tell you more of the story. At least the part he is willing to share. Here we go...

Roy was born in New Orleans in the late '20s. As luck would have it, he was born on Thanksgiving. We all know that's a day to celebrate and eat, eat, eat. It's funny how that worked out over the next few years. We will get back to that later.

His childhood dream was to become a soldier in the Infantry. It had to be the Infantry, I'm not sure how you know at 6 or 7 years old the word Infantry, but he did. He has a picture of himself standing at attention in overalls, saluting when he was about 6. Hell, I'm 59 and don't know what I want to do next Tuesday and he knew at 6 he wanted to be a frontline solider. That's wonderful!

As soon as he was old enough, he went to Crowley, Louisiana, and signed up at the Army Recruiting Office. Twelve weeks later he graduated Basic Training at Fort Chafee, Arkansas. He was assigned to the Medium Tank Battalion and then got orders for Fort Lewis, Washington, 2nd Infantry Division. Dreams do come true. He was in the Infantry!

At Fort Lewis he marched all day and trained with a .50 caliber machine gun. Then he marched and then he trained and marched and trained and on and on. Then one day in 1950, he got on a ship headed for Korea. He wasn't out of his teens when the ship docked in Korea. Only six months earlier, almost to the day, he had been standing in the recruiting office in Crowley and now he was in Pusan, Korea. Think about that for a minute; six months ago you might have been trying something for the first time and now today, you are ass deep in the addiction and you honestly don't remember how you got there. Roy knew how he got to Korea; he just didn't know what was awaiting him! Do you know what's waiting on you?

He romped and stomped around South Korea until November that year when he was transferred to HDQTS, Infantry Division, driving for a Col. Brown. On what Roy remembers as a pretty cold night, he and his company were over-run by North Koreans. All hell broke loose. Col. Brown was taken out by a mortar attack along with most of the company. Now Roy was attached to Lt. Col. Cody.

A few days later, in a place called Kuniri Valley, somewhere between North and South Korea, Roy and his group were completely surrounded and being mowed down. He was trying to get wounded and dead out when he was ordered to take off, get out, and get some help. He crossed a mountain and found a jeep, went to a tank battalion and sought help for the encircled troops. When they got back, Lt. Col. Cody had been shot in the hip and was helicopered out. Roy rejoined what was left of the outfit and preceded north. He eventually fell back when they encountered the Chinese Army, which kept coming in droves.

It was give, and take, back and forth, gain ground and lose it. By now it is late November and getting really cold. Eventually, somewhere between North and South Korea, Roy and his group were completely overrun by Chinese soldiers. The order was given to "Run, get out, every man for himself, reassemble south of Suwon." At that point, it really was every man for himself, run and turn and fight and run and turn and fight. For 72 hours it was total nonstop madness. Killing and wounded and no ammunition and thousands and thousands of Chinese Communists coming and coming and coming. And the temperature dropping and dropping each day and night, less and less food, and more and more snow.

Remember, the fighting went on at night just like in the day. It was so easy to be in a group and then find yourself alone. Imagine, alone 10,000 miles from home, freezing in a hostile land and a nonstop supply of enemy forces coming at you constantly. Sounds a lot like my mornings, doesn't it you? I mean, I woke up this morning and there were about four birds chirping outside my window and I think that is soooo rude of those birds. Then this girl called and woke me up again, and the nerve of her! I was so upset, that I just had to go get some apple flip caramel pecan pancakes to make me feel better about how unfairly I had been treated. We really don't have it so bad, do we?

As I repeat this story, it makes me sick to think of what a worm I was for so many years. I would drink myself to sleep and eat my weight (like a Kiwi bird) in bad food and cuss and moan because of some woman whose name I can't remember didn't show up at my house at 2 a.m. because she was too drunk to drive. I am so sorry for the time I wasted, forgive me, Lord. On with the story...

In order to get south to Suwon, Roy would travel at night and try to sleep during the day. One morning he slipped into a clump of rice stalks tied together in a field and fell asleep. When you are sleeping, and freezing, you toss and turn and his foot had worked its way out of the stalks and was sticking out with his boot attached. Now remember, this wasn't the Marriott or the Holiday Inn. There was no polite wake up call, no coffee service on a night stand, no room service, no newspaper, no shower, no TV, and no friendly maid to check and see if more towels were needed. A North Korean solider shoved a bayoneted rifle into Roy's boot and began screaming, what Roy quickly translated as "Hi, Good morning, would you mind getting up, shaking it off and coming with us?" Maybe that's not exactly how it translated, but ladies might be reading this, so we will leave it there. He also remembers a train station and bullets flying around him.

That wake- up call was estimated to be on December 1, 1950. With the exception of an attempted escape that we will discuss later, Roy L. Broussard was an unwelcomed guest of the North Korean Army for the next two years and eight and a half months. Now the story begins.

For the next three to four days, it was a steady march north. Finally the Prisoners Of War (POWs) were turned over to the Chinese. On the march to this point, there was very little to eat and no showers, no tooth brushes, and melted snow for water, and let's just say things were real bad. Let's also say they were about to get worse. Finally, Roy was reunited with what was left of his original Regiment. Then the real march began. They were headed north all the time and were forced to move constantly. The sick became sicker, the wounded got little to no attention, and the weather got worse and worse. Roy can remember several men who were bleeding but the blood flow stopped because their blood froze. I cannot imagine an ice sickle made from blood hanging from a man's arm or stomach or nose or rectum or mouth or foot. Roy saw a lot of that. The medics did what they could with almost no supplies. Men died on the hour, every hour, hour after hour. Food was whatever they had or what the villagers would throw at them, maybe a ball of rice or some vegetables of some sort. It was bad, real bad, and the temperature was dropping by the minute. And sometimes the guards would take the shoes off the POWs for themselves. This was sure death.

Marching, marching, marching, dragging, dragging, dragging, over mountain after mountain after mountain and then, welcome to your new home: Pyktong, POW Camp #5.

Roy was moved into his new wood hut. He could have a fire if he could find some fuel… there was none available. There was no bed, no bathroom, no lights, no window, no curtains, no sleep number adjustable mattress, and no nothing. Sleep on the dirt floor in whatever cloths you were wearing when you got captured. Welcome home! Your room is being prepared… enjoy your stay!

Roy refused to write home for over a year (his mother thought he was dead and actually received a letter from the Department of Defense stating as much) because the return address on all letters was "Against American Aggression." He chose not to write or receive mail rather than sign a letter saying America was the aggressor. His main diet was sorghum seed. That is cattle feed. He finally got a well and did have fresh water. Once in a great while he would get molded calves liver. He ate it without question. On trips to the Yalu River, he would get seaweed from the fishermen and boil it in his helmet. On a rare occasion, there might be a piece of fruit or vegetable, but not often. Men continued to die, some from illness, some from starvation, and some froze to death, and others just gave up. Roy remembers having to duck and run a few times on the march to Camp #5 because American planes were flying over. They were dropping leaflets saying help was coming… it never came; some men didn't want to wait on it any longer.

So, it's about December   (Merry Christmas) and Roy is in Camp #5 and he had just settled in for a long winter's nap. Unfortunately, there were no visions of sugar plums dancing anywhere. How to get out, how to survive, how to get warm, how to find something to eat, and how to not get a beating, pretty much were in the forefront of all of Roy's Christmas and New Year's dreams. I remember Roy telling me the number one Christmas wish was to get rid of the body lice that were eating him alive… no such luck.

There is no way to explain the following two-and-a-half years. Roy reported he did finally get some blue Chinese uniforms to wear, but the Red Cross never made it to where he was. There are some photos on the internet showing some GIs playing ball and big bushel baskets of apples and a big pig pen with lots of fresh pork and everybody is smiling and the guards are smiling and these photos look like it was a winter camp for the YMCA. When we were looking at them Roy said, "I never saw anything like that, and the only time anyone ever took my picture was when they finally gave us new Chinese Communist fatigues and blue hats." I sort of believe Roy's version of what it was like. His records indicate he weighed about 90 pounds when he was liberated and had to come home on the USS Haven Hospital ship. Probably too many apple pies and pork chops caused his poor health at the end of '53.

I know this little book is supposed to be about addiction; I haven't forgotten that. Remember, addiction is that thing that is probably killing us that we think we just can't live without and make it through the day (or night). But we can and we will and some of us have and I know in my heart that so can you! Listen, I am an expert on my addiction. I can vividly remember chasing my girlfriend all over town trying to catch her doing something wrong so I could throw it up to her and prove I was right. When I didn't catch her, I would go home and be madder than if I had caught her. Well, there is nothing else to do at 4 in the morning; she was at her house asleep, and so I would calm down by drinking a shot or two of liquor. I did that over and over and over... tell me I wasn't an addict! And an idiot and a fool. I was all of them.

It didn't much matter who the girl was, I knew my fair share, it was the pattern I was in. Being in the bar business where everybody was lying to everybody else, if a girl said good morning, I would go outside and look. My friend Joey told me if you are not an addict, you can drink 100 bottles of booze and it won't make you an addict. You either are addicted to it or you aren't. I believe him but, I promise you this: the results are the same. You're drunk.

Here's the difference: I was trying to party my life away, and Roy was trying to save his. I had too much food to eat and he had very little to none. I would sit and drink till the bottle was empty, and he sometimes drank out of the Yalu River. Don't you see the point here? What I and maybe you or someone you love and care for was doing (or is doing) is killing us, and there are other people who would die for a glass of clean, cool water. When I was drinking and running around and spending all my money being a big shot, I wasn't thinking about what was important. Now I know. Thank God, now I know.

Let me share three stories Roy told me. There is no question about them being true; that doesn't even come into it. These are true stories and you can look him up on the Web about Korean POWs and MIAs. From December 1, 1950 until August 18, 1953, his name is in the POW book as a guest of the North Korean Army.

Story one. That first winter, the temperature got down to 30 or 40 below zero. I have no idea how cold that is. I have been a Deputy Sheriff in the Rocky Mountains in Colorado when it was 13 below zero. I had on enough cloths to look like the Michelin Tire man and was in a heated patrol car and still was freezing. Roy reports some guys' blood froze in their bodies. They weren't cut or gushing blood, they just froze to death. No space heaters, no electric blankets, no comforters, just whatever sticks they could find to burn and whatever cloths and animal blankets they could put over them. (There is a pretty good book about this called "The Coldest Winter" by David Habersham.)

So anyway, it's freezing and almost everybody is sick and Roy's tonsils get infected. Sore goes to inflamed and one day his throat is so bad, he can't swallow. In each camp there was GIs assigned to different tasks. Some guys were medics and others were cooks and others were chaplains or whatever. This morning, Roy got up and walked up a small hill to the medic tent and wrote out the note about his throat. Upon inspection, it was immediately clear they had to come out. They had to come out right now. The instrument used was a bamboo stick with a wire noose around one end. The bamboo stick was pushed down his throat and the wire hooked around the tonsils and twisted until the flesh was sliced open and the tonsils came out. Roy swears he walked back down the hill and just made it to his bunk area. He was left for dead; he couldn't eat or swallow for days. He doesn't remember if it was summer or winter or spring or fall, he only remembers the pain. It had to be winter because he had snow in his mouth to stop the bleeding… the inside of this throat looked a little like someone who had eaten a pack of razor blades at some point in their life. I asked him about anesthesia and he wouldn't answer me. I knew when to quit talking about it. The end of that conversation had come.

Are you burning your throat up with two or three packs of smokes a day? Are you spending all your money and all your family's money and all you can steal on meth and smoking it in a glass pipe? Do you have any idea what the temperature of smoke is when it hits your throat? Not important? You're right, just like it was Roy's throat, it's your throat. Do what you want with it. Drinking straight shots of booze? If you're interested, look up what happens to your throat, esophagus, and stomach when you shoot straight booze… have you ever heard anyone talk about that burning sensation?

Each and every solider has a responsibility to try and escape if possible. Roy found that opportunity one afternoon at the Yalu River. They had been in Camp long enough that the guards didn't follow them to the river day after day after day. The prisoners were hundreds of miles from anywhere in the middle of North Korea or Communist China… where were they going to go, Las Vegas? This was Roy's chance. Enough was enough; he was going to give it a try. He meandered down to the bank and when he saw nobody paying any attention, he bolted. His plan was to follow the Yalu to anyplace but where he was. He would again travel by night and sleep during the day. It seemed like a good plan. After two or three days he was well aware the guards were looking for him. The daily life he knew back in camp and intended to report wasn't going to have stories of apples and softball games and smiling guards. He was going to tell quite a different story.

You don't need to try not eating for two days to imagine how low your strength is. Not to mention how you smell running all night and sweating from fear and no toilet paper and no soap, etc., hiding not only from the guards but from farmers and airplanes and not knowing exactly where you are and you don't speak the language and being hungry all the time. Then all of a sudden, like a gift from heaven, there was a live chicken right in front of him. Needless to say, the chicken didn't have a chance. Roy grabbed it and rang its little chicken neck. He ate it raw. He couldn't have a fire for two reasons: no matches and the farmers and guards would see it. Roy plucked the feathers and chewed the chicken right where he was sitting. I have read about sailors at sea during WW ll who were drifting in life boats and a seagull landing on the raft, soon to be eaten raw. Roy didn't have a seagull, he had a skinny little raw chicken and he ate it up! Viva Col. Sanders!

Big mistake for the chicken and for Roy… he learned something in the next few days. He learned that animals don't pluck chickens; they pull out a few feathers and eat from the hole they have made in the skin. Farmers don't pluck feathers and leave bones in a pile by the river; they put the whole bird with bones in a pot and cook it. Only runaway POWs who are starving would do something like pluck and eat. So, they called in a few more guards and slowly tightened the perimeter and they had him. Now it was time to pay the consequences for disobeying the guards. The price was several beatings and no mail and no exercise and being made an example of in front of the other POWs. Roy told me he didn't give a damn, he would have run again if he got the chance.

Are you caught in a relationship that you don't think you can get out of? Are you under the threat of being beaten or left or that you better not dare think about leaving because "you're mine" and nobody else will ever have you? Friend, that ain't love. That is being a POW here in America and you chose the head guard! Get out as soon as you can. Roy was running for his life, and if we stay in an abusive relationship, sooner or later we will be running for ours. I'm not going to go on and on about this but you get the drift. This is present-day America, not a POW Camp in North Korea or China in 1950, where starving and beatings are the price for freedom. Here you and I do not have to spend one more minute in a relationship like the one Roy and the thousands of other prisoners had with their guards.

One more story to go: There were prisoners from other countries in the different camps in North Korea, and in Roy's camp, there were several French Foreign Legion troopers. None of these guys spoke Korean or English, but they did of course speak French. Guess what? So did Roy. He was from Louisiana, and his family is French (Broussard) and the guards figured out he could translate a ton of propaganda from English to French. They even thought he was a French solider when he was originally captured. As luck would have it, Roy was pulled out of his area and sent to live with and to teach the French troopers about the wonderful life of a communist. Korea was well known as the first brain-washing propaganda war for the enemies. The guards saw an opportunity to spread the word. Roy agreed, like he really had a choice, and would hold class with the Legionnaires and speak French all afternoon about girls and Paris and families and girls and hamburgers and wine and girls and just have a big time. Nobody else spoke French, especially the guards, so Roy would pick up the communist literature, go have the lectures, talk about girls and come back in the evening. All was well.

One day a skinny little Chinese communist officer went along with Roy for no apparent reason. All this guy spoke was Chinese, so no big deal. Roy got the literature and started the lesson in French as usual, and after about 45 minutes of making fun of the officer and talking about girls and nothing in particular, Roy got the hell beat out of him. The new officer had studied in Paris and spoke fluent, perfect, flawless French! To quote one of my favorite philosophers, Gomer Pyle… Surprise, Surprise! Now the trouble for Roy really did start. These Communist understood trying to escape; they probably would have tried it if the tables had been turned, but to make fun of and refuse to teach the literature he was given, Roy was going to pay dearly. For sure he got several beating when he ran and ate the chicken, but that was the warm up show for this.

After the initial beating, Roy was taken to what he can best describe as a bank vault. It had cement walls and a concrete floor and a huge metal door that was almost too much for one person to open. The room had no light, no table, no chair, no shelves, and no air. It was just that, a cold ice floor, pitch black room. That was to be his new digs for the rest of his incarceration. Once a day he was allowed out for a few minutes to stretch or get a drink of water or be interrogated by the officer who checked him in there. He got a ball of rice or a bowl of cold soup or whatever they gave him. He said his treatment changed according to how the peace talks were going. Some days he didn't come out at all; other days he was out for an hour. Beatings came and went, it just depended. The guards made up lies and told stories to the other POWs about where he was. One interview that Roy remembers well was when they asked him what he had been talking about in French all those days when he was supposed to be teaching the communist literature. Roy wouldn't tell them. They beat him again and finally put a pistol to his head and told him to confess to his crimes in French for the news or die. Roy recited in his best Nathan Hale impersonation, "I've got one life for my country, go ahead and kill me." Well, they didn't shoot, but they did pound on him some more and threw him back in the bank vault.

One day out of nowhere, they drug him out of the vault. He had been in there so long, he couldn't see for a long time. He went from total darkness to daylight in a few seconds. He was taken back to his fellow prisoners and that day they were all put on a Chinese truck and driven away from the camp. They had no information at all. Some thought they were being taken out to be shot.

The truth was they were being driven to Panmengong. Upon arrival, there was the Red Cross tents and American uniforms and a few helicopters and some press people. Roy tells me he didn't wait for orders or direction or permission. He jumped off the back of the truck and ran into the first Red Cross tent he reached, it was over.

Roy was in bad enough shape that he was one of the solders helicoptered out. He traveled on the aforementioned ship USS HAVAN back to San Francisco and met his mother at the hospital. She had come to take her son home. He spent the next few months at the hospital in Camp Polk, Louisiana. He told me he later saw a news reel of the very truck he was riding on approaching the exchange point and saw himself jumping from the back. He knew it was him but he didn't recognize himself. Maybe it was the 80-pound difference that threw him!

At the end of our discussions, I asked my step-father to try and sum up his POW experiences. He listed a few thoughts for me.

1) He thought about the person who loved him the most every day, his mother. He told me he simply wanted to see her face one more time and then he could die after that. "Please, dear God, let me see her one more time."

2) "You can't lose the will to live. If any of us were getting out of there, I wanted to be one of them."

3) "Something in me kept me alive; I don't know what it was. It was nothing I learned, it was just there. They could kill me at any time, but I wasn't going to kill myself."

4) "At one point I had rock-hard frozen mucus in my nose and sinuses. Till this day I have trouble with my nose dripping, and I sniff unconsciously at times. I have never forgotten why."

5) "Regardless of my troubles, there were others in worse shape than me. I can't forget one solider whose feet were frozen and he developed gangrene. His toes and ankles were rotting off his legs and the only hope was to amputate both legs. I don't know if there was any ether or antiseptic or how they did it but, they cut both his legs off to save his life. I'll never forget him."

(I want to remind the readers that this was not done at Johns Hopkins or at the Medical College of Georgia. It wasn't even done in a MASH unit. It was done by captured American Medics with little to no medical supplies in a Prisoner of War Camp in North Korea, in order to save this man's life.)

6) "I don't like Christmas very much, that time of year I begin to associate the cold with being frozen in North Korea. I can't help it, something in me just drifts back to being cold and hungry, and so miserable those Decembers."

The day Roy was free, he began living his Life! The past was there, but it had no part of his future. He spent the next 20 some-odd years in The Army. He graduated from the Jungle Expert School in Panama and served with the Infantry Division. He was transferred to the Calvary and served in Ft. Riley, Kansas. From there it was off to the Airborne Division at the famous Ft. Bragg, NC. From there he visited lovely Vietnam. When he returned he became an instructor at the signal school at Ft. Gordon, Georgia. He had served several tours in Korea and Vietnam and had moved from pillar to post all over the world while in uniform. He had willingly paid his debt to this country in full and before he had to pack up and go back overseas, he retired. Enough was enough.

Along about 1975, my mother decided Roy was going to get his college education, he deserved it. She went with him to Augusta College in Augusta,

Georgia, and he enrolled. He had not been to school in almost 30 years but, he wasn't afraid. He had faced a lot tougher obstacles than English 101. Some quarters he was on the Dean's List and some quarters he didn't quite get there. Nonetheless, he graduated in three years with a double major. Not bad for a young man from Crowley, Louisiana, who lied about his education to join the Army back in '49.

He is always after me to do what he did and go sign up at Augusta College and get my education. I keep coming up with every reason and excuse in the world why it's too hard, and I honestly didn't do well at all in public school and I would rather have all my teeth pulled than try to understand algebra and on and on. He looked at me and said, "Oh it's not all that bad, it's air-conditioned in the summer and heated in the winter. They have a great Student Union Building and a pretty good cafeteria… and you won't have to spend all day with a limb in your hand, trying to catch a chicken for dinner."

What do you say to that?

Several years ago a letter came from Washington, D.C. It announced Roy was being awarded a Bronze Star (with V for valor) for action in Korea. If you look it up, you will see it's a pretty high honor. It came about 50 years after the fact but during war and especially in a POW situation, papers are lost, people are killed, there are a lot of urgent, more important issues than documenting each and every action. I am very proud of him and love him just like I do my real father. They have both been good to me, and they are both good friends. When we were talking about his Bronze Star, I asked if he received the Purple Heart. He smiled and said, "After Korea and Vietnam, the only heart I got was a broken one, let's leave it at that." I had heard that once before from a Vietnam veteran.

I said, "Yes sir."

Korean War: 103,284 soldiers; 36,568 killed; 8,177 MIA; 7,140 POW; 2,701 POW died in POW camps (none of old age); 4, 418 POW returned.

My troubles cannot compare to a story like this. All the crap and hard times that I invited into my life were by my own selection. I could have said no at any time. We are not talking about the death of a loved one or an innocent child with an injury. That is part of life and at some point, we are all going to have to deal with it. I want to know why I and so many others have opened the front door and welcomed trouble into our lives and at some point convinced ourselves we couldn't live without that very same trouble.

It's like the little boy who is told he can't have a cookie and when mother is out of the room, he sticks his hand in the jar and wraps his fist around the cookie. Now he can't get his fist out of the top of the jar. If he would drop the cookie, he would be free, but he wouldn't have the cookie. Mother walks in and he is caught. He just couldn't let go of the cookie.

Isn't that just like us and our addictions? We stick our hand into something and it goes in real easy. We grab whatever it is and refuse to let go, not realizing it has a hold on us. As long as we keep holding it, it keeps holding us. Let go! Let go before you can't let go. There is a great line in a movie where a bunch of tough guys go into a bar in New York and they are raising hell and the manager comes out and asks them very politely to leave. They continue raising hell and all of the sudden about 20 of the manager's pal's show up and lock the front door. The manager walks up to the toughs and says, "I asked you to leave and you didn't; now you can't!"

I get it! I swear I finally get it. What real value does our addiction bring us? Mine brought me hangovers, heartache, maxed-out credit cards, 75 pounds of heart-clogging fat, and a total loss of self-respect. What dividends is your addiction paying you? What is really, honest to God, important in your life? Do you think what the latest styles were meant a *&^% thing to Roy and the other 4,000 POWs who were freezing? Probably not. Today the men and women serving this country in Iraq and Afghanistan are probably a little more concerned with not fainting from heatstroke and not being blown up by a car bomb than so and so was seen at the Awards last night with such and such and Hollywood insiders with the real scoop have all the information that everybody is just dying to know. Arrrrrggggggghhhhhhh! I can't stand it anymore.

I was a certified idiot for about 15 years of my life. What I was addicted to didn't amount to a day-old want-ad after the item is sold. I was never addicted to anything illegal, thank God! That would have just made it worse and more dangerous. Everything I was hooked on was legal and available. Remember, drinking is the only thing you start out doing legal and end up doing illegal. I always had respect for the law and followed the rules to the letter. Never dated anybody's wife, never ran off and hid in a hotel room where I wasn't supposed to be, never did drugs, never took any money but my paycheck. But if a cute girl winked at me, and she liked to drink, I was in love! Love, drink, argue, over and over and over. Then we would go to Denny's and eat 5,000 calories and then go to sleep! Don't you see... stop right now and make a list of what you have to have to stay alive and what you need to get to work tomorrow. Then add family or real friends who won't let you down and want nothing from you. Then add the people who LOVE YOU, not the ones you love. Who really loves you? Not the people who are trying to control you or the ones who "can't live without you"... yes they can. If you have a loved one in the hospital, the level of care they are receiving is important; what the nurses drove to the hospital or who that young Intern is dating doesn't make a bit of difference. If your mom is at death's door, who is dating who at the gym is NOT IMPORTANT. It never was and it never will be. Took me 47 years to figure that out. Roy and the thousands of other POWs didn't wake up and wonder who was dating who on "Days of Our Lives"... they were lucky to wake up and then spent the day wondering if this was going to be their last one!

Ask yourself this: What is more important, the kind of watch you're wearing, or how much time you have left?

Thank you to Roy and each and every person who ever put on a uniform from any branch of the U.S. Military... everything we have is because of you. We read a lot about WWII and a lot about Vietnam but we don't hear too much about Korea. That's a shame. Those soldiers paid just as high a price, and we owe them a tremendous debt of gratitude. Thank you again to all men and women who have, are, and will serve. Thank you, thank you, and thank you.

Note: I may have a few dates or places wrong in this chapter. It was difficult getting Roy to talk about something he has tried to put behind him for nearly 60 years. A few times he would get Korea and Vietnam mixed up and would have to rethink the time and place. He reports the jungle in Panama and the jungle in Vietnam look pretty much the same when you're under a canopy and its 105 degrees.

I can't remember what I watched on TV last night, so I hope you will join me in giving Roy a little "benefit of the doubt" on exact days in February of 1950, '51, and '52. He is sure of one thing: It wasn't the Ritz-Carlton!

94

December 16, 2010: I wrote the above chapter back in 2009. A couple of things have happened since I wrote it, both bad. I lost my dear friend Jim Wade. He was a USMC Korean War veteran. He and Roy had met and talked and agreed it was the coldest place on earth. Jim came home from the war and served 27 years on the Florida Highway Patrol. His class graduated in October of 1956. After the Patrol, Jim served 13 to 14 years with the Orange County Florida Sheriff's Department. He retired to Lake City Florida. I miss him, he was a good man. Semper Fi, Jim.

The other bad thing that happened will be discussed in detail in the chapter entitled "Hate"… read on.

Chapter 7
Hate

I feel sure we can be as addicted to hate as any other emotion, maybe even more. There are a couple of stories and a few examples that follow. Keep in mind, we can hate all sorts of things... people, events, places, religions, political parties and the folks in them. We can actually hate the fact that we hate... another endless list. I am beginning to hate spell check, but that is a whole other story!

Let's begin with two examples from the same place.

I have a dear friend named Kim. This is an extraordinary lady! She is in her early 40s, is in great shape, takes care of herself, takes tremendous pride in her job, and owns an amazing history. She has seen a lot in her 40-plus years. She is respected and trusted and has earned everything she's got. Every day she comes to work, her staff and the public's safety is priority number one. I appreciate that very much.

Kim had served in the U.S. Army for 10 years, been a correction officer, a police officer, a school recourse officer, and now works in a law-enforcement environment for the feds as a supervisor. She has been married, divorced, and remarried. She is a loving mother and a loving daughter and wife and one other thing... she has buried one of her children.

I never had children, but my mother did. I've known a lot of parents in my life and as wild as my imagination is, I cannot imagine the pain of holding your own child as it breathes its last breath on this earth. You were there when the child took its first breath and there when it took its last; there is just something wrong about the second half of that.

I will get around to this hate thing I'm writing about shortly (keep reading and see if I don't), but let's talk about losing a child for a minute.

Remember, I don't have any little Porters, but as all of us have, I know and have been close to people who do have children who have passed away. As it was explained to me, the pain is like no other and never goes away. As Kim explains it, "If your heart were a hotel, there is always an empty room."

I imagine you become so hollow that you don't taste food; you couldn't tell someone what is on TV if you were looking at it. You drive from point A to point B, but you get lost and have to pull over and remember where you were going, and it usually doesn't matter unless it's to the cemetery.

When you see another child run or play or hear it laugh, the pain settles in your heart and stomach for a long winter's nap. I have been told that no matter the age when a son or daughter dies, the parent can hear that child giggle for years and years and forever. I have been told a parent can hear a child cry, and it is so clear, they have gotten up and run into another room even though the child has been gone for a long, long time. The silence of Adrian Mabry Powell born February 25, 1985 and put to rest February 21, 1988 is deafening.

It's not like losing a husband or wife or sweetheart or parent... those are terrible, but losing a child is a world-class pain like no other. Some days you feel like part of your arm is missing or some of your teeth are gone or at the very least they hurt all day. Some days you feel like your legs don't work and your eyes burn from all the endless crying. I am told you feel that way because part of you is gone; part of you is in that casket and part of you—arms, legs, heart, eyes, hair, ears—hurts every day. The pain moves around because if it settled in one spot, you couldn't take it. The pain is always there, but it moves around in order to keep you alive.

Think of the parents at Columbine High School, or the parents of the children at Oklahoma City. Don't forget, the parents of the young men and women at the World Trade Center, they had parents too. Remember the mother or father who looked up and saw two military officers come up the sidewalk in dress uniforms... that happened to my next-door neighbor during Vietnam. I swear to God, you could taste the pain and agony in the air after those officers left. Have you ever gotten in a car and you could smell and feel the pain and sorrow of the people who had been in the car? It's real and I'm not sure it ever goes away. I remember one of the trucks that belonged to a Columbine student sat in the parking lot for a few days after the shooting. It was covered with flowers and teddy bears and cards and notes... but... all that failed to compare to the presences of his spirit. It was there. Even I could feel it. I will never know how his parents dealt with it… I don't know that I could have.

The late-night knock on the door or the phone call from the local police and you know your child hasn't come home yet… and before a word is spoken, you know the child won't be coming home ever again. I have had to do that once or twice in my law-enforcement career, and I will never know how doctors do it all the time. I guess it just has to be done.

All the above is the pain that Kim gets up with and goes to bed with. But, she can't sit down and wallow in it. She has other children and she has a husband and she is very much alive (except for the part that dies and aches and comes back to life every day.) I tell you all of this because we are identifying hate, and Kim hates the day her child went to Jesus. She hates the disease that took him, and she hates the pain it left. Don't misunderstand, she loved that baby and she loved the few years they were together here on this earth, but she hates the day it happened and the reason it happened and that hate is very real and understood. She hates it!

Here's another hate: Back when Kim was a deputy sheriff, a call went out from dispatch concerning an elderly gentleman with severe chest pains. An ambulance was dispatched and as protocol demands, a deputy also responds.

Both Kim and the EMTs responded at about the same time and approached the house. Let's review: 1) a call is made to 911 from a lady, concerning an older man with pretty bad chest pains. 2) The call is forwarded to medical and fire and the zone deputy riding that area. 3) Several people respond ready and willing to assist the caller. 4) The responders arrive "on scene" and approach the front door. All this is done in a matter of minutes. No crime has been committed, nothing is on fire, no neighbors in the yard, just a call went out and the first responders are there, ready to assist.

When the front door opened, the lady stopped in her tracks. She told everyone to wait right where they were and not to come in.

The old man was sitting in the front room, and he and the lady had a short, not-so-quiet conversation. It was obvious he was in some discomfort but not on the floor and not unconscious. Again, no crime had been committed and the responders had no choice but to stand on the porch and wait.

The lady turned around and said, "You can't come in."

Here sits this old man as pale as concrete holding his chest, his wife or daughter or whoever she was had called 911, and now they can't come in.

Naturally Kim and the EMTs ask why not?

"Because we ain't never had no blacks in this house and we never will."

Did I mention Kim is black? I didn't think it was important until now.

I don't know that it is important at all... what the hell difference could it possibly make? Here was a state-certified police officer, a 10-year honorably discharged veteran, a mother, a wife, a public servant, someone who knew death real well, and she was not allowed in the house! On with the story...

She and the EMTs had no choice but to leave... that was that. They went to the corner and stood by. Shortly another call went out and the coroner was called. The old man had died. He and the woman there chose death over being helped by a black deputy... now, friends, that's hate. And stupidity.

Here we have two distinct kinds of hate that will eat you up. If you hold on to them and pull them close to your heart, your heart will stop, not the hate. The first hate is that of a mother... she hates the day and hour and minute her precious child was taken to eternity. An innocent little heart quit beating and a mother's heart full of love was broken. Again, she hates the disease and the pain it brings. Then we have an old man and woman who were taught hate long, long ago and hate Kim without ever knowing her or who she is so much, that they prefer death over being touched by her hand. Did they think she was the Angel of Death? Just the opposite, she is an Angle of Mercy; she was there to help save him.

I would like to go on record right now and tell you that 40 hours a week, I am a police officer. I work with the Richmond County Marshal's Office. I don't think my level of danger is as steep as one of our Richmond County Deputy Sheriff's (I am a little too old to do what they have to do), but nonetheless, I wear a gun and there is a degree of danger involved with my job each day. That said, if you see me getting my ass beat or if I am in a wreck or if for any reason I need help, I am giving you permission to do whatever is necessary to save my life! I don't care if you are gay, straight, male, female (or in between), black, white, or any other shade of the rainbow. I don't care if you are Christian, Jew, or an Aztec Sun worshiper... if you see me hurt and there is anything you can do to come to my aid, DO IT!

Here is one reason to do it... I am willing to do it for you! Any person who puts on a uniform and gets on a fire truck or in a police car or ambulance or goes to war is there to save your life. Don't you think there have been lifeguards at the beach who have drowned trying to save a swimmer who they were not friends with, who they didn't know, who they will never know, yet they died trying to get them out of the water? Don't you think Kim was willing to give her life to save that old man? She was and she has told me if he had changed his mind between the refusal of help and the "big chest pain," she would have gladly helped him.

Police officers and firefighters and EMTs don't get paid to die. There isn't enough money to pay that salary. What they get paid to do is protect and defend and help the rest of us and if they give their life doing that, then all I can pray is they died doing what they loved to do and were willing to do. We have lost four officers here recently: one military police and three road patrol officers. They are all true heroes and gave their life in uniform protecting the rest of us. I hate the fact that they are dead, and I hate the people who killed them. Sorry to all the bleeding hearts reading this, but it is what it is. I wish it had been the shooters rather than the victims! We simply cannot act on that hate, but we do hate it.

Now this isn't just about Kim, and hate isn't owned by any one person or group. There are some more examples coming... stand by.

If you hate something or somebody or some group of people, or anything so much it affects your life, how is that different then addiction to porn or smokes or booze or the wrong person or food or exercise or shopping or any of the things that control us? It isn't different. Suppose a father hates his daughter's boyfriend, you think that can't create problems that separate families for years? It does and has. I even read about one guy who hated his daughter's "western" ways so much he ran over her... he has to have some addiction to some screwball religion and he is eaten up with hate for anything other than his ideas... that is insane!

Some people hate all policemen. That is so stupid I can't comment on it. Some people hate the IRS but love our soldiers. Who do you think collects the tax to pay the soldiers... the IRS! There are a few people I hate. I wish I didn't but I do. There are only a few, but I do so much hate them. One way or the other, they have harmed me or my family or my friends. It's hard not to hate someone who has done a horrible deed to an innocent loved one. I don't know how people get over it; I haven't gotten over it yet.

Just a few chapters back, you remember reading about my step-father Roy Broussard. He is loved by me and my sister and just like he had to either quit hating the guards that beat him and starved him for two years and eight months during the Korean War, or his other choice was to relive it day after day after day for the next 60-odd years. He hates it happened, but he put it behind him. The hate would have kept him there every day he let it control him.

Now let me tell you who I hate. On January 2, 2010, I was pulling my first day shift. A deputy named Al Grossman and I were on duty at the Augusta Regional Airport. I believe it was a beautiful, crisp morning and everything was going smoothly... until the phone rang. The conversation went something like this: "He got me Porter... I'm hurt pretty bad, son, I want you to know I love you."

WHAT! What are you talking about?!

"Carjacked me, bleeding pretty bad, the son of a bitch cut me."

Roy, what the hell are you talking about? Have you been in a wreck? Where are you?

"He was in the driveway next to our house."

At this point Roy mumbled something about he wanted to kill the bastard. When he finished, I said very firmly, "Roy, hang up the phone and call 911. Do it now. Call 911. Hang up, Roy, they will send an ambulance."

I am going to move fast on this story because, like anybody who wants to get past the addiction to hate, I don't want to dwell on it. Here goes.....

Al Grossman heard the conversation, got sketchy details from me, and started calling dispatch and deputies he knew in the sheriff's office. He had been an Augusta Police Officer and knew a lot of guys and gals who worked at the sheriff's office. He found out that the ambulance got to Roy and had transported him to the Medical College of Georgia. Roy was in the ER and was being attended to. I called my brother-in-law and he went to the hospital immediately. Al made more calls to "God only knows who" and found out Roy was in stable condition but was being transported to Eisenhower Hospital at Ft. Gordon in Augusta. My brother was with him.

There was nothing I could do, and that's a bad, bad feeling. Is there someone you gave birth to or someone who gave birth to you who is killing themselves? Is there someone who you love and cherish and have promised to love honor and obey till death do you part and you are watching them kill themselves with a fork or with a bottle or a match or gambling or the wrong person or some off-the-wall religion or whatever? You hate it but they won't quit and you can't quit loving them. That's how I felt that beautiful New Year's morning! Somebody I loved had been minding their own business and was cut, stabbed, sliced with a combat folding knife, and robbed and carjacked, left bleeding to death in a driveway and there was absolutely nothing I could do about it... nothing. You can't un-ring a bell.

My brother-in-law called from Eisenhower and reported Roy was in surgery and to come on when I got off work. Right now there was "nothing" I could do but be in the way. I want to go on record right now and tell you good readers that I would have walked off my post that minute if there was anything I could have done. But there wasn't. My supervisor, Lt. Steve Johnson, came in immediately (it was his day off) and stayed till I said I wasn't going to leave till my shift was over and I appreciated him but to go on home and I would keep him posted. I want to thank him and Al Grossman; I won't ever forget them.

Now you have the picture, my step-dad, Roy, is in the driveway next to my house, getting out of his car and minding his own business, not bothering anyone when a complete stranger runs up behind him and sticks a knife to Roy's face and says, "Give me your wallet or I will cut you" and the fight was on... 80 years old, Roy Broussard was a man 60 years ago in Korea, he was a man 45 years ago in Vietnam, and he was a man on January 2, 2010. Roy had paid for every stripe on the American flag against a hell of a lot tougher guys then this punk. &^%$head had picked on the wrong man.

Roy looked bad... he had almost 70 stitches and staples in his head and face and mouth. The worst injury was from a direct stab to his cheek. The rather large blade went in Roy's right cheek and broke four teeth and punctured his tongue. I can't imagine the pain. The other problem was Roy had had massive bypass surgery on his heart back about 10 or so years ago. During the fight in the driveway, something went haywire in his heart and a stint had to be inserted at Eisenhower. So let's quickly review: Everything is going great at work on my first dayshift. I am working with my pal Al Grossman and in the matter of a few short minutes, our family is devastated, sheer terror has rained down upon us, we don't know if Roy is going to live or die because of some *^%$head's addiction to crack! Either that or the guy simple loved Roy's car and just had to have it. One or the other.

Let me thank the ER staff at the Medical College of Georgia and the staff at Eisenhower Hospital... they gave us a few more years with Roy that we might not have had. How do we come and thank you? I don't know the answer... they do it day after day and sometimes the people they save never know their names.

If you want to cut the fool or show your ass around Richmond County Georgia, if you want to rob and carjack and be a gangster, you better hope Tim Rzasa from the Richmond County Sheriff's Office doesn't catch your case. He is like a bulldog when it gets its teeth in you... he don't quit. Now I want you to know he didn't ask me to write this and he probably will get made fun of at work when it's published but... it's my story and I get to write it.

The next day a couple of street patrol deputies saw Roy's car go sailing by and gave chase. The bad guy got away, but the deputies recovered the car... and all the evidence in it! Tim and the crime scene technicians went over that car like a fly on flypaper. Nothing was left undone. After a few months, we get a call that Roy needs to come down and look over some photos at the sheriff's office. Roy looks at six photos and says NO! He's not there. OK, fine... let's look at six more. Guess what? Roy looks at the second set of photos and immediately says, "That's him, number four!" Guess what? Number four's blood and DNA were in Roy's car... what do you know... how about that. Thank you from the bottom of my heart to the Richmond County Sheriff's Office. Thank you.

So this is a chapter on hate… addiction to hate. I hate the guy who did this to my 80-year-old step-dad. I think about it a lot. Sometimes I day dream about it. Roy was minding his own business and taking our neighbor to the drugstore because she was ill and couldn't drive. He was in his own car and with God as my witness, he was going to do an elderly sick lady a good deed, asking nothing in return. As he pulls up the driveway to get her (she has since died), this human piece of $#%& jumps out of the bushes and stabs Roy. He gets caught and goes to trial and he pisses and moans about how unfair and unjust the system is and waa-waa-waa. Man up, $#%&head.

After a week in court, the jury comes back "guilty on all counts"… there is a God. $#%&head gets life plus more than 50 years for a car he drove one day and enough money in Roy's wallet to get a few rocks of crack. Did I mention $#%&head is in his early 20s? Did I mention he had a criminal history about a notebook long? Did I mention he was black? Just like Kim being black, it didn't make any difference. It wasn't important that he is black, black had nothing to do with it… but he was and probably still is. I wouldn't care if he was Oriental purple, I would still hate him. Half the jury was black and after the case was over, most of the jurors came up to us and said thank the Lord $#%&head was off the streets. I concur. I love Kim, but I hate him, so black ain't got anything to do with it. I hate him a lot. Also, tremendous appreciation to the Richmond County DA.

Take a few minutes right now and think if there is anyone or any group that you hate. I'm not the one to tell you that you should or shouldn't, that's your call. But, if the hate is burning a hole in your chest, if it is controlling your life or your family's life, if it affects your work, if you are obsessed with it, try to let it go. Maybe get some professional help. It will eat you alive.

Neither I nor nobody else can tell you who or what not to hate… I don't know what evil someone has done to you or caused you or if they have hurt your family. What I can't do and what you shouldn't do is act on that hate with severe consequences. Roy's health has improved and he is getting better. He's going to make it. Pray for me, I'm doing better with my hate for the bad guy… but not much.

I heard a long time ago that the most dangerous person is one with nothing to lose. I agree… the most difficult person is one who doesn't care. How true. And the one most easily persuaded is the person who is emotionally involved. You can write that in stone. I am emotionally involved with $#%&head, so I am getting off the subject. I'm starting to daydream about beating his ugly head in.

Get over the race thing... there are some God-awful white people in this world. Ted Bundy comes to mind. And there are some wonderful white people in this world... Billy Graham comes to mind. There are some God-awful black people in this world. Try the four blacks who slaughtered those two college students in Tennessee. And then there are some wonderful black people... Colon Powell and Condoleezza Rice come to mind. Nobody, no one group, owns Thugville. A hell of a lot of people, from all walks of life, live down there. What a shame. What a waste of effort and energy. What a waste of life.

A few years back I lived in Golden, Colorado. A buddy of mine worked at EAS in Golden and he was headed to Kansas City to watch the Broncos-Chiefs football game. Thousands of fans go back and forth each year to see this game, and it is played in both states equally. When he gets to the stadium, he and two or three friends are walking from the parking lot and three or four Chiefs fans start screwing with him. Why? Because he has on an EAS jacket and EAS is in Colorado. We made sports supplements, not weapons of mass destruction! Naturally, a fight followed and all hell broke loose and the cops show up and there are arrests made and as I remember, a court date was set and all over a couple of people WHO DON'T PLAY THE GAME wanting to beat up someone from the opposing state. Please tell me how you can hate a fan of the other team so much that you are willing to attack them and go to jail yourself?

A girlfriend of mine was in Connecticut at a gym and happened to have on a New York Jets baseball cap. She was on the treadmill minding her own business when another lady (she didn't know and had never seen) came up and said, "What trash-can did you get that hat out of"?

How can some woman be willing to get her teeth knocked out over a hat? Maybe one of the Jets had done her some wrong a long time ago and she hadn't got over it... who knows? How stupid! Can somebody need an identity so bad that they have to fight and go to jail over a baseball hat? I think the problem is much deeper than team pride, don't you?

I believe some of the fans in England do that all the time. Fight at soccer games? The players aren't fighting, the fans are… great idea. Hate anybody that doesn't like your team? I guess if we all get to Heaven and I happen to like Paul more than Luke, and you like Luke, then we should each get a band of Angles and all meet over on cloud 26 and beat the $#%& out of each other. Hmmm, maybe God could referee.

If this doesn't get your attention, I give up. There was a television program on a few years back that interviewed some folks who took hate to a whole different level. This is a true story. I believe it was real life, not actors. I know for a fact it was filmed inside a prison. Here we go: This guy and his wife don't get along. That's not news worthy, it happens all the time. Finally it gets so bad they get a divorce. That happens all the time, no big deal. Problem was, the guy hated the wife so much, he killed the only thing she loved more than life itself… he killed their daughter. He went to jail for the rest of his days, and the wife went down to the cemetery every day, the rest of her days. Can you imagine killing your own child because you hate the mother that much? I'm speechless… I am paraphrasing this but remember the guy saying, "I am going to rot in here the rest of my life, and she (wife) is going to be in agony every day the rest of her life." Don't be like him… get some help.

You have to be asleep not to notice there is a lot of hate floating around these days, and it's getting worse. Political parties are becoming more verbal and saying mean things and making mean hateful half-truths in commercials in order to get or retrain power and purse strings. Funny thing about that, and I'm just putting this out there, if you listen real close to some of the political radio and TV commercials for one party or the other, it's the same voice doing the information. Somebody with a great radio voice is telling you this party is no good on Monday and that party is no good on Tuesday. They are like hired guns; they shoot for whoever pays them. Wonder who they really vote for?

Some folks hate all the illegals and some of the illegals hate us. You know that's the truth. Some illegals sneak in here and rob and steal and join gangs and bring gangs and sell dope and are leeches on our tax dollars. You know it and I know it. Others come here and pay their bills and work seven days a week and do jobs that nobody else will do. What is easier, sitting on your ass collecting a welfare check or getting up at 4 a.m. and walking to a chicken slaughter house to work in guts and blood and chicken $#%& all day? The next time you have a delicious fried chicken dinner with all the fixings, think about the poor person who had to kill, clean, and chop that bird up for less than minimum wage and live in fear of getting caught... yummy, yummy, lick them fingers.

Some religions hate other religions; don't tell me they don't. You know they certainly do. There are people who hate and despise successful people. They are jealous and wish they were successful but so far have not been willing to do the work. I'm not talking about "don't like," I'm talking about hate. There are people who hate lazy folks who always have an excuse to do nothing. What did President Truman say, "When it's time to move the piano, they always want to carry the stool." Some people HATE folks who live off welfare and WIC and Snap and Section 8 housing... and some people on welfare hate people who work and have something. Hate, hate, hate, hate... there is plenty of it out there, and it's getting worse.

I am writing a chapter on addiction to welfare. I don't think anyone begrudges helping another person sometimes. We all need help now and then along the way. I know I do. What I, and about half the population, am talking about are the people and families that have made welfare a "lifelong career." Again, don't think it doesn't and hasn't happened. It happens all over America every day. I guess if you think lifelong welfare is the way to go, then communism is right up your ally. Your motto should be, "When you overload the wagon, don't buy another mule, just get a bigger whip."

After September , my roommate went out and bought the Koran and read it. He wanted and needed to know exactly who we were up against. That's a pretty smart move for all of us, know your enemy. Anyway, he read it from the beginning to almost the last page. It is written that if you read the Koran and then you don't pick up the faith and follow Muhammad, you will be cursed and die a thousand deaths like the infidel pig that you will become. What a great religion... hate the infidel (anybody who isn't a Muslim) or get cursed. I beg you to read ISLAM and TERRORISM by Mark A. Gabriel, Ph.D. What a book. I didn't know whether to put it in the chapter about religion or this chapter, it could go in both. People can say the book is about religion; I think it is about addiction as much as anything I have read. One of the most revealing parts in his book is the awakening that it is perfectly acceptable and expected, for a devout follower to lie to the infidels (anyone who is not a Muslim).

You read the book and make up your own mind; don't take my word for it. According to his book, the jihad might want to come kill me because I wrote about them. Nothing I can do about that. But, if you speak jihad, do me a favor and tell them this for me, in the state of Georgia, I am a duly sworn police officer and if I've got my clothes on, I'm armed. Suit themselves.

It's hate, plain and simple. Why can't we call it what it is instead of milk toasting it. The jihad Muslims hate us infidels. When they make contact with us, they have three options: convert us to Islam, make slaves of us if we can't be converted, or kill us. Wow, what a great religion. Not only is it a religion, it is addictive; it gives the follower a sense of being and purpose and belonging to like-thinking people. The more you practice, the better you get at it. It is as addictive as any drug out there. If I am wrong, I will learn to sing Kumbaya in Arabic! By the way, I wonder if Muhammad Ali hates the infidels. Just putting it out there...

On one of my trips to Washington, D.C., I was picked up by an Egyptian cab driver. I saw his name on the ID in the cab and asked where he was from. We chatted and talked about how long he had been here, etc. Long story short, I made a point of asking if he HATED all us Christians? No, of course he didn't. He believed in live and let live, worship however you wanted. Great, I saw this as an opening to convert him to Christianity... why not... by the time we got to where I was going, he had revealed to me his intentions. With God or Muhammad or Buddha or whomever you believe in, these are his true words. "When we get to eternity, my brothers and I will slaughter the infidels." Now that's what he told me, take it or leave it. There are no guns in eternity, just swords. A lot of cutting will be going on. What a wonderful loving religion... trust them, take them into your home. They are your brothers and they don't hate you. Yeah, right!

One of my pals works for a very big police department. He is a hate-crime investigator. That's all he does, he and about seven other cops spend 45 to 55 hours a week trying to solve and prevent hate crimes. He's overworked and can never catch up. There's a stack of cases on his desk that seem to never get smaller. Here's the deal: He told me it isn't against the law to hate someone or some group or to belong to a group that does hate someone or something. Government control hasn't quite gotten to that point yet. What is against the law is when you act on that hate. You could probably go to a number of VFWs and find a group of old fellows who hate the Japanese. They sit around and relive the war two or three days a week. You know they are there, I know they are there, and they know they are there. Some of them are married to Japanese women, but that's a moot point to them. Anyway, they can relive the stories and talk about whatever they want. They earned the right to drink beer and tell their stories. What they can't do is form up in the parking lot and with fixed bayonets and lead a charge on the sushi buffet down on Main Street. That's acting on hate, and that we can't do.

If you don't look like me or if you don't think like me or if you don't worship like me or if, for any reason, you are not on my team or from where I am from or if you are not the same color as me, then for some folks that's reason enough for hate. I work for Pepsi and you work for Coke, should I hate you? I live in Colorado and you live in Kansas, should I hate you? I drive a Ford and you drive a Chevy, reason for hate? I'm black, you're white, is that enough reason for hate? You didn't want your wife or husband and somebody else did, is that enough reason for hate? Trust me on this, somebody in America, at some point, for one of the above-listed reasons, has committed a crime and gone to jail for it.

A coach somewhere didn't play a mediocre child enough and the parent hates the coach. I cheerleader mom hates the girls who got selected and her daughter didn't. A high school girl hates the new girl who is prettier than her. The list is endless.

I admit I watch the investigation shows and the military channel on television. These are true stories and one of my favorites is America's Most Wanted. I can certainly understand how a father or mother or husband or wife or any family member can hate some piece of trash who killed, raped, hurt, or destroyed an innocent victim's life. There is never an excuse for the crime and you can't un-ring a bell. Once the crime is done, there is no getting it back.

God, I hope you have never been the father of a young lady who has been raped and/or murdered and left in a garbage can. I pray you are never the mother of a son who was hurt and killed by some perverted sex offender. I cannot tell you how my heart hurts for you, and I just stopped typing to say a prayer for you and your family. I have had two family members and two girlfriends who were victims of violent crimes. All four were here in America, done by other

Americans. This wasn't war, it was here and now in the good old USA. The point is, I do not blame the survivors one bit for hating the guts out of the slime that committed these crimes. I do so much hate them also. But none of these crimes were done by one race or one sex or one nationality or one religion or in one location.

That would be like hating everyone named Ted because of Ted Bundy. How stupid would that be? Should we hate all people named Jeffery because some idiot named Jeffery liked to eat people? How stupid is that? Then pray tell me, why should we hate all people of a different color? How stupid is that? Why do some black people hate me, and some do? They don't even know me. They have never talked to me and all they have done is see me as a white cop. I am the enemy. Do they not know I would give my life for them if I had to? I guess the same way they saw Kim as just a black cop. How stupid is that? To hate a group of people because of an injustice done by one or two of them is as stupid as it gets. Suit yourself.

While I'm wrapping this up, I thought of a couple of other things I hate. I hate Pimento cheese and eggplant... the thought of it makes me lightheaded. I hate the Rosetta Stone language program. It's a good thing they don't ask me to do a testimonial. My dad bought me the Spanish program two Christmases ago. It still isn't playing. I had trouble getting it loaded on my PC for starters. In their commercials, they say, "If you can click a mouse, you can get started." I say if you can call the help line, you can get started. I had to call for assistance and believe it or not, I got connected to a guy in India or Pakistan somewhere. Now I admit, I don't know anything about computers and I admit I have somewhat of an accent. You should have heard me and this guy named "Billy" trying to understand each other 10,000 miles apart on a cell phone and his accent was as thick as hops! He was very nice and if you talk to him, I suggest you take the Hindu Rosetta Stone before you call. You got a southerner talking to an Indian trying to learn Spanish... good luck. Did they mention you have to put on earphones and talk into a microphone to make this thing work? If you live alone, make sure the doors are locked and windows shut because you will never hear someone enter your house... whatever. I'm happy for the 100,000 or more satisfied customers. I'm one who ain't and my dad is out 300 bucks.

I hate the Sports Authority. I don't go in there anymore, and they don't come to my house so we are even.

I hate bullies who try to force their way through life. I don't just mean physical force, I would like to include emotional force and financial force and religious force. There is a lot more to bullying than the schoolyard tough guy. Right or wrong, the bully has to have it his or her way and you are wrong if you don't go along with it. Bullies are the weakest people I can think of because they don't have to be the way they are, they can change. They chose not to.

Last but not least, I have a reoccurring dream (nightmare) that I hate. In my nightmare, I am driving a station wagon across the country. I have to load up eight people in New York and deliver them to Los Angles nonstop. In my nightmare it is always daytime and I can't get out of the car.

Sitting next to me the entire trip is Rosie O'Donnell and Michael Moore. Oh God help me. We have to stop at every donut store we pass, but I never get a donut. Mine is already eaten before Rosie and Michael get back in the car. In the back seat sits Ellen DeGeneres. She keeps sitting cross legged and won't stop trying to dance. It annoys everybody. Next to her is Nancy Grace and beside her is Paula Dean. Paula keeps trying to put a fried egg and sausage patty between two of the donuts. Nancy won't stop accusing everybody in the car of doing a "Smelly." She threatens all of us with a full investigation. I have to slow down, I am getting double vision. In the back row sits Al Sharpton, Pastor Reverend Dr. Mike Murdock, and next to him is Jesse Jackson. Al and Jesse keep threatening Mike with a boycott, and Mike keeps telling Al and Jesse they better send him 43 dollars and 61 cents or they will not be the chosen ones and will miss an anointing. Oh God, the horror of it all. When we get to California, Joel Osteen is there grinning, telling us it's all going to be all right!

At some point I wake up, usually sweating and shaking, and realize it was all a bad dream. As a law-enforcement officer, I would defend these people with my every breath. As a free-will American, I would turn down an invitation for an all-expense, First-Class paid trip to the Vatican to have lunch with the Pope if any one of them was tagging along. I don't hate these people; I just hate the dream!

I truly believe none of these folks give a $#%& what I think of them. They couldn't care less about me, and that is fine with me. I couldn't care less about their opinion on anything. Worked out well, don't you think? Remember, it's just a dream.

Ecclesiastes 3: There is a time for everything and a season for every activity under the heavens. 3:8: A time to love and a time to hate.

Leviticus 19:17: Do not hate your brother in your heart. Rebuke your neighbor frankly so you will not share in his guilt.

Psalms 5:5: The arrogant cannot stand in your presence; you hate all who do wrong.

Chapter 8
Jessica

I have no idea what a perfect life is. Could be it is different for all of us. There are some basics that might be as good a place as any to start. Maybe having a beautiful home is a good start. The lady you are going to meet lived in a beautiful home on 40 acres of farmland near the Blue Ridge Mountains in western North Carolina. For a location, it doesn't get much prettier than that.

She had a loving family and a second-marriage family that she cared for very much. We all like some kind of family, and she had two to choose from. She had a husband who loved her and a job she looked forward to every single day. There was money in the bank, food on the table, and everything was coming up roses or corn or potatoes or whatever they planted. Life as we know and appreciate it was looking pretty good for Mrs. Jessica Brasington.

Jessica was 45 years old, college educated, with a background in law enforcement and was now working in human resources. She never smoked, had an occasional glass of wine and does admit to eating a southern diet of probably too much fried food. She still maintained a wonderful figure and there was no history of any illness in her family. Working around the farm on weekends kept her in pretty good shape, and all her yearly physicals came back excellent. She had never been to the hospital except to deliver two beautiful daughters. That's it.

Along about July of 1997, she and her husband made plans for a weeklong vacation. It was full of travel and there was a lot of preparation. Jessica had to get everything covered at work, had to tie up a bunch of loose ends, phone numbers for the children, and on and on. You have been on vacation; you know what it's like. She admits to forgetting her yearly physical until her doctor called with a reminder.

Damn it, how could she have scheduled a vacation the week she had her yearly physical? There was just too much going on at work and home and she just wasn't thinking. There was nothing to do but reschedule and also schedule her mammogram so they could get on with life and summer vacation! Yipee!

Jessica got her physical out of the way, passed with flying colors, and now the mammogram was the only thing left. It was scheduled for the following Thursday.

She reports for the mammogram, gets in her gown, sits down in the waiting room for the first time that day, waiting, and picks up a magazine with an article about breast cancer. Jessica told me she thought, "Gosh, wouldn't that be something if I ever got breast cancer?" Little did she know. Little do any of us know. She didn't give the article a second thought. Remember, she had received excellent results from her physical and really didn't have time for this breast exam, but she knew it had to be done so let's get on with it and go on vacation.

Jessica was called for the screening and everybody knew her and hello and how have you been, etc. She went through all the steps and went back out to the waiting room and waited on her "good report, permission to leave" review.

The nurse came out and for the first time in her life, Jessica was asked for a second screening. It's no big deal, just a little gray area in the X-rays and it won't take but a minute. Nothing to worry about. OK, let's go, I have to get back to work and get packed and so much to do and "let's get the show on the road." Back in she goes and out she comes and back in the waiting room and now she needs a phone because this is taking a little longer than she thought and she has to make some calls. Jessica was sitting there when the nurse came back in and said, "We need one more screening."

The nurse said not to start worrying, they just needed a different angle or something, and sometimes it takes three screening to be sure and it's not unheard of. "OK, but now you are starting to worry me." After the third screening, Jessica returns to the waiting room and is there for about one and a half minutes when the nurse returns and very calmly says, "The radiologist needs to see you."

Jessica walks in the doctor's office and the doctor is standing next to one of those lit-up walls with the X-rays hanging on it. She told Jessica to come look at a darker cloudy area on the X-ray. "You see this area here, we need to do a biopsy and find out what is going on." As an afterthought, she also said, "We need to do it quickly."

Jessica was sorta laughing and remembers replying, "Can't be cancer, it doesn't run in my family. I'm closing on a condo, I'm going on vacation next week, just too much going on right now. I ain't got no time for no cancer." OK, the doctor said, she understood. But, "I really strongly urge you to make time for this."

Jessica got dressed, went out, and sat in her car then called her husband. She got his answering machine and left a message bringing him up to speed on a cell phone. She was still lighthearted about it and not overly concerned. This was a simple inconvenience that had to be taken care of. Oh well, back to work.

But, when her husband got the message, it became a much greater priority. According to Jessica, he agreed with the doctors. This was urgent and had to be addressed immediately. It was his wife and her health we are talking about. The biopsy was scheduled for the following Monday. Tuesday and Wednesday morning passed and everybody was on pins and needles and the call came in. Maybe the first indication that something was wrong was the call was coming from the doctor himself. Nurses bring good news, doctors bring both kinds. The conversation went something like this:

"Hey Jessica, how are you?"?

"Doctor, I hope you are calling to tell me good news."

"Afraid not, Jessica, it is cancer. It's a garden-variety type. Intraductal Carcinoma. It means cancer within the milk ducts. What surgeon do you use?"

"None, I've never had any surgery."

"All right, Jessica, I will refer you to one of the best. I think I can get you in pretty quickly."

Remember, dear reader, Jessica had never missed a physical or a mammogram. Somewhere between July of '96 and July of '97, this mass appeared and began to grow. Jessica had not done anything wrong. She did self-exams and was in good health. The question is, when did you have a physical? If it has been a while, don't put it off any longer. It's one train we can't afford to miss.

Friday that week she meets with the surgeon. He looks over the X-rays and reports the good news. He can get her in real soon and go in and get that

115

pesky little mass out, and if he has to take out the lymph nodes, then she will wake up with some stitches under her arm and be sore on her vacation. It was good news.

She was going on vacation and didn't mind being a little sore. This would finally be over with. The surgery was scheduled for the following Monday. Let's review:

Thursday she gets her yearly mammogram.

Monday she gets her biopsy

Wednesday she gets the phone call from her doctor.

Friday she meets her new doctor, the surgeon.

Monday she is scheduled for a lumpectomy (removal of the mass).

A total of 11 days has passed.

Monday morning at 6, Jessica is at the hospital in great spirits. "Let's get it on! Get me in and out of here and get that lump out and sew me up for my vacation." All the nurses and staff loved her attitude and smile and optimism.

The first thing Jessica thinks when she wakes up in recovery is: If I can't move my arm, if there are stitches, I'm good to go. Vacation here we come. She thinks, OK, it's time to try and move it. It moves just fine, no pain, no stitches, and no nothing. Not good news.

As she puts her arm down the surgeon comes in. The happy, laughing, joking, neat doctor who she talked to on Friday is nowhere to be seen. He is dead serious now. There is no B.S., no joking, and no laughing. This guy isn't fooling around.

"Jessica, can you hear me?"

"Yes, sir."

"When I got in there, I couldn't just take the lump out, that mass had tentacles. I could not cut around it. I wasn't convinced I would get all the cancerous cells. My only option is to take the breast. I have scheduled you for a mastectomy on Wednesday. Do you understand?"

"Yes, sir."

Wednesday came and the breast left the same day. Unfortunately, that's not the end of it. It's far from the end of it. Now the real discomfort and pain and sickness begin. Now we start the "chemo."

As I understand it, which isn't much, just taking the breast doesn't ensure all the bad cells are gone. After a few weeks of recovery, Jessica had to go in for chemotherapy. To cut a long explanation short, this involves getting a dose of radioactive stuff shot into your veins and you get violently sick from it. What it does is kill all the cells to make sure the bad ones get killed. Then you get good cells back and hopefully the bad ones are dead and gone.

She told me the names of the drugs she was taking, but I have no idea what they were or how to spell them. I do know she said they were like a cocktail of Drano and Round-Up... she couldn't eat for three to four days and then she couldn't eat enough!

Jessica told me she was so thirsty and her throat was so sore after the treatments that she lived for ice cream. That's OK, Jessica, I know some people who live for ice cream who haven't had cancer. All of her beautiful, long, thick hair was falling out by the handful. She reports that one day she was on her front porch just standing there looking out at the beautiful mountains trying to sort out all this trouble when a cool breeze blew by. In front of her eyes she saw long strands of her hair begin to fly away. It was so loose and she was on so much chemo that the evening air could pull her hair out. All Jessica could do was hope a bird would find it and pick it up and use it to build a nest. What other possible use for it could there be?

Couple of months of chemo and one or two operations to get her figure back and life went on. The breast augmentation wasn't a walk in the park. There was a lot of muscle tissue cut and a lot of damage in there and there is a story about some stomach muscles being brought up to the chest and it gets so graphic that we will pass on the details. Let's just say this is one tough, determined woman! I hear that childbirth can be a little uncomfortable, but getting stomach muscles pulled up to form chest muscles... get my drift? P.S., these doctors get

117

an A+ from Jessica... she says she is completely happy with the results regardless of the pain.

Life continues for Jessica with the normal speed bumps and detours and roadblocks along the way. She moves to another town and starts a new job and becomes very involved in the Susan B. Komen Foundation. She and one of her daughters begin walking and running in the events, and Jessica begins really taking care of her health! And then out of nowhere it hits her in the middle of the night! Hot searing pain in her eyes... what the hell, where did this come from?

You probably know the rest of the story... guess whose back? That's right, after endless tests and biopsies and tests and drops and exams and waiting and specialists... the cancer has returned and is in her eye! Jessica laughs now and tells me, "I guess the cancer wanted to see where I was going."

Well, she could have told it she was going back to the lab for another round of chemo... same church, different pew. This time it's bad, real bad. The treatments leave her exhausted for days and after three or four days, she is starving again. This time the side effects were always different. Sometimes it was diarrhea out of nowhere. (I guess that is the only kind there is.) And sometimes it was simply handfuls of hair falling out during a meeting. Back to the old scarves and hats.

Don't eat for 72 hours and then get as much soup and soft food as possible in you. And more ice cream. Ice cream by the gallons. Thank God for ice cream.

Back to the hair again. She told me only about 75 percent went this time, but it went quick. Remember, she is a working administrator at a full-time job and has to make sales calls and schedule people and run an office and meet clients and do reports and look good and dress good and be upbeat and fight cancer all in a day's work. She's a woman, a W-O-M-A-N, I'll say it again... it's an old song about what all a woman can do. She did it.

After a few months of that and a lot of other tests and keeping her job, she gets a clean bill of health... thank God!

Along about this time, she reads about the Body-*for*-LIFE Challenge and decides to enter it. She gives the Challenge the same effort she has given recovering from the two cancers. She gives it all she's got. What a great job she did. The local television station interviewed her and did a segment on the recovery and the tremendous physical transformation she had. It's 2001 and Jessica has a new job, a new figure, a new chance at life.

Around 2002, all is well and just as quickly, the pain is back in her eyes. It is just as bad as before and came unannounced and is white hot! What, what, what... how can this be? Again, without all the gory details, there are tests and drops and goo and needles in her eyes and biopsies and more tests and trips to major medical teaching centers and more fear and more pain and more suffering and absolutely nothing to blame it on, nothing.

This time a different form of radiation was used to try and correct the problem. Jessica reports it wasn't the most comfortable thing in the world, but it wasn't chemo! She was afraid she was going to start glowing in the dark and in the daylight! After months of this new treatment and everything else life can throw at her, she gets a good bill of health from her doctor. It may not be gone, but it ain't there anymore. It might come back, but nothing is showing on any test, and there is nothing more anyone can do. Jessica can see, and there are no more searing headaches, and she feels pretty good, finally.

Listen, I'm not trying to write a report to be published in the *American Medical Journal*, and there is no chance of me doing a doctoral thesis on anything. This story won't be on television or in any history book. I certainly could and probably did make a mistake about the exact timeline or the exact type of medicine used, but so what? It's a life lesson, not a biochemistry paper. If you want to correct me, let me urge you to take that time and effort and go out and try to raise a little money for the CURE of all types of breast cancer. I'll stay an idiot, you go cure breast cancer. Thank you.

What in the world would this story about an innocent girl in western North Carolina have to do with anything about addiction? Here is the answer: Try and get her to smoke a cigarette... go ahead and try. Try and get her to eat deep-fried, grease-laden food again... go ahead and try. See if you can get her to down five or six shots of hard liquor to burn up her throat or rot her liver... go ahead and give it a whirl. She won't do it. Jessica refuses to put anything in her body that will invite, encourage, or entice Mr. Cancer to move back in. I honestly do not believe there is enough gold in Ft. Knox to get her to miss an exercise session if she can help it. There is nothing more important than her health, NOTHING!

Remember when I wrote about Dianne Weeks and she said she loved her family and she loved her grandchildren and regardless of all that, she was going to go work out and exercise come hell or high water? These two women mean it. They both have a running love-hate relationship with death and being paralyzed and with the end of their life, and they were both completely innocent. They weren't sitting in a bar drunk; they weren't in a hallway with a needle in their arm. They weren't having unsafe, unprotected sex with multiple partners; they were married, hard-working, intelligent mothers and wives. No fouls, no strikes, no anything but going through life minding their business and taking care of their families. And in a matter of minutes, all hell broke loose.

And here is my point: What are we doing that is shaving minutes and hours and days off our lives when we have a choice of being well or continuing to be sick? What, do you think it can't happen to you? It damn sure can. Do you think Dianne wanted that car to crash into her leg? Do you think Jessica woke up and looked out the window in 1997 and said what a beautiful day for cancer? How ridiculous!

A strange thing I noticed about both of these ladies is neither one wanted to use the world-class narcotics they were given for pain. Isn't that funny... they had prescriptions for some mind-blowing, mood-altering dope, and both of them report they threw away the bottles with more than half the pills still in them. On the other hand, you will read about a pal of mine who lost everything, and I mean everything, trying to find those bottles. How does that happen? How can five people stand in front of a bottle of booze and four of them not give a hoot about having a drink and the fifth one (me) wants the entire quart of liquor? Maybe five people stand in front of a line of cocaine on a bar and four of them would wipe it on the floor and the fifth one would get down on a filthy floor and lick it up. How can five people stand in front of a key-lime pie and watch it melt and the fifth one would eat the entire thing, even if it was melted and turning rancid.

It's addiction! It's the merry-go- round that rides you. I am going to try and act and live more like Dianne and Jessica. There ain't nothing been born that is going to get these Champions to hurt, kill, or abuse themselves. I hope you get to meet them one day; they are amazing people.

120

As a closing note, I live here in Augusta, Georgia, and one day last year the local newspaper (Augusta Chronicle) published the entire paper in pink! It announced a big party for some locals, and I was writing this story so I decided to attend. It was me and about 10 guys and about 200 ladies! I wish they would have a party like that every week!

The theme was Coping with Breast Cancer. I don't know if the ladies all had cancer or their friends had it or what, but they all wore pink. Pretty cool. After lunch, a lady got up to speak. That's why I came, to hear what she had to say.

This first lady was 29 years old when she got Ovarian Cancer. She said words like unfair, discouragement, anger, fear, hope, love, and then she said something amazing. She said, "Cancer happens to everybody who knows the person who has it." It can show up even if you are pregnant. What do you do? It will test your faith in ways you never thought possible. The wigs and hats and the vomit. Lots and lots of vomit. She said she couldn't find the words to express the importance of support from family and friends and other survivors. I stopped eating my dessert and from 20 tables back, just stared at her, what a lady!

The next lady to speak begged the crowd to get that checkup. She admitted she skipped a year and when she went back, it was there. The price she paid was far too high for missing a one-hour appointment. She couldn't remember what had been so important to have missed her yearly checkup. She talked about the dash! The year you're born—dash—the year you die. She asked everyone to give their life the best shot possible.

Next lady: Breast cancer will teach you what is really important, and what isn't. She said that every prayer counts. She said to buy a ticket for the future and she meant it. She told everyone to go buy a ticket to Disney or to a cruise or to somewhere for next year and get the clean bill of health to go.

Several ladies spoke and there was a common theme. They were all glad to be there and none of them thought it was fair that they were the one out of eight women to get cancer. And every one of them speaking begged every one of them who was listening… take care of yourself and get that exam.

There is a picture in this book of Jessica standing in a kitchen with no hair and no breast. She is as pale as Dracula and grinning from ear to ear. When

121

she showed me the picture, I had to ask why she was smiling; it was obvious she was sick as a dog.

She just looked at me and said, "Because I was still alive."

Go ahead and see if Jessica will lie in the sun and bake for hours to look tan and fit. She won't do it. See if you can get her to bake in the tanning booth a mile from her house; the answer is no thank you. If she goes in the sun, she has on a pretty good coat of a high SPF sun lotion. Again, do you think she is going to burn a pack of smokes this afternoon? Nope. Think she might smoke a bowl of crack or shoot up a baggie of black-tar heroin? Nope. I know, she is going to take her insurance payment this month and bet it on Old Ragmop in the fourth... nope, not that either. Does she watch her weight and try to eat clean and healthy? Yes she does. Why? Because she knows life ain't a joke. This isn't a dress rehearsal for the big Christmas play in the school gym. It's real and it is fleeting, and each and every second and minute and heartbeat is precious, and it only comes once in our lives.

What do you think the chances are of Dianne Weeks going out to the bar this afternoon and downing four or five doubles and trying to drive home? I'm guessing it isn't going to happen. Do you think every time she sees a wreck, she doesn't wish they hadn't been speeding or prays they weren't drunk and nobody's hurt? She does. Do you think she ever walks between two cars that she doesn't get a little chill even just for a second? She does. She never wants it to happen to the people she loves and the ones she doesn't even know. She most certainly doesn't want you to drink and drive or text and drive or look for your lipstick and drive or do anything behind the steering wheel of a car but drive. Good idea, Dianne.

These two women only have one addiction and that's to living.

Neither of these ladies was doing anything wrong or unhealthy when travesty struck; it just did. Somewhere along the line and to some degree, the fact that they both were in pretty good health and had been seeing their doctors and had been exercising and did lead pretty healthy lives helped in their recovery. Remember, if Jessica hadn't had a mammogram the year before, the cancer might have been too far gone to do much about. If Dianne had been way overweight or not strong enough to hold herself up, she could have either bled to death or, at the very least, lost all of her leg. Thank God both these ladies took care of themselves, and it proved to be greatly to their advantage, but it still didn't prepare them for what lay in store.

MATTHEW 5:48: He causes his sun to rise on the evil and the good and to rain on the just and the unjust.

It can rain on anybody... be ready.

Chapter 9

Now Boarding... Welfare, Food Stamps, Gravy Train... ALL ABOARD!

What a silly name for a chapter. There is no such train leaving any station in America that I know of. The problem is, the train is there, it just ain't leaving. It's staying, it isn't going anywhere. It can't really be a train because trains move, they leave, and come back. The good old Welfare train is stationary; it's here to stay. And, it's in your town and my town and his town and her town.

Here's the problem: There aren't fewer people boarding, there are more people boarding, and the train station is adding new cars every day. The train is growing longer and the price to get on board is getting higher and higher for those of us paying for the tickets.

I am convinced (and if you are not convinced, you can say so when you write your book) that welfare and food stamps and WIC and Snap and every other program in this category are as ADDICTIVE as any drug or lifestyle known to man. Don't believe it? Get in it and see how difficult it is to start turning down hundreds of dollars of free money and instead, go get a minimum-wage paying job. I do believe the roots and vines that bind some people to this "gets me mine" welfare system are innocent children... the more children... the bigger the check. And it is guaranteed for at least 18 years or until mom's uterus gives out, whichever comes first!

Where in the world am I going with this? Probably broke... let's find out.

I read somewhere that a fish ain't wet in water. That makes sense to me. A fish is born in water, grows up in water, and dies in water. A fish doesn't know it is wet until it is pulled out of the water and is surrounded by air. Wonder if the same thing applies to welfare? Born in it, grow up in it, it becomes a way of life.

Let's start with a couple of the worst abuses of the welfare system that I have firsthand knowledge of. In a book about addiction, why bring up Section 8

Housing, free school lunches, books, pens papers, WIC (Women-Infants-Children), etc.? Because just like the fish in water, some people find themselves on the "Gravy Train" and either can't get off or have learned how NOT to get off until the end of the line (or the end of the money, whichever comes first). With our economy in the shape it is in, that end may be soon, real soon.

I was listening to the radio and heard a guy say, eventually enough parasites will kill the host. Do you think too many people on the Gravy Train will ever overload it and make it stop running? Do you think it's possible that a person can get on welfare and learn the system and figure out how to do 1/ the work of going out each morning and doing manual labor and still at the end of the month have the same buying power and money in his or her pocket as an honest day's labor? Damn that's a big sentence, read it again.

Let's review: Get up, have some coffee, go down to the welfare office, no education, fill out three or four applications a day for a while (all of which you are not qualified for), list the horrible headaches and back problems you have, get some EBT cards, get an apartment for next to nothing to share with two other guys in the same boat, go to the soup kitchen or Salvation Army kitchen and eat lunch, go do a little under-the-table, no-tax-taken-out work (like selling a little dope), and watch television with your pals, smoke a blunt, slam a few .40s, and enjoy the rest of the night. Yep, that's a full day for some folks.

Don't give me the story about that being the exception. I don't think so. Prove me wrong. Now I know some families that lost their jobs, they try every day to find work, will get up and go to the Man-Labor each morning and do any work to survive. That's what welfare is for, to help people for a short period of time while they get on their feet. It's to help the truly disabled who would give anything to be able to get out of that wheelchair and go to work. It is for the mother or father who lost their partner and has to have some help so they don't starve until they are on their feet. IT IS NOT FOR THE LEECHES THAT ARE PLAYING THE REST OF US FOR A FOOL!

Do me this one favor… if you like the system as it stands now, don't do a thing about it. If you think there is a little hanky-panky going on, DEMAND that people getting city, county, state, or federal assistance take a simple urine test for drugs and or alcohol.

I am a police officer in the state of Georgia, and they demand that I take a drug and alcohol test. Why, if the same state of Georgia is giving some deadbeat Gravy Train expert a couple hundred dollars a week, why don't they have to take the same drug test? I guess the same way it's illegal to ask an illegal alien if they are illegal because it's illegal to ask an illegal if they are illegal. WE ARE FOOLS and NO ONE IS GOING TO DO ANYTHING ABOUT IT. So the people addicted to the welfare game keep on playing. And that's my opinion. Let me give you a few examples why I think this way. WAIT! Forget the drug test... all that will happen is we will have to pay 30 or 40 bucks for each test (and it only checks for the two basic drugs) and if the person is caught with dope in their system, what are you going to do about it? Are you going to put a mother and her four kids under the age of 6 on the street in the rain and snow and have them stand on the sidewalk? Hell no... so why even spend the 30 or 40 bucks to pretend you are going to do anything about it? What a waste of time that would be! Who is going to pay for the rehab? Who is going to care for the kids while mom and dad are in rehab? If mom is clean and dad or boyfriend isn't clean, who is going to force boyfriend to move out of the apartment until he gets clean? Are you going to hire more cops? If the 12- or 13-year-old child is on dope, does the child have to live on the street until he or she cleans up? Forget the drug test, unless you are prepared to pay thousands of dollars to support the "kids" while mom or pop gets straight.

I'm standing in line at a local grocery store and there is a guy right in front of me with a backpack on, buying some kind of groceries. I didn't pay much attention to him until he started loading up the counter. He looked like a student or a traveling man passing through Augusta. I'm going out on a limb here and say he was a traveling man because it was about 9 p.m. and there were no schools anywhere near the store. Probably clothes were in the backpack, not college books.

He starts putting food up on the checkout counter and the first three items were boxes of chocolate cereal. You know the kind, they have a cartoon monster on the box. I guess this guy liked cereal, nothing wrong with that, I like oatmeal. Then the next four or five items are more of the same chocolate cereal. I guess this guy is on some kind of new diet where you eat a bowl of chocolate cereal with every meal. Sounds good to me. Then he puts up four more boxes of the same cereal again. I was trying to count but the cashier was good at her job

126

and the price was all the same so it went by fast. I will go on record and say it was an even dozen boxes of Monster Chocolate Cereal, and not one drop of milk to wash it down with. Then the traveling man hands the cashier a green state of Georgia EBT credit card, she hands it back. It isn't really a credit card but looks exactly like one. I was told it took the place of food stamps because it is easier for the store and not as embarrassing for the customer.

The guy swipes the card, she never looks up, and he loads the cereal in the shopping cart and heads out the door. Now it's my turn. I pay cash for my can of tuna, my apple, and my six pack of Diet Coke. Now I am out the door behind the traveling man.

He's about a third of the way through the parking lot and loading the back door of a car driven by an Asian guy. If my life depended on it, I couldn't tell you if he was Hawaiian, Korean, Chinese, Japanese, or from Tibet. It was dark and he was in the front seat of the car. I don't care if I offended anyone by saying he was Asian... he was. I saw him, I looked in his face, and I have seen Asian people in my life. This guy was Asian. If the Southern Poverty Law Group wants to sue me, I will leave my email address at the end of this book. If the Asian American Council on Discrimination wants to sue me, please contact the Southern Poverty Law Group. If Al and Jesse want to fly into Augusta on private jets and protest how cruel I am to Asians, don't come during February... I will be on vacation with my Chinese girlfriend. We are going to meet her parents. I'm very excited!

So the traveling man loads the backseat with the boxes of cereal, and I slowly walk to my car about two rows over. When the traveling man is done loading, he hands Asian man something, and Asian man hands traveling man one of the little plastic shopping bags. Asian man drives off into the night. No idea where he went. I didn't follow him. Traveling man reaches in the plastic bag and pulls out a pack of smokes and fires one up. I have no earthly idea what else was in the bag. It might have been more smokes or a can or two, I honestly don't know. Traveling man heads off across the parking lot in the general direction of a bridge where some people sleep under the stars; the bridge is directly behind the Salvation Army barracks. Now here is what I think: This has one of two explanations... 1) Traveling man and Asian man are roommates and Asian man dropped traveling man off at the store to buy three months' supply of cereal for the two of them. Remember, there was no milk so that just means they simply enjoy eating it dry. Instead of going home with Asian man, traveling man wanted to go over under the bridge and write some poetry or at the very least volunteer at the "CLOSED at 9 p.m." Salvation Army. That's the first explanation, here's the second: Asian man traded some drunk a bottle of wine and/or a pack of generic smokes for an EBT card. He then found another guy (traveling man) to go into the store and buy 12 boxes of cereal on the above listed card. Traveling man probably got a pack of smokes and maybe two beers. Asian man gets $50 worth of sugar-coated cereal to feed fat little kids and it cost him maybe two packs of smokes and two beers. Asian man total cost: $7. Cost to taxpayers: $43. First lesson concerning Gravy Train rip-off... priceless.

If you think that is the first time either of those guys did the swap food for smokes or beer routine, you're nuts. If you think it's the only time and my town is the only town, you're nuts. If you believe it is happening all over America, you're right. You know it, I know it, and nothing is going to be done about it. At least not until somebody comes up with a mark of the beast or something to ensure the right person gets the right food... hmmm, where have I heard that before?

The second example is much quicker; I'm tired of typing. Same store, same checkout line, different day. It's Sunday after church and the store is busy. This time I am two people behind a good-looking woman and her daughter (I guess). They are both dressed to the nines. They have matching outfits and in all honesty are beautiful. They seem to know just about everybody and are all smiles and manicured nails and both have perfect hair. The little girl's hair has rows with beads on each end and matching shoes and pocketbook. Mother has matching shoes and pocketbook. Just beautiful!

I again cannot tell the good reader if mother's diamonds were real or glass. I cannot say if her wedding ring was gold or from the county fair. If my life depended on it, I could not tell you if her pocketbook was plastic or rich, fine imported leather... I didn't get to feel or examine it. I can tell you they both looked like "money in the bank."

The lady bought ribs and barbeque fixings... she had veggies and sodas, and I was hoping she was a widow and was going to turn around and invite me to dinner. She had biscuits and cake and everything for one hell of a cookout. The little girl got one candy (that's all mom would let her have. Good for mom) and when it was all rang up, mom pulls out the state of Georgia EBT (electronic benefits transfer) card and swipes it. The whole time this was going on, the cashier was talking about how pretty the child was and have a good day and tell everybody hello and la-de-da. Something was said I couldn't hear but mom did open her purse and drop two $20s on the belt for something. I saw some personal items that I guess weren't covered by the green EBT card. I could not wait to get outside and see where they went.

Have you jumped ahead of me? Have you figured it out yet? Winner, winner, chicken dinner! There they were in a brand-new Chrysler 300 automobile. And here's the kicker: The car was the exact same color as their outfits! I stopped to let them back out. I went and got in my 1996 Honda with 80,000 miles on it. I have trouble finding 2 socks that match and these two looked like Ferragamo dressed them.

I want one of them cards! I want to barbeque on Sundays instead of going to work. I want a new Chrysler 300! I want $50 worth of oatmeal for two packs of smokes! I want one of them green state of Georgia food cards. I want mine... where's mine? I don't want to pay for those cards and not be able to have one, that's not fair! Or is it? You be the judge, it's your money. Some people get on the system and learn the system and work the system and get their relatives on the system and use and abuse the system and it becomes an addiction, and you and I are paying for it. Instead of saying "Play on Georgia" like they do with the lottery, why not say "Pay on Georgia" 'cause that's what we are going to do. And it ain't just Georgia... trust me on that.

I repeat: This is not everybody; it is not all people on welfare and assistance who beat the system. I do not begrudge one person who is hungry or homeless, for asking for help. I give to my charities and church, and will continue to do so. I learned a lot from Bill Phillips and here is one lesson: Give some of your money to a good cause and ask nothing in return. Don't be a big shot about it, don't tell everybody you're doing it, just be thankful you can share and do it quietly. That's what he did. Very few people will ever know how much or who to or how often he gave. I was fortunate enough to work with his mom and help with Charity Affairs and have a small idea. So please don't get the impression I want anybody to do without, I don't. But, I also don't want anybody to beat the system and get what they do not deserve! The chocolate cereal and barbeque folks listed above are making fools of the rest of us and grinning while they do it.

I have more firsthand examples but want to share two or three other people's stories. Hopefully they will make you cringe.

A dear friend of mine worked part time for a tax firm. Her job was at the front desk and when clients came in, she would get their name and make sure they had all the paperwork in order and had their ID with them. Then she would assign the clients to one of the preparers who was most familiar with the type of return needed. My friend did this during tax season for several years. After a year or so, she got to know and would remember returning clients, sometimes even on a first-name basis. According to her, the following is a true story. Another funny thing: You have to have an ID to get WELFARE but not to vote for it... hmmm!

In 2009, a lady walked into the tax office holding a new baby. I don't mean brand new, but like about 3 months old. So my friend recognizes the lady from coming in for the previous two or three years and they "hey, how are you, how have you been" each other for about five minutes. Now according to my friend, this lady had four children, no husband, and worked a minimum amount of time each week as a maid for a cleaning service. My friend said, "Oh my goodness, you've got a new baby." The lady smiled from ear to ear and replied "Yes, Ma'am! I tries to have one every year!"

You're getting ahead of me again, aren't you? The way this lady saw it, if one fatherless child was worth, say, $2,000, then two fatherless children was worth $4,000, and the more children she had, the more money the IRS and the Federal Government sent her at the end of the year! Do you think she didn't know what was causing those children to appear? I think she did. Do you think she found the children in the cabbage patch? Here's what I think... she was at the club one Saturday night and she was getting her dance on and some guy was getting his dance on and then they were getting their groove on and they went back to her Section 8 apartment 'cause the kids stay at their grandmother's and her and lover boy did one of the two most important things anyone can do on this earth, they created a life... and you see, friends, the circle was unbroken. This mother of five children was born in welfare and grew up in welfare and has survived as an adult for seven years on welfare and now is introducing all her children not to the Wonderful World of Disney but to the Wonderful World of

130

Welfare. Congratulations! Somebody else is paying for all of those innocent children to get an EBT ticket and ride the new, exciting "broken back of the working public." There is no height restriction; you can ride it the minute you are born!

There was an article in the local paper that stated in our county, 70 percent of all the school children get free food at school, or pay a tremendously reduced rate, something like a quarter. All the other children pay $1.50 to $1.75 per meal. That sounds fair to me. No child should be hungry; no child should be without a winter coat or a pair of comfortable shoes. No innocent child on this earth should have to go to school dirty or with rotting teeth or ashamed of their tattered clothes.

This isn't about race or religion or location or anything else, it's about worthless parents who know they can pop out children like a gumball machine because somebody else is going to care for and feed and clothe and educate the child and send the parents a check! Great system. How about this... I'm just throwing it out there, just kick it around a little bit and see what you think. Don't have any more innocent children that you and who the hell ever the father is can't care for and love. Ahh forget it, that ain't ever gonna happen. Sorry I brought it up. It's like owning a car lot and not wanting to sell all the cars. The more cars you sell, the more money you make. On welfare, the more children, the bigger the welfare check.

Here is a perfect example... you can say it's not true, that's your call. Go ask the girl and see what she says. This young lady is out of high school and going to a junior college, working part-time nights and weekends. She is a great girl, pretty with good, loving parents. So, she meets this guy who is a little older than she is, but they hit it off pretty good and go out a few times. She gets swept up by Mr. Smooth Operator, and you know what happens... she presents him with her virginity. It was going to happen sooner or later, and it was her business who she wanted to give it to, and it turned out to be this aspiring young Casanova, Mr. Smooth Operator. Remember, you can always give your virginity away, but you can never get it back.

After a few visits to his pad after work and on the weekend, guess what happened? That's right, you got it, there is a little Smooth Operator in the oven. Now an abortion is out of the question, she thinks she might love him but he ain't never said the word love and has no intention whatsoever of marrying this girl. What does she do? She goes home, works as much as she can, gets all the WIC and EBT and assistance as she can, and has the innocent child. She doesn't see Smooth at all anymore. Life goes on, until she runs into him at one of the old familiar places... where they both used to work. Guess what? Two months later, she calls her mom and tells mom the great news: Mom is going to be a grandmother again... how wonderful! Abortion is again, out of the question. He not only doesn't love her, now he no longer likes her and has a new girlfriend. Too bad, so sad! The girl goes back (it's easier this time because she knows where to go and how to work the system) to get her WIC and SNAP and EBT and assistance and has a second baby with Mr. Operator, who is again out of the picture. Plus she gets more diapers, formula, car seats, etc.

Now, finally, somebody somewhere with some &^%$ brains asked where is dear old dad, Mr. Operator? The girl reports he works part time at such and such and the ball starts rolling in that state for dad to show up in court for a little something, something on the child-support payments. I wasn't there but heard this from one of the relatives who was there. This is unbelievable... our girl shows up with her two children in tow, another young lady shows up with her child in tow, and Mr. Operator comes through the courtroom doors with his pregnant girlfriend. That's a minimum of four illegitimate children (there were rumors of more) with no father and all on some type of welfare.

He was threatened with jail time if he didn't cough up some do-re-mi for the children. No problem... go to jail and cost the residents of that county and state (not Georgia) about $15 to $20 thousand at the very least to keep him in jail, plus he had a right to an attorney and he had a right to give the girls a DNA test and he had a right to bring in any of his friends to say the girls were trash who slept around and he was a Smoooth Operator!

By the way, think back and see you if you paid any taxes in your state or to the Federal Government in the past 10 years because you helped those four children with clothes, food, meals at school, after-school programs, health care, dental work, school supplies, formula, car seats, cribs, diapers, utilities, rent, summer school, and summer camp for the next 18 years! Did Smooth Operator send you a Thank You card? Funny, I didn't get one either.

How many more addiction to the Gravy Train stories do you need? Want to hear the one about the eight family members who camped out for the summer in the air-conditioned waiting room at the hospital? This is a keeper. Somebody's cousin was in the hospital and it looked like they were going to be there for a few weeks. That's bad; I don't want anybody to be stuck in a hospital. It ain't a place to be. So, cousin is in room 1400 and the first few days one or two or three relatives are there visiting. No problem. By the end of the week, I am told there are about five people waiting day in and day out to see how dear cousin is getting along. They get there at 6 a.m. and stay till 10 p.m. When cousin takes a turn for the worse, three children show up and different shifts of the family stay and spend the night. Do you see any problem with this? I don't, that is until...

Now the children have built a fort out of the couch cushions. The television stays on cartoons all day (it keeps the children busy), and no other family can sit in that waiting room... all seats are taken. The family goes down to the cafeteria in shifts with their EBT cards and loads up on carryout and eats and keeps food in the waiting room. The kids are beginning to learn their way around the hospital and visit random waiting rooms and floors and enjoy the elevator when visiting the children's play area for child "patients" of the hospital.

What in the hell could this have to do with welfare, you ask? I am told by the eye witness who was there every day the adults went to one of the doctors raising hell because the kids couldn't get any pop or candy out of the vending machines when the cafeteria closed. The machines would not take an EBT card. It was completely unfair and all the vending machines should be changed to accept EBT cards. What were the little children supposed to eat when they got hungry after 10 p.m.?

I cannot report the final solution to this problem. My friend's family member was discharged, and I will never know the end of the story... I bet the machines get changed. I bet the day is coming when all machines must accept welfare cards. I bet, we (the taxpayers) are going to pay $2 for a soda that goes on an EBT card.

So, on a major news station recently it was reported the average amount of assistance available to people using the welfare system is... drum roll... $37,000 a year. That includes reduced rent, school everything, EBT and cash cards, and on and on. At minimum wage, to get up and actually go to work five shifts a week, you will earn about $12,000 a year before taxes. Call me crazy, but I will pick door number one, the $37,000 one.

Let me tell you about the lady who worked with a friend of mine. Again, it is hearsay because I wasn't there. This lady works in an office and gets paid the same as everyone else. All things equal, she always has more money than her cronies. How does she do it? Inquiring minds want to know. Simple, she says. "I get about $250 a month in food from welfare." How? How in the world does she do it? Of course, all the other ladies want to know the secret. Simple, she tells them, I use my maiden name, same social security number, and they just don't know I am married. Guess where she reported she learned to pull this little $2,000- a-year stunt? Give up? She learned how to do it from her CHURCH! According to her, there was a group of ladies who actually taught groups of other ladies "HOW TO WORK THE SYSTEM." God helps those who help themselves.

A college-educated girl who I did work with did the same thing (so to speak). She and her boyfriend lived together and saved their money in order to buy a house. They found one they liked and he made the down payment and then moved in. It was in his name, but they both paid for it. They are living together and decide to have a baby. How nice. Both have jobs and both are educated and both are in their mid-twenties. Now after a few months, she starts coming to work sitting on a pillow and gaining weight and all the girls are ooohing and ahhhing over her and everybody is excited for the baby.

I have contact with this girl about twice a week and she is showing me pictures of the little tyke in her tummy and grinning and all is well. One day I ask her in passing if she thought she and the child's father would maybe get married. She said sure they would at some point but not right now and no time soon. Why not, I ask? Are you ready, do you see it coming? "Because we are not paying anything to have this baby, as long as I am single, welfare and Medicare will pay for it. So far I have spent about $3 on medical bills."

How about my friend who tells me the story about a lady who came to him to rent one of his rental properties. She filled out all the necessary paperwork and waited to hear back from him. As it turned out, she just couldn't afford the unit she had her eye on and was offered an alternative apartment. Just hold it for a few days, she told him, I'll be back.

She was a woman of her word. A few days later she walks back in and fills out a new set of papers and this time the only difference was... drum roll... she had quit her full-time job and taken a part-time job and now with the help of welfare and HUD and a slew of other government agencies, she got the same $600 apartment for less than $300, and he gets the difference each month from the good old USA! Exact same person, exact same apartment, exact same location, exact same rent, except now you and I are paying for half her rent and most of her utilities and phone. All she had to do was quit her job and file the right paperwork. Maybe she went to the same church as the other lady.

I almost forgot, the second half of the story was, she told my friend she needed a new refrigerator. Certainly my friend told her refrigerators do give out and he would see she had a new one delivered. This is his story, not mine. When he and a helper delivered the new icebox, they were walking it in the front door when he tripped and almost killed himself on her new (in the box) 42-inch flat-screen television. According to my buddy, the apartment was cluttered with expensive electronic children's games, men's cloths (and she was a single mother maybe she liked to cross-dress), the list of furniture and furnishings goes on and on. But you and I and any person working helped pay her rent. Let me say thank you on her behalf (wonder if those were Smooth Operator's clothes? Could be).

It is addictive. It is available, and it is being used by both those deserving of some assistance and those who have been taught and encouraged to take full advantage of welfare on every level. The key word is "CHILDREN." If you are just hanging out being unproductive and you can chat up some stupid woman into getting pregnant, the world will pay her and she will in turn pay you. Not bad work if you can get it. Try to get three or four girls pregnant and your monthly checks will triple. It always helps if you claim a bad back (that's a hard one to prove) and that you have trouble breathing and have constant chest pains. Unfortunately, you may have to start smoking. Most of the people I see on welfare have a pack of smokes on them, and you will have to start buying your beers one at a time. It doesn't look good if you get beer by the case.

One of the deputies here in Georgia was telling me about the "burglary" call he took. He arrived at the address and went in. It was a Section 8 (welfare assistance) housing project. The call was concerning some shoes missing. Now remember, this is a WELFARE address. That means a great deal of the rent and utilities and phone and Internet is being paid for to some degree by our taxes. I wish I could get a drum roll for the punch line... except it is anything but funny.

The complainant reported his 100 Nike athletic shoes were missing. All he had left were his Air Jordans because he was wearing them. There were about 50 empty boxes thrown back in the closet. Estimated value: $5,000. Where is Imelda Marcos when you need her?

I repeat, it is not one race or one group. It is not one sex. It is not one religion. It is not one illegal alien. Here's what it is: several programs with little to NO supervision or consequences for abuse. If you think about it, welfare and Social Services is about the only program that pays you for what you don't do.

Do me a favor and look up the lady in Michigan who won $1 million in the lottery and continues to collect unemployment from the state. Look up the guy in Atlanta who won $500,000 in the Georgia lottery and continues to get 14 months of unemployment. Look up a lady named Angel Adams in Tampa who has 15 children. Remember, she was living in one room in a hotel. Her sweetie and the father of 10 of her children is unfortunately in jail... so it is reported. On camera, she DEMANDS somebody (not her) is responsible for these kids and is going to pay. Look up Larmondo Allen. If the news article I got is correct, he was shot to death in New Orleans at 25 years of age. He leaves nine children behind with his girlfriend. That is about one child a year since he was 16. I wonder who is feeding those children now that their father is gone.

Does your town have one of the following? This past summer I joined a new gym and on my days off, I drive a different route than I was used to. I drive to the gym about 11 a.m. every day that I go, and I notice a soup kitchen a few blocks from my house. That's a wonderful thing; people who are hungry and have no job can get something to eat. Anyway, every time I go by, there is an elderly grandmother-type lady there with a car full of small children. I don't know exactly how many, eight or nine little kids all in and around grandma's station wagon and all are eating their lunch.

About twice a month, I go visit a chiropractor across town that happened to have an office across from a Mission House that feeds the hungry, God bless them. Guess who I see at the Mission House? Guess who I see when I drive past the Salvation Army headquarters? Guess who? Before I tell you who makes the

136

free food circuit with car loads of children, I want to go on record telling you I think the Salvation Army is priceless. They are (in my opinion) going to get a reward in Heaven as great as anyone. They are one charity that I willingly give to. OK… it's time to guess who I see at all the free food kitchens, missions, churches, and the Salvation Army… granny and her station wagon full of kids. She has the route and times down like a city bus driver. Those kids are eating two or three meals for free. What are their parents doing with the EBT money?

I don't know if it was always the same kids; they were running all over the place like cats. But I do know this: I'm betting (call me crazy), but I'm betting I am watching free enterprise at its best. Granny don't work so she gets paid to pick up all the little neighborhood tykes she can haul and she babysits and feeds them while mom and dad work or sleep or do whatever they do, and she gets 5 bucks a head. Prove I'm wrong… and remember, when you write your book, you can say there is no WELFARE addiction and it hasn't created any jobs other than government jobs. Granny will disagree with you… she's knocking down about three bills a week and getting lunch thrown in for free!

I quit. This chapter will never end. It gets worse and worse, not better. Write your book and say whatever you want. I am not now nor was I ever talking about or reporting about the innocent people who absolutely have to have a helping hand.

What a liar I have turned out to be. I admit it. I thought I was finished with this chapter on welfare addiction when another story that demands reporting pops up. This one is too good!

A girlfriend of mine works at a really big and really famous shopping center. It's like Wal-Mart or Kmart or Target or one of those type places. She is pretty much retired and works there part time more for something to do than anything else. She works all over the store but this is one of her cashier stories. One bright sunny afternoon, a kindly lady comes in and buys about a hundred dollars' worth of groceries. No problem. The kind lady swipes her EBT card and asks for the balance in change. No problem, except… the change is a little over $700!

When the kind lady is told no, she goes ballistic! It's her G&^ %$#@ money and the store can't stop her from getting her money. Of course, the manager comes rushing up to see what the screaming is about and discovers the kind lady can't get the money BECAUSE THERE ISN'T 700 DOLLARS in the register. The kind lady replies, well you better G&^ %$#@ get it. I want my F&^%$#@ money, M*&^%F^%$#@. You ain't cheating me out of my F*&^%$ money B%$#@.

They went to several registers and "borrowed" the cash to pay the nice kind lady and get her the hell out of the store.

Now it gets interesting. Come to find out, this happens a lot during the first of the month or whenever all the welfare cards are reloaded. There was just never a time when that much was asked for that early in the morning. So the store has a secret in-house policy that they try and only give back about $200 in cash if people want a little spending change off their EBT card.

You're ahead of me again… now people come in and buy something, close out their transaction, buy one more thing (gum or an aspirin or whatever) and then they can get up to $200 back from the second transaction. They simply go from one register to the next to the next until they get all the cash off their EBT card.

I am told you CANNOT ask for ID… it's too embarrassing for the cardholder and all, and I mean all in this world they need to have and enter to get the money is the PIN number. That literally means the governor can come in with an EBT card that has the name Winker Butterfly Johnson on it and if he or she swipes the card and knows the correct PIN number, the deal is sealed. No questions ask. Sounds like a good system to me. What's coming is a tattoo or a "mark" on the head or arm or something like that. I think someone has already thought of it and written about it: John in Revelations. Don't believe me, go read it.

Let's review: First of the month, welfare card is reloaded with a predetermined amount of money, good as cash. Person goes to the store and buys $25 worth of food. Person buys one more item after the $25 purchase and gets all the remaining credit back in cash. Now these people obviously know where to shop where they can get a better value for cash than my friend's store is offering. Bull^%$#… they are taking that money and buying smokes or booze or dope or movies or Powerball or Mega Million or paying off their court costs or whatever.

138

And you know it and I know it and it happens day in and day out and it is going to get worse, not better, and you know that also. I wonder if condoms are included in EBT purchases, if not, they should be.

The smallest amount my friend reported was change from $200; the most she returned was over $700 in cash that morning. It happens over and over and over and over. If you bought and paid for this pitiful book, you paid tax about three ways. Some of that money went to help that poor nice lady who gets back her change from her EBT card. As soon as she saves a few dollars, I feel sure you are going to get a really nice thank you card... just be patient.

By now you should have heard of the guy arrested and in jail who calls his buddy and tells him to go to the ATM machine and run his EBT card in order to get the cash to bond out of jail. It's his money and he can do whatever the hell he wants to with it. You and I gave it to him. Do you really think this is the first time it has ever happened? You have got to be kidding me. It happens all the time. All the correction officers I know and all the police I know have known about this for a long time. I can't understand why this is newsworthy? Hell, the people who own the ATM and the bank are getting their taste of the EBT transaction, what do they care?

You know the old story about the genie that appears with three wishes when someone found the magic lamp and rubbed it. It is just a child's tale, but if it were real, I would like to know the answer to this question: How much WELFARE money has gone to making a car payment, a flat-screen TV payment, paid for new Nike's? How much EBT and WELFARE money has gone to pimps who have three or four or more "ho's" working for them and all are on some sort of government assistance? How much WELFARE money has gone to buy guns and ammunition that was used in the commission of a crime? How much WELFARE money has bought prescription drugs that were traded on the street for street dope? What is the sum total of the amount of tax-generated WELFARE that doesn't go for a little hungry mouth that needs feeding?

I think the answer is the same as the answer I got when I asked a friend of mine how many people worked at his company. He thought for a minute or two and replied, "About half of them." That's about how much WELFARE goes where it is supposed to, maybe.

139

The only addiction as bad as or worse than welfare is the scam going on with prescription drugs. I have two friends in the health business. I have to be careful about HIPPA here, so let's just say one works in an office and the other is a state-level health fraud investigator. Both know what they are talking about. Do you think some patients might see several doctors and get the same prescription from each of them? Do you think there are any senior citizens who get prescription drugs and have their son or daughter sell them? Do you think there are any people who visit the VA and then go to free clinics and to their personal doctor to get three times the "scripts"? Do you think it is generational? Can it go from mom to daughter, dad to son, and on and on? It can, it does, and it will continue to do so.

Get strung out on some mood-altering legal drug and see how many ways you can think up to get the pills. We are going to talk about how smart addicts are in the "wrong person" chapter... they are brilliant when it comes to deception. There is a great Andy Griffith episode (they all are great in my book) about a new druggist that comes to Mayberry and takes over her father's store. When she examines the books, she finds out this old woman in Mayberry has been getting a dime's worth of "pills" for years. The pills don't really do anything, but the old lady just has to have them and throws a fit when she can't get them anymore.

By the middle of the show, the old lady is sick as a dog and on her deathbed without her (sugar) pills. Andy comes to the rescue and gets the old lady her pills and all ends well. Everybody learns a great lesson and the world is a better place to live. The only difference in Mayberry and the pills I am talking about is: We weren't paying for the ones in Mayberry. The old lady did. Medicare and welfare and all kinds of programs are paying full price for drugs that end up on the streets. Unfortunately, we don't have Barney to help stop the abuse. Get used to it. Lie down, take a pill, lunch will be ready soon.

Chapter 10
The Shark

Recently a television program came on one of the 24-hour news stations. As they go through the day, they have little news stories of interest that pops up here and there and this one caught my eye.

This footage was of a large shark lurking just beneath the water, looking for some food. That's what sharks do, they look for food and then eat it. I remember reading and going to see Jaws back in about 1971. When I got home from the movies that night, I flushed both my Goldfish down the toilet! I didn't trust them any longer.

The news film was being shot from a helicopter or airplane, and as the plane panned out, it showed a beautiful sunny beach with sunshine and a few people here and there. It also showed two small children playing with a sand bucket about 30 feet from the water. The adults were within yelling distance, but they were NOT 30 feet from the children. If either child had jumped up and toddled into the water, the parents or babysitter would not have gotten there in time.

This was a big fish! It was a huge fish. Nobody knows what it weighed or its length; they were filming it, not measuring it. I feel sure that unless this shark had lost all its teeth or was a vegan (which I doubt), it could and probably would have swallowed those children in two bites. After a little while, the shark drifted off in search of an easy-access buffet.

This is a book about addiction, so what could that story have to do with the subject at hand? Just this: The news lady said, "Oh dear, that could have turned out really badly, oh my."

What the hell did you expect? Sharks have been swimming in the ocean a lot longer than we have been sunning at the beach. We are visiting the beach; they live there. There might not be a shark in every foot of the ocean, but do you know exactly where all of them are at all times? Of course you don't, they move.

Sometimes they are close to you and sometimes not. Sometimes they get you and sometimes they don't, but they are always there.

So the point is, if you mess with something that can hurt you, if you go where it is, if you invite it onto your beach, what do you expect? Thank God those children didn't run into the ocean... and don't you knowingly run into addiction. Stay out of the Addiction Ocean... you have no idea what is lurking just beneath the surface.

Chapter 11
Sex Addiction

No matter what I write, this will be a very touchy subject, so to speak. My first question is, did the Internet create sexual addiction or was the addiction already there and the Internet only exposed it? Hold on to your seats (so to speak again), here comes some unbelievable statistics: If you just want to see Asian men who happen to look exactly like females, whew, this is going to be tough... there are 1,960,000 sites to go to. That absolutely amazes me. The list of adult Web sites gets serious after the Asian "she-males."

If you happen to be looking for gays, there are 1,020,000,000 Web sites to go to! WHAT! Yes, 1,020,000,000 different places to click on and it becomes a gay or gay-related site... that just floors me. If you are interested in plain old, every day, run-of-the-mill porn stars, you have 52,700,000 sites to visit. Want (straight) Asian sex stars, try the 24,100,000 different sites. Not to be outdone, the lesbian sex sites number 73,300,000 and coming in on the hit parade is gay porn stars (not to be confused with just the word GAY) Web sites at a meek 8,750,000! If you are planning on viewing all these Web sites, you better pack a lunch or at least have some Chinese or have a pizza delivered, you are going to be awhile... This one I really had a problem with: Type in "grannies" and you will find 310,000,000 sites, slap dab full of places to view, meet, watch, and chat with mature ladies, old ladies, grandmothers, and great-grandmothers all of whom are in a semi-nude or completely nude state or engaged in full-blown sex or having a lot of sex by themselves. I have to stop here and thank God that there is no chance of you seeing my grandparents on any of those sites... I would puke if I saw my grandparents on anything like that, but somebody's mother and grandmother and father and grandfather are on there. Try plain old "women in porn" and you get 300,100,000. Lord, help me...

I simply typed in the words I used in the above paragraph and the computer tells you at the top of the page: 1 of 10 of however many sites there are. I didn't open any of them because I don't want a record of that mess on my computer. And, I certainly didn't type in anything beyond what I have listed. Well, I did type in World Sex Guide and got 435,000,000 places to visit! I believe I am starting to get addicted to looking these places up. Wow. I didn't go for the whips and chain crowd or "men that love small farm animals." Or anything gory or illegal or falling in love with dead people... none of that. But, I bet it's on there somewhere. God help all of us! If you know the name of one porn star, just one... type it in and hit search. I bet there are millions of sites for just one name. It's crazy! Attention: Attention....s#&t, I just got a virus and it's probably from looking this crap up, damnit! I had to call a guy to come over and work on my PC... what a bunch of s#&t. OK, back to the story.

I remember at EAS I was asked to contact a couple of fitness models for a show we were going to do. I typed in the words "fitness" and "model" and red flags went off and my computer went nuts! It froze and scared the s#&t out of me. I thought I had broken it. The nice guy from IT came immediately and was laughing about it. He said the title was so large that it would include all sorts of XXX websites... he monkeyed with my computer and got it all taken care of. I later found out that typing in the word fitness model will take you to leg models and that takes you to 170,000,000 sites for models, and about 75 percent of those are porn sites!

It makes me think of one of my Police Academy instructors. He said you know why there are so many weird laws, covering so many strange actions in the law books? Because somebody somewhere tried it and got caught. It's the same thing with sex and the Internet and porn shops, if you want it, you can sure find it... it's there somewhere. God help us again!

I am absolutely sure prostitution is illegal here in the good old USA. I am also absolutely sure that pornography is legal. Here are a few thoughts to mull over. Are porn actors/actresses SAG (screen actors guild) carded? Do they belong to a union? Do they pay Union dues? Maybe yes, maybe no. Regardless, prostitution is illegal and making porn is not illegal. So... if you meet a lady in a bar and ask her to go home and touch pee-pees with you for a hundred dollars, that is a crime. If you ask her to let you film you and her touching pee-pees because you are making a full-length porn movie and want her to be in it, wouldn't that be legal? Don't actresses and actors get paid to act? Hell, most women I dated were acting anyway... what's the difference if you paid them to act nasty? I bet there are a bunch of elected officials running to the city/county charter to see if they are covered legally right this minute.

Since porn is legal, I wonder if a person could get a BA degree in porn filmmaking? Maybe UCLA could offer some classes like "Light positioning, couches to king size beds 101. Or maybe Saxophone music and butt shots. Lab required. I know I am being silly, but think about how silly staying glued to the computer for hours, watching 11 or more people have sex is. One is legal because a camera is there and the other isn't because a camera isn't there. Either way, I just don't get it.

There are two points here: First, I think it's strange that a piece of equipment like a computer can have such an endless wealth of information and be such a wonderful experience. Then the same piece of equipment will be happy to take you to a site that offers five or six people completely naked in positions that will need a coat hanger and protractor to figure out how to get them apart. Maybe the computer is like a gun... it can perform whatever task the handler has in mind when they use it. Second: For there to be that many Web sites committed to sex, somebody somewhere is using it on a regular basis. You think?

We get figures between $2 billion and $16-$17 billion a year spent on porn. (I believe the real number is around $4.6 billion.) I guess the truth depends on which side of the camera or couch or Bible you are on. Pretty safe to say as long as this world lasts, there is going to be sex and adult movies, Web sites, and book stores and on and on and on. What I want to address and make the good reader mindful of is this: Don't use sex as an emotional comfort food. Don't throw your body away to feed your ego or whatever empty hole is in your chest. We talked about addiction being like the fog, remember? It takes whatever shape you bring into it. Food, smokes, drugs, the wrong person, alcohol, sex, whatever, it doesn't matter. Addiction is Addiction. We have an expression on the Police Department: Probable Cause is Probable Cause is Probable Cause... same thing with sex addiction, it is an addiction. Except one small difference, if it ain't safe sex, it just might kill you!

Those numbers of sex-related Web sites blew me away. I did a little test and typed the word "roses" in the search engine and got 233,000,000 hits. Then I thought I would try something a little less common so I tried bar-b-que... got 176,000,000 hits on that. I tried cows and got 83,600,000 sites to visit. They have pictures of cows and breeds of cows and anything and everything about cows! Next was "railroads in China in 1900"... guess how many sites there were... 1,560,000. My last subject was "bicycle horns" and I got 913,000 sites about bike

145

horns. Now things are in a little bit better perspective. Total bike horn and bell sales are in the millions of dollars a year. It makes the porn business a little more realistic. At first those numbers were beyond belief. Not really, if they weren't real and people were not using them, they wouldn't be there. I went back and did two more just to see what would happen: God got 236,000,000 hits and Devil got 63,500,000 hits. Good to know we are still in the lead!

I have a pretty sharp Sergeant on my shift at the Marshal's. His name is Sgt. Clayton Evans and he gave over 20 years of his life to the service of our country as an Airborne Infantry solider. He is also a parent and has concerns about the safety and well-being of his and all children. He came up with a real smart idea when we were talking. He thinks every porn site should have xxx. in front of the site. There are laws that allow people to look at any trash they want to on a PC, would it be against the law to make porn sites have "xxx." as their Web address? That way there would be no mistaking what you were looking for. There would be no "oops, I opened this by mistake!" There is no word in the English language that starts with the letters "xxx." That way it would be real easy to block anything on a child's PC that started with xxx. I thought it was a great idea and only wish that I had thought of it first. Maybe it will happen one day. Hoorah, Sir! An afterthought... I wrote the beginning of this chapter in about 2010. Today is December 12, 2011. I see that people are buying up xxx websites as fast as they can... it's all over the news. Funny how things happen... my sergeant knew this was coming almost two years ago. Several smart people know what's coming and the masses aren't listening.

I thought a lot about whether or not to report this story... I finally decided to clean it up and give a short version. It is the truth. There is a video on the Internet concerning a pretty blonde-haired girl and a horse. Don't read any more if you think you see where this is going... I understand it runs about 25 minutes. I did not download it or any other porn and never would, but evidentially it was filmed in South America or somewhere because they are not speaking English. I don't know what language it is. Maybe Mr. Ed or Francis the talking Mule could translate. At this point you should apply your wildest worst imagination and you would be close to the truth. I will leave it at that. My point is this... somebody filmed it and somebody was willing to buy it and somebody saw where there would be a demand for it and it was produced. The craziest thing about this video is: the girl is attractive, looks very healthy, is not being forced to do anything, seems to be enjoying herself (if not, she deserves the world Academy Award) and when it is over, she laughs and cleans up and then kisses the horse on his jaw! Maybe later they had a cigarette together or perhaps shared a blanket and bag of oats... who knows. It is out there, folks, and somebody is buying it. God help us again.

Of all the chapters in this book, this one and the chapter on food abuse are the two most difficult. I don't care who you are, more than likely at some point in this life you are going to get hungry and maybe a little horny, hopefully not at the same time. Maybe so, but all I have to go on are my experiences. How do you tell someone who is killing themselves (or at the very least burning up their character) not to do something that their body urges them to do, that others are doing and seems perfectly normal? You have to eat or die. I don't think you have to have sex to live but you do to procreate. I have known a few people who abused sex and sex ruined their lives. So sit back and struggle with me through a couple of stories and lessons. A hell of a lot of people are having sex... unfortunately, some of it is for the wrong reason and with the wrong person.

I have a trip coming up to Thailand and I promise to give a full report when I get back. I can already give you one on Singapore, Germany, Costa Rica, Brazil, Amsterdam, South Africa, Spain, Italy and a slew of other places... at some of these places, sex is legal with anyone (18 years and older) who wants to trade it to you for cash. Now in America, it isn't legal except in a few places, such as in Nevada. (As of this writing, some lawmaker is trying to get a law outlawing the legal places... good idea, drive them into the street.) What an idiot. I have never been to these places, but I understand they pay quite a bit in tax dollars. Am I right? As I understand it, you go to these places in Nevada and you pay the house and then you pay the girl and nobody says anything about laws being broken or morals or anything else. Some grown men and women pack their suitcases under no duress and move to cities in Europe and Asia and everywhere else that sex is legal and go to work. Not all of them are kidnapped and held against their will. I think that is awful when it happens and especially with children. Those people responsible for that (both male and female) should be fed to the lions. But one more time, most of the people in the sex trade that I have talked to love working when they want to, love the money, love the hours, and left full-time jobs to do sex. You don't believe it? Go tell them they are liars. I'm not making it up.

147

Now, let's see what happens if the sales tax and the property tax and the surcharge isn't paid! They would close the Nevada place down in about a zillionth of a second... kinda reminds us of the lotto, doesn't it? As long as the Tax Man is getting his cut, the party goes on. It makes me wonder if there were any way the government could control prostitution, would it (like alcohol) be legalized tomorrow morning? Anyway, that's a subject for another time... let's get back to good old, everyday, barnyard sex.

I started looking up AIDS and HIV on the Internet. I also found a book called The Epidemic by Jonathan Engel. You should read it. That is a shocking lesson. The numbers keep changing, but each year they go up. More people are becoming infected, not fewer. Guess where people get AIDS from? It's not from hip hop or country music, it's not from fried chicken or sharing coffee, it's not from singing in the shower (assuming you are alone), and it's not from wearing white after Labor Day... it's not from about 10,000,000 things. It comes from about four places. Let's name them. Blood transfusions that are contaminated. I believe today the hospitals and blood clinics do a world-class job of keeping the good blood and throwing out the bad. Some innocent people did get infected by accident. They are totally innocent and have our most sincere prayers and respect. Another place it comes from is sharing dirty needles. Let's see... if you can go out and steal and rob to get hundreds of dollars a day to buy crack and heroin and dope, couldn't you steal another dollar's worth of something and get a clean needle? If you really want to be the top crack and heroin dealer in your neighborhood, why not give away a complimentary needle with every purchase? Your sales would boom and you might keep your addicts alive a little longer to buy more dope. Silly me... forget that, addicts are going to buy the dope regardless.

Another way is exchanging bodily fluids. That can mean being born to a crack-addict mother who is HIV positive or from what I have read, exchanging live fluid with another grown person. Let's think of the ways to exchange fluid from one person to another. How about this: SEX, UNPROTECTED SEX, with someone who has the AIDS virus. How are you going to know if they have AIDS or not? Are you going to make them raise their right hand and double promise that they don't? Have you read about wives who go to the doctor for a checkup and come to find out they have the virus? I have seen them on television. Their own husbands have lied to them. Do you think a one-night-stand is going to tell you the truth? This isn't just men, it's women also. Do you think the street walkers and lounge lizards who have sex for a living are doing it to meet new people and have a fun and exciting life? I think they are addicted to the lifestyle and/or drugs and some poor dumb yahoo comes along and falls for the fake eyelashes and perfume and high heels. Little does he know that everything that happens in the big city doesn't stay in the big city if you take it back home alive and roaming around in your bloodstream? By the way, I just heard there is a new case of AIDS every 9 minutes in America. I hope it stops but it probably won't.

UNPROTECTED SEX is the biggest cause of AIDS and people have been told and told and told and told and "the spirit is willing, but the flesh is weak"… they are going to go right on playing Russian roulette but not with a gun, with their libido.

Easy now, I am sure I should catch my breath and slow down here. I am all over the place when it comes to this subject… I will try to stay on one or two topics. I repeat, I am not talking about innocent, honest people who contracted the virus without knowing or being able to do anything about it. That is fate and I am sorry for them. I want to focus on the fools who have the choice of sex and needle partners… the addicts.

OK, three categories: 1) people who have SEX and produce parentless, poverty-doomed children. 2) People who have unprotected SEX and produce AIDS and HIV patients. 3) The "real" price you pay when you pay with, or for, SEX.

About three days ago I picked up a newspaper and there was an article concerning a lady who was homeless. That's terrible. This is too big and too rich a country to have anyone homeless, unless they want to be. I don't think she wanted to be. She has several small children and no job and no husband and no grandmother to hand the kids to. The article didn't report her age but all the children are less than 10 years old. I have a few questions… where are the fathers? Why didn't this lady demand the fathers use a condom? Would she be in this predicament if she had not gotten pregnant? Do you think she knew what it was that caused her to develop those children? It was SEX! And here is the big question… does she know how the process works? You would think so after the first baby.

149

Drinking a beer won't get you pregnant. Listening to Billie Holiday won't get you pregnant. Going out on a date won't get you pregnant. Reading Erskine Caldwell novels or Jughead comics won't get you pregnant. What will get you pregnant and cause you to make life miserable for little hungry mouths that need medical and dental and social and normal, everyday life expectancies, like utilities and Christmas gifts and television and education and toys and on and on? It's SEX! SEX, SEX, SEX. Somebody was getting their "groove on" and somebody else pulled their drawers off and laid down and stuck their feet in the air and without any protection, the two of them committed the most important action that can be done on this earth. They created a life… but, they didn't accept the full responsibility of that creation. Remember, the two times you are closest to God is when you create a life or take one… you are acting like God both times.

Now here is where I am going to lose half my audience, but I accept that. I think it is as big a sin to have a child and dump it on the footsteps of poverty and food stamps and assisted government living and doing without and secondhand clothes and hunger and cold, empty Christmases and no mother and no father and going from one relative to another and back to a Foster home (thank God for some good Foster homes) as it is to have an abortion. You're killing the child either way, one is just quicker than the other. At least the guy got his "groove on" and the girl got a double cheese burger and a date to the dance out of the deal… that's just wonderful. And it was all because of the wild, unbridled need to ejaculate. Couldn't use a condom 'cause "it just don't feel right, baby!" And she went along with it. Can you hear me screaming? Oh yea, by the way, in 2010 at a conference in Europe, the estimated number of HIV cases is 33.4 million. I beg you to stop by the gas station on the way to your big date and slap 2 quarters in that funny machine on the wall of the men's room and buy a damn RUBBER! STDs or an unwanted child or a condom… you choose. We're going to pay for it either way.

Please don't send me letters saying that I hate children. I do not. I hate stupid people who want the orgasm but refuse to practice safe sex and refuse to not have sex. They are saying to the world and everyone in it, "I don't care if I get pregnant, I love him," and the guy is saying, "I don't care because I ain't got to pay for it, you will!" If this chapter is rubbing you the wrong way, I insist you not read the chapter on welfare… it will make you holler.

I'm not sure where to start, how about with one of my friend's father. This guy had it made. The dad was college educated, some sort of a manager with a bank or loan company, and they lived high on the hog and the hill. This happened about 50 years ago, but I remember my mom and dad talking about it. Everybody was talking about it. Times were different that long ago, but it is still the same 24 hour clock today.

This guy has a wife and two or three children and that great job and his son had a new bike every Christmas and it was just a "Beaver Cleaver" household. Then guess what? The dad meets a young waitress in some diner and he is a big shot executive and she is a blushing bride freshly arrived here from Japan. She no speaks a good English and Mr. Big Shot Big Tip is more than willing to help her after work with her grammar. If I can recall the story, her solider husband was shipped out and she stayed here in the states while hubby was overseas. Honestly, I think you know where this lesson is going.

Mr. Big Shot is bragging to his buddies about all the "gishie" loving he is getting in the front seat of cars and the backseat of cars and down on Lover's Lane and once in a while, in seedy motel rooms across the river. Go ahead and guess what happened. You got it, she comes up pregnant. Remember, her husband is in Korea (I believe) and there is no way he could be the father. Also remember it is about 1960 or '61 or somewhere in there and abortions aren't as available as they are today. Without boring you to tears, I will tell you that everything you think happened did happen. The solider got a divorce, Mr. Big Shot's wife got a divorce, and Mr. Big Shot now has two families to support.

Addiction to sex. That is the first time I remember my mom telling me the father should have been home with his wife and family and not down on Lover's Lane... and at the very least, if he absolutely could NOT keep his wee-wee in his pants to at least use a condom. I wonder if kissing counts? I remember mom telling me not to be messing with someone else's wife or girlfriend and not to be like this fool who couldn't stay away from a willing 19-year-old girl. The father was out of control. He was unable to say no. The drive and desire to do something sneaky and forbidden was overwhelming. He kept on and kept on until the trap door slammed shut. Don't be that guy.

You think men are the only people who can't say no? Think again. I have known several ladies who wanted and needed to be loved so badly, they needed

151

everybody to love them. One was never going to be enough. If it took sex to get some attention, then so be it, sex it was. If they didn't have a boyfriend, then several boyfriends for an hour apiece was better than none at all. These girls were looking for something they couldn't find. I don't know if it was acceptance or love or attention or revenge or all of those things. If they did find a person to love them, it wasn't enough; they had to hear it from someone else. It was the same old story of the hole in their chest that couldn't get filled. One drop-dead beautiful girl I knew needed to be loved so badly, she took in every single stray animal she found. It was a funny thing that nobody was ever invited into her apartment. That was OK because she was so good looking, you didn't question why you couldn't go in, you just wanted her to come out. So one day she calls work in hysterics because the sheriff is there with the landlord and they are evicting her and taking away her nine cats... she lived in a one-bedroom apartment with nine cats. She was screaming on the phone that the cats needed her and she loved them. In her case it wasn't sex with different partners, it was loving all those cats. Same difference.

Let me share this next story because it is a textbook example of addiction to sex and to the wrong person at the same time. I'm not sure if this guy liked the girl more or the sex with her more or if it was dead even. Maybe he can tell you, I just watched it happen. I think it was a simple case of the wrong person and out of this world sex. Something I am familiar with.

We have hit on a subject here that I am an absolute expert in. When it comes to losing your mind for the wrong person, I hold a Ph.D., an M.S., a B.S., an M.D., an MBA and a WTF! I have every advanced degree known to man on the subject and have done extensive studies concerning the wrong person. You could say I have devoted a large portion of my life doing personal research. I think Richard Pryor may have said it best, "You ain't graduated in this life till you had your heart ripped out of your chest and stomped on in front of your face and then you go back for more." Sometimes it's because the sex is out of this world! Nobody else moves you (or themselves) like that person, and you keep paying an inflated price to return to the trough for more.

At this point I have to direct you to one of the best songs ever written and performed by The Allman Brothers....it's called Whipping Post and goes like this: I been run down... I been lied to... I let that mean woman make me a fool... took all my money... wrecked my new car... and now she's with one of my good-time buddies, drinking in some cross-town bar... sometimes I feel, sometimes I feel... like I been tied to the whipping post, tied to the whipping post, good Lord I feel like I'm dying...

My friends tell me... I'm such a fool... it goes on and on and absolutely fits perfect for the "wrong person addiction" chapter. Look it up, it's well worth listening to. And you can change the words from "she to he" depending on your situation.

No way can I forget both Eric Shrieves and Joey Vincent telling me at different times the same thing. They didn't know the other one had said it so there must be something to it. Let me set the stage...

I'm a single guy and I do not believe there is anybody on the face of this earth that likes or liked women more than I do, not Hugh Hefner, not Charlie Sheen, not Elvis Presley. The major difference is, they had a lot more ladies to choose from and got a lot more attention when they did. That said, they didn't like being around women more than me. If Aunt Jemima was the last girl on this earth, I would get busy eating her pancakes. I like girls, end of subject.

Sorry guys, I am not gay. All the gay people in the world are welcome to it, but it just ain't in the cards for me. I was born this way, please respect that. I adore girls! Hope all the gay guys and gals find a loving, caring partner and happiness the rest of their life, but as long as one woman (not related to me) has a pulse and likes men, I hope to be a candidate for that position. Knowing all this, here is what Joey and Eric told me:

"Porter, if you got invited to a cocktail party and it was just you and 100 single ladies there, if 99 of them had advanced degrees from the best colleges, if 99 of them had interesting histories and bright futures, and if 99 of them were successful in business and in life in general, if 99 of them were completely independent and had money in the bank, if these 99 spoke two or three languages and had traveled worldwide, you would seek out and discover the 1 out of the 100 who was three months behind on her rent, needed to go to the dentist, was in rehab again or at the very least on probation, couldn't find a babysitter, had missed her last period and had two outstanding warrants for unpaid parking tickets because the car wouldn't start and she didn't have any jumper cables...

that's the one you would chat-up and try to save and the sex would be out of this world!

Dear God... I know they were right because I have done it. Wonder why? Maybe some of us find our self-worth in saving other people. Maybe we can't see that some people DON'T WANT TO BE SAVED! Maybe it's us that need to be saved from them. That's me. I think I have a handle on it now, but when the wrong person builds a nest in your heart (or underwear), either by accident or by invitation, it is as hard to quit as heroin or crack or alcohol or any addiction. Now add some good old-fashioned barnyard sex to the mix, and it's like being addicted to heroin and the needle. Now there are two hooks in.

I hope all this ties in for you and at some point makes sense. It does in my head and that's all I can tell you but here goes: I don't care too much for Oprah and that's OK because she probably doesn't care too much for me. She probably doesn't have a clue who I am and probably couldn't care less. Not exactly sure what her talent is, but it evidentially works because she has been real successful at whatever it is she does. I don't dislike her; I just haven't bought any of her records.

It was a funny thing about her... she had a program once and invited people on who had got in great shape and then either gained all their weight back or had gained all their weight back and more. A friend of mine was on that program. I'm going to always wonder if Oprah did it to make herself feel better about gaining all her weight again. Only she knows. I bring this up because she probably has enough money to hire Arnold Schwarzenegger to be her private trainer. (I guess being addicted to food doesn't have anything to do with money, does it?) I don't think that would help her. I believe she had a trainer named Bob Greene, didn't she? What happened to him? Did she fail or did he? With all her cash she could buy the next world-class gym in Chicago or put one in any of her homes. That won't get it done either. She continues to gain the fat and lose the fat and gain the fat and lose the fat and lose the fat and gain it back. Think there could be some form of addiction going on there? I am sure she can get one of the many doctors as guests to explain it to her. I do know she reported some issues in her background... that's very bad and I am truly sorry. But it doesn't change the simple fact of a hole in your chest that either food or booze or whatever fills it... until it's fixed, the hole always comes back empty.

154

Now this isn't a personal attack on Oprah, she hasn't done one bad thing to me and I haven't done anything bad to her. The truth is her weight seems to be like the childhood story about the Emperor who didn't have any clothes and all the little subjects were afraid to say anything. Why didn't somebody say, Hey, Sweetie... you're gaining all your weight again? Why didn't somebody come up to me at the party and say, Hey, Porter, she (not Oprah) ain't the woman for you? I want to tell you two things that Oprah did perfect in my uneducated opinion. She hit the Bull's eye on these. One was The Color Purple... buddy, she nailed that. It is one of my favorite movies of all time and Oprah was out of this world in that movie... at the Porter Freeman Academy Awards, she took First Place. The other thing she did (or said) that was the truth like you don't often get was when she said something like, "If somebody tells you they can't live without you, you need to get as far away from that person as possible." One more time at the Porter Freeman Academy Awards, she gets First Place... truer words were never spoken. I wish her a lot of success with the weight.

Am I making any sense whatsoever? It does not matter if it is food, porn, gambling, shopping, alcohol, smokes, drugs, or sex. It can be religion, money, pain, or a host of others addictions. It can be addiction to another person. With the other person addiction, there is always sex involved, at least for me it was. Never was addicted to any woman who wasn't taking me to see the stars and the moon. And like with Oprah's weight, nobody around me said anything.

Now imagine in our sick, addicted mind, we think the other person CAN'T live without us and we have to save them from themselves, when it's really us who are sick and the other people need to be saved from us! That one girl in 100 does not want to change or does not know how to function any other way and Oprah can do 1,000 shows on dieting but until she finds out why she won't put the fork down, and always picks it back up, the hole in the chest keeps getting empty. If she or anybody else wants to sue me for my opinion, as of today, I have $380 in the bank... you are welcome to it.

Back to the one in 100 person that we get addicted to... add sex and all bets are off. Remember I said it was like being addicted to two hooks instead of just one. If you do manage to get one hook out, the other digs deeper. I am as guilty as anyone alive about this. Argue, fight all night, swear you're leaving and then make up, if you get my drift, and then both hooks are back where they started. Here comes a true, true, true story of both.

I was working in a bar back in about 1992 or '93 and we had a pretty fair lunch crowd. It was a jumping place at night but that alone doesn't pay the bills, so we started a day shift with a young, good-looking staff and OK food. It was far from fine dining but for working crews to come in between noon and 3 p.m., it did pretty good. After a year or so, we started a happy hour from 3 to 6 p.m. The business grew and we did two for one draft beers and free snacks at the bar and the night shift began to get return customers. Business was good enough that a few of the night shift waitresses moved to days and that allowed them to work in the day and have the night off to party all they wanted. Remember, they were young and it was Orlando and there was plenty to do at night! Let the good times roll!

So it's Orlando and all of Central Florida is booming and business is good and about once or maybe twice a month a group of guys come in for lunch and have sort of a business meeting and laugh and have a few beers or drinks at the bar and it's no big deal. They are all well dressed and professional and I was glad to see them. I find out they are engineers and their offices are about 3 miles from the club and they come in once in a while to blow off a little steam. They are always gone long before 5 p.m. and they are never out of line or drunk or a problem. Oh, what I would have given for more customers like them.

There was one guy who always came with the group. He always picked up the tab and it became obvious pretty quick he was the business owner or senior partner of this group. They sat at the same place and always had the same waitress. She was a pistol. She was drop-dead beautiful, a wonderful figure, and had a personality to match. She had everybody laughing and guys loved her, and so did I. She was great for business and she made a lot of tips. Once in a while she would have a drink or two but I never said much about it… she stayed in control.

Stay with me. One afternoon the group comes in and they go nuts! They are yelling and high-fiving everybody and raising all kinds of hell. They buy the house a round of drinks and order a bottle of champagne and are all on cloud nine. Now remember, this is Central Florida and there is Cape Canaveral and NASA and the Orlando Navy Base and Martin Marietta and a lot of military businesses and an Air Force Base (Patrick) is only 45 minutes away. Guess what, lo and behold his firm had won and signed a contract with a different group of engineers that got one of the government contracts at one of the government

156

places and it was what they had dreamed of for years. It was Christmas and New Year's in February for these guys.

Eventually the party would wind down and the guys began leaving... all except one. He stayed. This is important. He had a wife and children at home and he was always gone by 2 or 3 p.m. or before, but not today. He was in a party mood. I remember him asking if the day waitress could stay after she clocked out and have a drink or two to celebrate his success. It wasn't policy but this one time was the exception. I said yes and the party kept going. What the hell, once wasn't going to hurt anything. How wrong I was. It was going to hurt and nobody knew that day how bad it was going to hurt.

I have no idea what transpired that evening between those two, but something did. Pretty soon after the big celebration my friend started eating lunch three or four times a week at the club, always on the days that special waitress worked. He never showed up when she was off. I didn't see any difference in her. She came to work, did a world-class job, and left. The change began to appear in him. He would sometimes show up at 11:30 a.m. instead of noon and stay until 1:30 p.m. His lunch hour was becoming two hours but he owned his business so I guess he could do as he pleased. He was never a problem. Once in a while he would show up at 5 p.m. and stay till 6 p.m. He had never done that before. On a very few occasions, he would stay until 7 p.m. when she got off work. Still, no problems.

It didn't take long for one or two of his partners to start calling the club asking if he was there. This was a little before cell phones and we would occasionally get a call for someone. No big deal, he would say thanks and go to a pay phone to call his office. Pretty soon it got to be three or four times a day. "Was so and so there, and could you ask him to call his office?" Eventually I had to say something to him and his answer was, "Those silly guys, they can't do anything without me... hahaha." Right.

Sometimes the waitress would cover a night shift and you guessed it, he was sitting right there nursing his beer and talking to her every chance he got. When she went back on days, he was back at lunch. I finally asked her about it and all she said was "he's got a hungry heart." I think his appetite was a little bit bigger than that, but it wasn't my business, yet. If she took a week off, he didn't show up until the day she came back. I have no idea what he was telling his wife.

Retelling this is giving me a headache, so I am cutting about three months out of the story. Before I get to the end of it, let me tell you he lost the contract he had, he lost his partnership, and he finally lost his business. The last night I saw him, he was well dressed but hadn't shaved in a couple of days and looked like he had been sleeping in his car. I have no idea what was going on at his home.

This last night I saw him, he was in the club and she was working. She came and asked me if she could get off early, company was in town or she was going to a concert or something. I said yes, we were slow and she had worked since about 3 p.m. and it was around 9 p.m. Sometimes in the bar business, you have to call someone in on their day off and tonight she was collecting on that debt. All right, goodnight. She went in the ladies room and changed and went out the backdoor. About 10 minutes later he walks up to me and asks where is so and so? I said she asked if she could leave early and she left. He went blank... what do you mean she left? She left! She ain't here, she got off work and has left the building. At this point, he rushes past me and out the backdoor to the parking lot. He hasn't done anything wrong, so I don't chase him or yell for help or have any reaction. She left, he left, and that's that. He can see her tomorrow.

Then we hear a scream and out the door we go. She is in the car with some guy and she is driving, or at least trying to back out of the parking space. Our friend is hanging on the door and trying to get the keys. She is screaming louder and finally gets backed up far enough to go in drive. He is still holding on and still has his arms in the driver's window. I swear to God this is the truth, I told the other employees to go back inside and back to work. I would handle this. The girl floors the car and this idiot keeps hanging on and taking 6-foot leaps, leg over leg, trying to keep up with the car. When she gets to the end of the lot, she turns right and floors it. He can't hold on any longer. I guess he understood centrifugal force being an engineer and all, because he went flying into a yard across the street.

I walked across the street and he was balled up hugging his knees. He was sobbing, not crying or weeping, he was sobbing like he had buried a child. I asked if he was all right and he said yes, that he was so sorry for acting like he did. I helped him up and he went to his car and said he wouldn't be back. He had lost everything over a girl that didn't love him. She had put something on him that he wasn't getting any other place and he was a big shot engineer and she was just a waitress with a drop-dead body and knew how to party. And he lost his damn mind. He got addicted to something and somebody that was passing through. Most of all, he lost his dignity and character. I never saw him again. She never mentioned it and I never forgot it.

Was it the sex? Was it just her? Was the whole bar scene too much for him? Was it his addictive personality? Was six months of his life worth what he paid for it? Why didn't he walk away from her? Why didn't he have a couple of laughs and tip her a big tip the day he got the contract and go home? Why did he have to hang around till 7 p.m. and get addicted to her and her little sumpten-sumpten that night? Or... was it that old country saying I heard a long time ago, "A bite of the bait ain't worth the pain of the hook"?

I'm going to write a few more things about sex and then we are done. Sex has been around since Adam and Eve... if you are a "slime up out of the swamp believer," then sex has been around way before Adam and Eve. Either way, somebody had some sex or we wouldn't be reading this. If you haven't had sex in your life, you are in for a real treat. If you start with the phonebook tomorrow, you can't sleep with all the A's before there will be new ones. You will never get to the B's or C's. There are too many people coming of legal age every day. My mother told me there would be women walking away from my grave that I would never get to know. Believe it or not, there are men out there who will use you for sex (and women out there who will use sex to get what they want out of you) and when they are through, they will hand you over to someone else to use. The perfect sex is (just my opinion) with someone you love and they love you. The best, most perfect sex in the world is with your wife or husband and it's just the two of you for eternity. No matter what kind of sex you are having, no matter how many people are participating, no matter if you are a sex worker and love your job (and some of them do) or not, remember this: Sex ain't a bar of soap, it don't get smaller with use"... .and you will never know if someone else has rinsed their hands with it!

Maybe there should be three titles here: Sex... Wrong Person... and Welfare. Sometimes they all three go together. I am going to try and keep Welfare out of it until the next chapter but it might run over... we will see.

Back to the sex... did you ever see the infomercial where the old white-headed guy comes walking through the worst part of some town with children

159

everywhere and he is on a dirt street and the kids are filthy and there is garbage and filth everywhere? He says little Ramón or Jose or whatever the child's name is and his four brothers and sisters have to live in this cesspool. They have no water and if lucky, they get a scrap of food once in a while. It is horrible and for only 50 or 75 cents a day, you can bring fresh water and food to the village and to Jose and his brothers and sisters. When they come to the part to tell you the phone number, a train comes by and you can't hear the guy talking so thank goodness, the address where to send your money flashes up on the screen. I guess that was bad timing about the train, but at least they had the number of where to call to send your money. No children should be living in that filth or be hungry.

After a few weeks of seeing this commercial, another commercial comes on. This has the same guy walking in a different slum, lots of starving children, all with rag clothes, no shoes, all hungry, all have x number of brothers and sisters, all live with their mom, no daddy, or with grandmother. If we will "adopt" little Mercedes, for only 50 or 75 cents a day, the price of a cup of coffee (I don't know where he is getting his coffee, it ain't Starbucks), it will completely change the child's life.

Let's see... 75 cents a day for 30 days equals about $270 a year. That sounds like a good deal to me, if the child really gets the food and water and clothes. Great. I say let's do it!

Unfortunately a taxi goes by just as the guy is giving the address where Mercedes lives... but once again, thank goodness, the address where to send your money flashes up on the screen.

I do believe there is a third commercial and I just can't remember exactly where it is filmed. I believe the old man is walking in a crowd of children and they are all pathetic and strangely look exactly like the other children in the first two commercials and they are starving and living in filth. Do I think it is real? Absolutely I do. I have been fortunate enough to travel pretty much all over the world and have unfortunately seen poverty that is unbelievable... I cannot describe it. Let's just say it is bad and I have seen nothing to compare it to here in the USA. It is real and does exist. This time a crop-duster flies over or a railroad arm comes down but something happens and the address can't be heard again. Thank goodness, the address where to send money pops up across the bottom of the screen! What were the chances of that happening for the third time in three different parts of the world... unbelievable!

Let me see if I can make a point or two here... first, they need to fire the director and hire a new one that can get a copy of the train schedule and not be filming every time the train comes by. How simple is that? I'm sure somebody in town has it written down somewhere and would be more than willing to share it with the film crew... makes you a little suspicious, don't it?

Here is the second part... for each and every one of those pitiful, starving children, there are two other people who took their clothes off, one got an erection, and the other stuck her feet up in the air and they had intercourse.

This might be a Nobel Prize breakthrough, but simple little me just figured out how to stop the famine and hunger and pain those innocent children are going through. They exist in horrible conditions and go hungry and have to beg and share anything they have because of one reason... their parents won't STOP SCREWING! Hello?

They don't have water and they don't bathe (according to the old man in the commercials), no electricity, no money, they are living in cardboard boxes, they have never been to a dentist, their teeth are rotting in their gums. They have no toothbrushes, no soap, no deodorant, no Tampons, no nothing... but by God, they have a sex life that could compare to the wildest swingers in Amsterdam. The mother doesn't have any trouble getting her drawers off because she doesn't own any... maybe that the problem... you think?

Here's a crazy idea, send some condoms to these people! Teach these starving parents how to masturbate; it really is easy to learn. Me and some of my friends can go show them! Maybe legalize oral sex if it's against the law in these countries. It's obvious that sex and getting their groove on is more important to the parents than food or water or getting out of poverty or their children. How do I know? Because all the kids have little brothers and sisters... do you think the stork brought them? Bull $#*@. Some places sex seems to be a poor man's only pleasure. Damn the results.

All children are innocent, each and every one of them. And all the parents are guilty of a sin as great as abortion if they continue to create innocent children to come into this world and starve and hurt and live in mud and filth.

These stupid parents' need the hell beat out of them every time they have unprotected sex, causing a baby to come and suffer in the pain and agony and filth that awaits them.

Did you see the news footage or commercials of people in Africa starving? I have and I saw it firsthand. I have been there and seen it up close and personal. If you think it isn't real, throw this book down and get all your friends together and go over there and see for yourself. What you are going to see are women with a child trying to get milk from a dry breast, a child on her back wrapped in a sling, two or three children holding hands and hanging on to the mother, all covered in flies and she is PREGNANT... I give up. Maybe they ought to outlaw fertility dances! Listen, forget about my suggestion for sending condoms to these people... it's not going to happen. It won't correct what is wrong right this minute and there are far too many churches that will fight you tooth and nail all the way. They will tell you it's not God's way to use contraceptives... God wanted these children born and shipping condoms is against God's Law... I give up!

P.S. one of my closest relatives goes to these countries and works building hospitals and churches as an UNPAID missionary, and I know in my heart how much of my pitiful little money I send with him. So please don't think me and my family are against helping these people... I am on record for doing anything possible to prevent more starving, sick, dying, crying babies being born. Can't they give it a break long enough to at least feed the children already there? It's a damn good thing they don't have any Barry White records, they would be screwing all the time!

Here's an idea: Why not let the old guy in the commercials go out at night with the camera crew and a flashlight and walk through the slums and sneak up on the shack where these families live. As soon as Gomez or Mobuto or George or whatever the hell the father's name is comes home after a hard day of smoking cigarettes and digging in trash for a living and as soon as he pulls his pants down and pushes the wife down and pulls her legs apart, the flashlight comes on and the camera crew starts rolling... the old guy could say something like, "Here is Gomez knocking his wife up again, they have five children, you met Ramón in an earlier story and here is dad going at it again. He can't feed the five he already has and he isn't wearing a condom. Your dollars will buy an electric dog collar to strap on Gomez and from then on when he gets an erection

162

and feels like getting his groove thing on, we will shock the $#*^ out of him. And for only a few cents a day, the price of a cup of coffee, we will eventually teach Gomez to wear a condom or have a little self-control... either way, your dollars will, one way or the other, help solve Gomez's problem. Then we will use the electric dog collar on the neighbors. Please don't look away, we are now going to hit him in the balls in mid stroke with a Louisville Slugger. Maybe this will teach him a lesson, maybe not, but either way, please help us by helping all the stupid men and stupid women in the world to STOP having starving innocent babies.

At this point it won't matter if the train comes by or not. It certainly has had a profound effect on Gomez. I apologize to all the people named Gomez in the world... it was just a name I dreamed up. The name could be Al or Bob or Susquanaway or whatever. You get the drift.

Think what would happen if just for one or two years there were no new starving, innocent children brought into this world. Think if for two years we could devote all our charity resources to the hungry, sick children who are already here, think how much good that could do. Do you believe it's going to happen? Hell NO! Here in good old USA, the more fatherless children you have (brought to you only one way that I know of), the bigger your monthly welfare check! That's what I'm talking about... this might sound crazy, so what? Think if you had had a child with everybody you ever slept with. How many children would you have? What would they look like? You probably didn't have a child with everybody you slept with because you either quit before you became a parent, used a condom, used some sort of birth control, had oral sex... remember one of our presidents doesn't even think that counts... I might vote for him knowing that... but somehow you prevented a child. In other words, you had childless sex. Great! Why can't they?

Unless you have been living on the frozen tundra or in the Amazon rain forest, you probably know the famous golfer Tiger Woods got in a lot of personal trouble with his family. That's not headline-breaking news. It's really nobody's business what he does or who with except his wife. It's not your business and it ain't mine. Nonetheless, there is a world-class sex addiction lesson here. Let's see if we can learn it...

OK, here we go, suppose you are a good-looking, 6'1 or 6'2" top-of-the-world athlete who is worth about a gazillion dollars and wherever you go, you are treated like royalty because you can get a ball in a hole or in a hoop or across a line or in a net with a ball, puck, hook, car, or plane better than anyone else who tries it. Remember what we talked about when we introduced Joey Vincent on the cover? He could walk in any bar in Orlando in 1975 and never pay for a drink. People wanted to hang around with him because he was "Joey Vincent"... imagine how many people want to hang around Tiger Woods... millions.

Now suppose you have a beautiful wife and family at home and you find yourself in a town 2,000 miles from home for the weekend. About half those million people who want to hang around you and act like "feeder fish" are females! OK, you're away from home and all kinds of women are hanging around to spend some quality time with you and you are more than willing to show them how to get more ball spin out of their wedge! Get my drift? I wish I were Tiger Woods, I noticed they were all tall, young, good looking and single... didn't hear about any of them being married. Are you going to tell me 15 or 20 ladies all of whom were in their 20s or 30s didn't know who Tiger Woods was and that he had a wife and children at home? Right. Tell me something, was it addiction or was it a lack of character on both their parts? If you sleep with someone who is married, you are as guilty as they are. If you are both single... party on!

Maybe it was addiction to sex, maybe him and Arnold (the former governor of California) and a slew of governors and senators and representatives and judges are simply addicts... oh yeah, I lived in Orlando and remember a judge or two who got caught with a mistress or two. Should they not be allowed to listen to divorce cases? Maybe all the above have a mental/emotional problem called addiction.... maybe not. Sex, Sex, Sex... neither one could say no. I never met Tiger's wife but I met Maria Shriver once. She is drop-dead gorgeous! Her eyes are the color of Key West water. She walked by me and smiled, at the Arnold Classic in Ohio, and I almost walked into a wall. Lord that's a good-looking woman. But we are all human... was it a mistake with Arnold or is it addiction? Is it still a mistake after two or three or four times? When does it become addiction? I think the answer is the minute you want it more than you want your life at home, it's a problem. Maybe that's why I stayed single so many years... if I am single and she is single, it might be addiction, but it ain't adultery. And it isn't just the celebrities I mentioned. A lady recently came out about an affair with President Kennedy. You think it was that one lady or were there more? Don't ask the Secret Service... you might not like the answer.

I'm going to tell you this next-to-last story about sex and leave it at that. You decide if the price you are paying for sex or the price you will eventually pay for sex is worth the ride... 'cause the ride ends, but sometimes the consequences don't.

These two California redheaded woodpeckers fly across the United States on vacation and end up down in a Florida swamp. They fly from tree to tree and finally meet up with two Florida redheaded woodpeckers. The two from California ask the two from Florida where is a good place to eat? The Florida birds say the swamp Cypress is full of bugs and worms but the wood is hard as Chinese algebra and you just can't break through it.

We'll see about that, says the California birds and proceed to peck away at the Cypress. Pretty quickly the birds are into the wood and all four birds have a big feast. After a few days of this the California birds fly home and before leaving, invite the Florida birds to come visit in California. The following summer, the Florida Woodpeckers fly out to California and meet up with their two new friends. Where do we eat, ask the vacationers? Well, says the California birds, these Giant Redwoods are hard as concrete but they are full of worms and bugs. They are just too hard for us to get into.

We'll give it a try, says the Florida Woodpeckers and like a buzz saw, they go through the wood and everybody has a big feast! Want to know the moral of the story?

The further from home, the harder the pecker.

Don't do it... the price is always too high.

Last story... addiction to sex... a pal of mine was in the NFL or AFL or WFL or one of those pro football leagues, I just can't exactly remember. Anyway, he told me that on Sunday all the players have to come through the same tunnel to get under the stadium and they all pretty much show up at the same time. His first day in the league and his first big game as a pro, he noticed a hell of a lot of beautiful ladies, all sizes and shapes and colors, waiting at the head of the tunnel. It was the last place the public could stand before they had to have a badge to go in.

He was a pretty smart boy but this was his first rodeo and he initially thought they were either fans or cheerleader-wannabes... he didn't give it too much thought. After the game and at the same entrance/exit, there are the same girls and usually a few new ones. They seem to know all the players and are calling them by their names and numbers. Damn! He thought this was some kind of sports town he wasn't used to in college. He smiled and chatted one or two of them up and went on to his car.

He reports Tuesday was the next practice day and one of the older veteran players comes up and asks if he picked up any of the girls after the game. No, he replied, he had gone home and soaked in a hot tub to try and get the bumps and bruises out after his first big game. Good, the veteran said, and don't you ever pick up one of those "jock-hags." Why would you say that?

And the old player, the veteran player who had been in and out of that tunnel and two or three more like it for a long time, explained that there are women who wait at the gate for any pro athlete to come to the game or leave the game. They hope the player will stop and strike up a conversation and get the ball rolling so she can show up nine months later with a lifetime meal ticket for her and any other children she might have. When you are making $5 or $10 or $15 million and the court says because of DNA that you are the father, you are going to be attached to that lady for the next 18 years come hell or high water... and sex was the bait and the innocent child is the hook.

Let me tell you something... it is just as easy to get pregnant with a millionaire as it is to get pregnant with the relief tire man at the carwash. These girls know the score and I don't mean the football game. I knew one guy who had several children by different mothers and he said he loved his kids but could not stand their mothers... too bad. He should have used some sort of protection. It was too late. He told me some of them actually have business cards made up with rather revealing (not nude) photos on them... they give them to basketball players and hockey players and baseball players and now soccer players, with their phone numbers and e-mail addresses. And don't forget, when you use cell phones or e-mail, there is a record of it and the girl has proof you called her. Again, use a condom. Not every girl at a sports event or concert is looking to get

166

a hook in. It would be ridiculous to think that. You know exactly what I mean… believe it or not, when it comes to sex, some men and some women will lie to you.

I like girls and I like to date them. What I wouldn't like is for her to ask me what I make a year and how much do I have in an IRA and what is my 401k and do I have any insurance… does she want to be my girlfriend or my accountant?

Like sex, love sex, know who you are doing business with and why are they there. Sex is wonderful and it isn't going anywhere. I truly believe it got better and better over the years and now I practice the Bob Hope sex method: "Thanks for the memories." It's the downside of getting old and broken down and my back hurts and my hair is white and falling out and well, you get the picture… please remember everything in its place and in its time and with the right person… and safe… and for your sake, put a high price and value on your body.

As with most of his movies, Woody Allen had a great success with one called "Everything You Always Wanted to Know About Sex *But Were Afraid to Ask." I don't expect anyone to remember it (1972), but it was hilarious and pretty wild for that time period. In the movie there are 10 to 12 different scenes and all pertain to funny sexual situations. The one I have in mind is perfect for this chapter and book.

There is a scene where Allen is a butler from the future and is painted silver. He is serving drinks at a party and answering the door and doing butler duties which includes bringing out the "pleasure" ball as the party picks up and people are getting into the swing of things. The way it works is, as you rub this basketball-sized silver ball, you "get aroused" and evidently get pleasure from it just like sex. The more the butler carries it around and handles it, the more he gets aroused and in the end, he won't give it to anybody else to hold. He can't stop holding on to the ball. I don't remember exactly how it ends, but you get the drift. Like Woody in that movie, some people can't get enough sex or can't quit using sex to get enough people!

If it controls you, it is no longer sex, now it's addiction. If it's on the computer or on the corner and you can't leave it alone, you've got a problem. If other parts of your life are being neglected because of sex, there is a problem. If you practice unsafe sex, you are a fool. One of the best infomercials I saw in my life was two people getting out of a bed. It was a double bed, not very big. The first two people got out and then three more got out then one more got out and then three more got out and then two more got out and it went on and on. All these people were getting out of the same bed. The announcer came on and said when you have unprotected sex with one person, you are having sex with everyone else they slept with and all the people those folks slept with and all the ones they slept with and on and on. It was a wonderful public announcement. I hope we all listened.

Remember this: Everyone is equal when they are naked under the sheets!

Well, I thought I was finished with the Sex Addiction chapter but I guess not. More and more and more information keeps popping up. Again we are not talking about normal (whatever that is) sex between two people who like each other and are pretty much monogamous. We aren't talking about strange sexual behavior (whatever that is), we are still talking about addiction and sex that will ruin your life or kill you, usually in that order.

Let me beat this dead horse. Not the one in the video, the imaginary one in the expression. I do not care nor do I want to know what anybody does in the bed, in the truck, in the hotel, or naked. It is none of my business. I am concerned about what they do in the pool if I am swimming in it. Other than that, I don't pass judgment on anyone for anything they do within the law with another consenting adult. I have my boundaries and ever since I lost my virginity, I have managed to stay within them. Let's move on...

If you want to put on an elf outfit and your partner wants to wear a baby diaper and talk baby talk while you hide in the trees, it is not anyone else's business. If you want to dress like that and invite one or two or 16 people over to play along with you and they all want to come dressed in their grandmother's hats and nothing else... have at it. After you come out of the trees and baby does a poopee, everyone can get in a pile and put each other in an Irish Whip with a small package and have a double tag-team elimination bout. Try not to break any of the furniture. It is not anyone's business as long as 18 is the minimum age and no children are present. Now here comes the kicker...

There is a pretty interesting article in a past April issue of Esquire magazine... some statistics that should hold your attention. It was a good reference. You should read it. If I may: Two of the questions were: #8 During foreplay, what's the one thing you would like to do more of to your current partner? I thought about it and decided on "stay awake." Question #9 During foreplay, what's the one thing you want more of from your current partner? I answered, "A pulse." I don't think that's asking too much, do you?

What difference will it make if everyone is gay, straight or somewhere in between? It won't. If you buy a lottery ticket, there are about 175,000,000 different combinations that can win. If you have 10 or 15 people in a pile, I am going to go with about 100,000 possibilities. Good luck on both... I have never gone to a 10- or 15-person party for several reasons. First, I wouldn't have time to write everyone a thank you note. Second, a wild night for me is when I leave the bunny rabbit night light on in the bathroom... that takes excitement for me to a whole new level and last but not least: I do not want to die from AIDS.

I have cut from the newspaper about 75 articles over the years concerning Herpes, HIV and AIDS. A lot of the articles were concerned with Gay Pride and involvement in the community. I have watched programs on television covering the funeral of AIDS patients. I watched a good dog come out and lay at his master's casket in one of those programs. It was heartbreaking. Unfortunately, most of the cases where AIDS is concerned came from dirty needles or the gay lifestyle.

Please don't be mad at the messenger. I am not now nor have been nor foresee in the close or distant future being gay! It's just not my thing. As close as I want to get to gay is when Barney and Fred sing we'll have a gay ole' time on the Flintstones... I don't think Barney was talking about taking Fred out behind the Bedrock for a "gay" ole time... this is not a rage against GLBT anything. It is a book about being addicted to something that will hurt you or kill you and unprotected sex damn sure will. I may be wrong, I may have got the wrong information and read only a few studies rather than every one that was ever published but, call me crazy, I think the flesh-eating, life-draining infection AIDS is much more active in the gay community than in the straight community. Like unwanted pregnancies (more active in the straight community) can be avoided, AIDS can be avoided. Get it, party on...

Gay folks have rights like everybody else. They are like everybody else, they just like and love and marry people with the same type pee pees as they have. No big deal. They get the same treatment at the VA as all veterans. They should, they paid the price to be a veteran. There is a new VA bill that addresses transgender care and support for vets who have decided to become a different sex than they were born. They are still veterans regardless. I am serious about this; if you went in the military and were in combat and you (thank God) came home and wanted to become Joan Crawford... who the hell's business is it? Not mine!

In California, a bill SB 48 will go to the governor demanding public schools teach the contributions of gays and lesbians, bisexuals, and transgender people in social studies. It will be mandatory. This has really divided the California Assembly. Groups from both sides are determined it will or won't become law. I think you know where Christians stand. Read the bill for yourself if interested. The bill's author is quoted as saying, "It's only beneficial to share with students the broad diversity of the human experience and that our democracy protects everyone."

The one thing the author left out was, will this Bill mandate this material be taught to children as young as 6. I don't know about you, but I couldn't match two socks when I was 6. I wonder how children are going to absorb information about gay pride when they are still doing a number 2 in their pants at recess. Whatever.

The list of newspaper articles pertaining to "sex" and lifestyle demands is overwhelming. All 75 articles concern who you can have sex with and what rights you have and discrimination and my lifestyle is right and you're wrong and the beat goes on and on.

And the bottom line remains the same: The old farmer who lives out in the country and has been married to the same lady for 30 years probably isn't worried about dying of AIDS. Maybe hoof and mouth disease, but that's another subject. And the young man or lady (gay or straight) who comes to the big city and starts partying with multiple partners without a condom isn't worried about dying of AIDS. Neither one of them is worried about the same thing... how sad.

Thank God we have some lawmakers who at least got this right. There are new penalties for trafficking in sex. The fines and prison time for trafficking underage sex workers is getting hefty here in Georgia. That's as it should be. What I can't get over is who the customers are? Who in their right mind wants to have sex with a child? What in the hell is wrong with them? What sort of screwball addiction is that? You and your husband or wife want to get in the bed with five other consenting adults, let me suggest rubber sheets. Have at it. You want to kiss, cuddle, star gaze, and do the monkey dance with someone the same sex as you, go for it... I don't care, but please wear a condom. Medicare is going through the roof! But if you can't control some sick urge to fondle a minor or force an elderly person to have sex, I think you ought to have your damn dick cut off. But that's just me. If you disagree, feel free to sue me, I now have $437 in the bank. Happy sexing.

1 CORINTHIANS 6:19 Do you not know that your body is a temple of the Holy Spirit, who is in you, whom you have received from God? You are not your own; you were bought at a price. Therefore honor God with your body.

REVELATION 9:21 Nor did they repent of their murders, their magic arts, their sexual immorality or their thefts.

LEVITICUS 18: 1 through 29... it says it all!

Chapter 12

The Dog

It's cold, it's always cold, and it's damp... always cold and damp. You stay cold and you can't stop shivering. Imagine you're stomping through the woods and snow is up to your knees and you can see every breath you exhale. There is no relief in sight. Night is falling and it is getting colder but you have to keep moving or you will freeze to death. You know these woods from the summer and you know you are almost half the way through them. Colder and darker and damper...

Up ahead you see an old farmhouse with smoke coming out of the chimney. There are lights on inside and it looks as if the door is slightly open. You head straight for that farm house and the front porch. You can't believe your luck, the door is open and there is a "Welcome, friends, come on in, make yourself at home" sign over the door.

Finally you peel off some of the wet, frosted clothes and begin to warm up.

There it is, the fireplace. It crackles and snaps and sizzles, and in front of it is a large cushioned rocking chair. The chair seems to be saying "come on in, take a load off, warm up, and sit a spell!"

Beside the fireplace is a cord of wood stacked high and wide and ready to be burned. On the other side of the fireplace in the corner is a large, happy, fuzzy puppy. His tongue is hanging out and his tail is wagging. Finally, finally... you are out of all your wet freezing clothes and wrapped in a thick calico blanket in the rocking chair in front of the fireplace, finally.

Now here's the catch: As you peel the wet clothes off, you got a little warmer, and as you add wood to the fireplace, you get a little warmer, and as you wrap the blanket around you, you get a little warmer, and as you cuddle up in that rocker in front of the golden fire, you get a little warmer, and then for the first time, you hear the dog move. You realize that while you were getting warm, you hadn't really paid much attention to the big, fat, fluffy dog in the corner.

You notice the dog is up on his front legs now and looking right at you. For the first time you hear a low growl. All of a sudden he barks. You sit there getting warmer and then you hear him growl a little louder. The more he growls, the warmer you get. The longer you sit there, the more he demands you look at him. When you look again, he is up on all four legs and his tail has stopped wagging. You stop looking and rock faster and put another log on the fire. He is now snarling and slowly inching toward you. For the first time you notice how large and sharp his teeth are. He is growing in size in front of your eyes. He is huge.

The dog's head is low to the floor, and he is definitely coming toward you and the fireplace. You notice drool and foam dripping from his razor-sharp teeth. The more he snarls, the more teeth he has. You have to do something quick.

When you reach for your wet, cold shoes, the dog stops moving. You take the blanket off, and he stops snarling. You get out of the chair, and he backs up. You begin to dress in your wet cold clothes, and the dog lies back down. As you head for the door, the dog is now wagging his tail. When you step out the front door, as you feel the bite of the freezing night air, you turn and look back at the dog. He is a big pile of fluffy puppy, and he is on his side almost asleep.

You step off the porch, and in your wet socks and shoes you begin walking in the woods again. It gets colder and colder and worse and worse and now the temperature has dropped to below freezing and the further you go from the farmhouse, the darker and colder it gets. You are not going to make it, you can't go on, there's nothing to do but turn and go back to the farm house. When you get to the farm house and look in the window you see the warm fireplace and there it is the handsome rocking chair and blanket. It actually looks as if there is more wood piled next to the fire. This time it's a little different with the dog. Rover is sound asleep on his back with all 4 legs sticking straight up in the air. His tongue is hanging out and he is snoring lightly. He does not look or sound intimidating in the least.

Outside it is colder and later and darker than before. In you go. Off come the wet shoes and socks. Off comes the damp coat and scarf. On goes another log and on goes the blanket and into the rocker you plop. This is heaven.

Then you hear the growl, very low, not really bad at all. Then it gets worse and you notice the dog is awake and looking at you. Next comes the snarl and the dog is up on all four legs. No more tail wagging, and this time the ears are pinned back and there are more and sharper teeth than before. This go-round the dog ain't playing, his eyes are on fire like the wood, and every hair is aimed at the ceiling. You are so warm and so comfortable and so happy but... the dog is so close you can smell his rotten breath. You get your wet socks and shoes and wet clothes and head out the door. As you turn back, the dog is curled up in the corner licking his balls and wagging his fluffy little tail.

Outside you start in the same direction again but you don't get far. It's too cold and the comfort of the fireplace and the blanket is overpowering. With each step another toe freezes; you can't feel your fingers. You get a hundred yards or so and turn to go back. You know you will at least get warm for a minute and then the dog will run you out again, but you go back anyway. When you are standing in the snow, that minute or two of warmth seems worth it. It's simply too hard and too far and too cold to push on and make your way out of the woods. The woods are a scary place and a dark place and a cold place. You are alone and the woods seem unknown and dangerous. The farmhouse is warm and you can still barely see it behind you. So you turn around and go back, knowing once you step on the front porch, it will be the same process over and over again.

This is what I had to learn, and it is a hard, cold lesson: Nothing is ever going to change. Each time you visit the farmhouse, the fire is warmer and the dog is meaner with more teeth. Eventually he is going to bite you. Unfortunately for some of us, that won't even keep us out of the farmhouse. We hope against hope that the dog will someday change. He won't. It's his floor and his fireplace and his wood and his blanket and his rocker and he is protecting it until his master returns, and you ain't now, nor will you ever be, his master... he's *yours*.

If I could have found whatever it was that would keep me moving out of the woods, if I could have only known how to get further from the center of the woods, I would have been getting closer to the edge where it wasn't as dark and cold. We can walk out anytime if we learn the way and put one foot in front of the other. We will get out if we keep going.

The problem with me and some of you good readers is, we go back to the warmth of the fireplace and the blanket and rocker and we get comfortable, knowing full well that eventually the dog is going to attack and eat us. One more time. We are visiting, he lives there and he will continue to protect his master's house until we quit coming in to disturb him, or die, whichever comes first. It doesn't much make any difference to the dog; he's resting and sleeping and staying warm when we're not there.

Welcome to addiction, come on in, sit a spell, take your shoes off... have you met the dog?

Chapter 13

Puppies

What a strange name for a chapter about gambling, or maybe not. Further down the pages I am going to relate a story about my first contact with a gambling addiction. It involved the dog races in Miami Beach back in 1967... that was a long time before the lottery, yet it was gambling nonetheless, and it was addictive. Let's talk about something else first.

Addiction, addiction, addiction, something that controls you... could there be a better place to see addiction in action than Las Vegas? I can't think of one. I had a free ticket to come out here for a few days (going home today) and instead of bringing my dancing shoes, I brought pen and paper. I'm not sure where to begin.

Let's start with gambling. To take a chance on success or failure; to place a wager; to put up money on the unknown outcome of a specific event to happen, to roll the dice, to contribute a thing of value not knowing the result of an action. I think we all understand what gambling is. It ain't a college in Louisiana; that's Grambling. You could gamble on the Grambling Football team and you would probably win, but it's two different things.

In Vegas you can bet a penny in a slot machine (and there are thousands of them) or you could sit in on some pretty high-stake card games. I don't know the largest bet ever made here; it was probably the one where someone's life was on the line.

No idea if anyone has bet a million dollars on a hand of cards, but I am thinking there are card games for several hundred thousand dollars all the time. I want to be crystal clear on where I stand on gambling. If I owned the world, I couldn't bet a hundred thousand dollars on the sun coming up tomorrow. It might not come up, and I just cannot see myself forking over that much money on something I have no control of. With my luck, it would be the first day of the end of time. Everybody doesn't look at it that way. There is no right or wrong; when you write your book, and I hope you do, you can tell about winning or losing your million dollars. I just don't have a million dollars, so I don't bet it.

This Vegas experience is GREAT! If you haven't been here, you need to come on out here. It is something to see. You want to talk about lights? These people have light bulbs down to a science. I have never been here at Christmas, but I think it would be like the Biltmore Estate, even more beautiful than normal. The shows are amazing! I try and see one per trip. This time I saw "The Amazing Jonathan." It was a scream. I laughed for two hours and it was the highlight of my time here.

This is my eighth or ninth trip, and I have stayed where they have a water show on the half hour and another place where the water worked about every half hour. You can stay where the least expensive room of one night costs more than the suite for a week at a different hotel. I have stayed at Bellagio and I have stayed off Freemont Street. Let me tell you what both places have in common: They both have slot machines, poker tables, craps, and blackjack. They both will serve you free drinks if you are gambling. They both welcome you and your money. And, let me add, they were both nice to me and both invited me to hurry back. One difference I recall is the lady at Bellagio had all her teeth. It is what it is.

As long as everybody understands the score, I urge you to visit this exciting, amazing, wonderful city. What an experience! But make &^%$ sure you don't bring one red cent more than you can afford to lose. Don't bring your ATM card if you think you will drain the account, because you might. Don't bring your wedding rings or your grandfather's pocket watch or your Rolex. There are pawn shops all over the place… must be a reason why. Bring the exact amount of cash you are willing to go back home without and not one cent more. Remember, Vegas was built on the backs of losers, not winners. The people who own the casinos are the winners. I love that commercial about "what happens in Vegas stays in Vegas"… how true, except I think they are talking about your wallet. It stays in Vegas. Obviously, not all people here or in Atlantic City or any of the casinos come here and leave flat broke. Some do win, or people would stop coming. The question is, with all the lights and all the bells and whistles and all the free booze, will you know when to cut your losses and go have a good dinner and go to your room? You better.

Enough about gambling towns, now let's talk about mine and your town. Here's a funny little story about the lottery. It used to be called the "numbers" and it was run by bookies. I think Florida was the first state to make it legal, but I'm not sure. Anyway, when it was the numbers, it was a sin and illegal. You could go to jail a long time for running numbers. Now that the states get the money, guess what, it's all OK. Hmm! Keep that thought in mind when we talk about dope. I bet if the state could control reefer, it would be legal tomorrow. We will see.

This isn't an attack on the Powerball or Mega Millions or Daily Double or Quick Pick 3 or scratch off or any of the 47 ways to give the lady behind the counter your money on a gamble. I play a dollar each week and my dad plays a dollar each week and we call each other on Sunday and say "well, we still have to eat hotdogs the rest of our lives" and we laugh and it's great. I plan to keep doing that until one of us isn't here and we can't do it anymore. I will miss it dearly. It is a wonderful $2 investment. Here's the flip side:

There is not one place I have found that will NOT sell you as many Powerball or Mega Million or Super 8 or Fantasy 5 or whatever tickets as you want. If you want a hundred, they will sell you a hundred. That will be a hundred dollars please. I have not seen one "state approved" lottery seller who has a psychologist or financial planner or addictions counselor or priest standing at the counter advising you not to spend all that money on lottery tickets. Have you? If a drunk staggers in a liquor store, they won't sell him (or her) another bottle of booze; it's against the law. If a drug addict staggers in a drugstore with a belt pulled around his arm and tried to buy needles, they would call the law. But in your life have you ever, ever, ever seen anybody try to stop or refuse a habitual gambling addict a lottery ticket? I didn't think so. And it's just as big a problem and as big a disease as booze or drugs or smokes or porn or the Internet or food or the wrong person... no difference.

On national TV a few weeks ago, a guy was saying that one-tenth of one percent of the state lottery money went to any type of addictions counseling or recovery. Oh, you don't get your money back, no sir, but you might, maybe, if you're lucky (and obviously you aren't), you might get some state-funded help. One-tenth of one percent of all lottery money goes for recovery. Think about this, if you buy two tickets on any one lottery drawing, you're betting one of them is a loser. Think about that...

I buy a couple of tickets a few different places each week; I noticed they have a lot of pictures pinned on the walls of winners. I looked real close and didn't see one picture of any losers. Maybe the person buying the ticket didn't pay the rent or maybe their children haven't been to a dentist in years or maybe the people buying five or 10 or more tickets are the ones least able to afford 10 or 15 dollars a day on a gamble. There is nobody from the state behind the counter asking to see their teeth or asking if their family has warm clothes or food or new shoes. There is NOT one state officer passing any judgment on a toothless, dirty, old tennis shoe bum who is buying a ticket. He is told, "Good luck come back tonight and play the evening 3… maybe you will be the big winner."

I live in Georgia, but I travel a lot and buy a ticket wherever I am. I have counted 37 kinds of scratch-offs and 10 lottery types in one store. The tickets have names like "Lucky 7" and "Jackpot" and "Million Dollar Winner." I wonder why they aren't named: "No Chance" or "I Doubt It" or "No More Winners on this Roll," but, they're not… if you can't afford it, don't go in. It's addicting.

Do you get the drift here? Have you seen the commercial where the big winners are interviewed on TV? Have you seen the two love birds on the beach and the sun is shining and the sand is white and the sky is blue and a voice comes over the TV and says, "What would you do if you were the lucky winner?" And then some state lottery scrolls across the screen. I've seen it, maybe you have. At the end, sometimes, not always, a different, very masculine voice blurts out, "Please play responsibly." Do they mean while I am at the ocean, or back at the counter buying the ticket? Never could figure that out.

I plan on playing the lottery. Even if I am out of the country, the brilliant people at the lottery have come up with a way to buy your tickets in advance. How wonderful. I can afford to buy my two tickets and look forward to calling dear old dad and laughing. I am going to do this as long as the light bill and the car note and the doctor bill and the gas bill have been paid, not before. If the day comes when I don't have a dollar, I guess I will have to depend on dad to get the tickets. It won't be the first time I have had to depend on him.

I was reading *USA Today* on one of my many trips back in 2007 and came across an article concerning a lady who runs one of the state lotteries. She made a whopping $250,000 that year and other lottery officials in that state got their salary plus over $3 million in bonuses. Good for them. I wish I worked for the lottery. There is nothing wrong with them making as much as they can doing their job. They were hired to do their job and that's what they are doing, regardless of where the monies go. Some goes to the few winners and some goes to education (that's the bait we talk about) and some goes to pay for jobs. I got no problem with any of that.

What I do sort of have a problem with is this: It's just my opinion, but I think gambling might be the worst addiction of them all, or at least in the top two. Look, if you are addicted to cocaine, you know %*&^ good and well, nothing is going to get better. It will just get worse. If you are addicted to booze, and abusing it, you are well aware that there is no bottom to any bottle and being drunk is a one-way street to either jail, the hospital, court, or divorce court, and maybe the morgue. Let's keep going. Addicted to the wrong person, there is no end to it until you leave or die. Addicted to food or sex, you will never get enough of either of them until you get fat enough to get on one of those TV shows or die of AIDS. The only addiction I can think of that gives you any real hope is gambling. You "hope" you are going to win. In all the other addictions, you hope you don't get caught, you hope you don't die, you hope you don't kill someone else. You hope you don't, don't, don't. In gambling, you hope you do, do, do.

We don't drink hoping we will get sober; we don't use drugs hoping we will kick them; we don't eat like pigs hoping we will be fit and healthy and look sharp at the beach; but we gamble hoping we will win.

Let me repeat: If you buy two lotto tickets, you are betting at least one of them is a loser. Do you think all the casinos and slot machines and card games have a winner each and every time? The odds are in favor of the house and at the end of the day, the house wins (or the state or whoever is running the game) or they would go out of business. I remember walking into a casino in Costa Rica and a real pretty girl was sitting at a slot machine. I sat down and started to play one of the machines and asked her if she was winning? She gave me the most dead-pan look and said, "The machine always wins." They should put that on a plaque on the wall.

OK, enough about Vegas... I urge you to come visit this place and enjoy the entire experience. Just remember to bring what you can afford to leave. P.S., don't forget the old joke about the guy who drove a $3,000 car to Vegas and went home on a $50,000 bus... a Greyhound.

I started the chapter with a reference to Miami Beach. It was the summer of 1967 and I worked at a club on Collins Ave, and my sister was a flight attendant for Eastern Airlines. She let me stay with her that summer, and I got a job parking cars. After a week or two, some of the guys I worked with asked if I wanted to go see the puppies run. Remember this was long before Mega Ball and Powerball and the lottery. Dog and horse racing and Jai alai was the only game in town. The greyhounds ran at a place called the Miami Beach Kennel Club. I think it was down around street or near there. It has been a long time since I was there.

So anyway, I go and had a ball. It was my first time at a race, and I was star struck. Lights, action, fun, and I made my first bet on some dog named "Fawn Muff." It didn't win but I did. At the end of eight races, I had spent a total of $10. That included a program, parking, a hotdog, two Cokes, and three $2 bets. What a night!

Stay with me, it gets better... or worse. The next time I went, one of the bartenders went with us. This guy was about 40 years old and was married and had two kids. He was a nice guy and sometimes let me barback to pick up a few extra dollars. Now we get there and he studies the program and starts to bet on the first race, and I can't remember if he won or not. I bet my $2 for a certain dog to "show" and had a great time. He starts yelling at the dogs. Now I understand yelling at something that can't hear you because you are excited, like the TV when your favorite college team scores or when a favorite boxer wins, something like that I think is normal... to a point.

This guy takes it a tad too far. He starts screaming and storms off to the window for the next race. Evidentially, he lost that second race because he is now cussing at the top of his lungs. He must have won one along the way because he had some money from somewhere and he quit screaming for a few races. Then it happened; he was yelling at the dogs and his face was turning red and he was starting to draw a little too much attention to himself when an usher told him to calm down. I thought we were going to get thrown out. He calmed down for a few minutes.

181

Here comes the punch line: On one of the races, he bets all his money on three of the dogs to cross the finish line before the other six dogs. I think it is called a trifecta... if you get it right, you win BIG! If not, you drop whatever you bet. Simple. So the dogs break out of the shoot and start chasing this electric rabbit. Everybody is yelling and my friend is jumping around like his ass is on fire. He is in the aisle and his face is red and the vain in his neck is popping out and I am sitting there watching him borderline have a heart attack. I was 17 years old and honestly had never seen anyone act like him.

You guessed it, his three dogs didn't finish like he thought they should. He went ballistic. He is screaming and cussing and ran down to the rail that separated the fans from the track and is yelling at the dogs. This is the God's truth, he must have realized the dogs didn't speak English because he started screaming in Russian or Greek or whatever was his first language. I didn't get a word of it. He followed the dogs as far as he could go and still be in the stands. The dogs got off the track and everybody got ready for the next race. He came back to where we were and sat down. He tore up his tickets, then he tore up the program, and then he just sat there. Sweat was pouring off him and he had a complete blank expression on his face. Nothing was said.

I had had enough. I went home. When I counted my money, I figured in the hotdogs and the Cokes and the parking and the admission and all the $2 bets I had made, and at the end of the night, I was 50 cents ahead. I had a good time, he didn't. Back at work he was perfectly normal. He smiled and was quiet and seemed as if nothing had happened. The next time we went to the puppies, same thing, he went ape! This guy was like a walking zoo. He went to the dogs, then he went ape because he had a monkey on his back... back at work, he was completely normal. Go figure.

Finally I asked him if he enjoyed going to see the dog's race. He told me yes and no. I asked how much he had won on a single race and he reported (with some pride) $1,400 on one race. I asked how much he had lost over the years and he reported thousands and thousands of dollars. Where is the joy in that? This guy had a problem and didn't know how to deal with it. I have no idea what happened to him. I hope he either won big and quit or just quit and then won big. Either way, quitting was half the solution; winning wasn't.

I finished working that summer and went back to Georgia to start the grade. That was 45 years ago, and I remember his face like it was in front of me. Maybe that is why I don't care 2 cents about gambling. It's there and if you can afford it, great. If you can't afford it, don't do it. Don't get red in the face and throw furniture around the room if your team doesn't win, and don't get evicted because you can't pay the rent due to gambling debts. Don't sell your family's jewelry because you need to place one more bet. Don't rob and cheat and steal to get the money to buy more tickets. They will simply print more.

There can't be many more points to make on this subject. If you or someone you know has a gambling addiction, please get some help. These days, it's legal in every state, and there are people being paid to come up with new games and new ways to get your dollar. I absolutely understand the draw, the excitement, the thrill. You always want to win, and you always want to win big. Who wouldn't? I think it's fun to bet a couple of dollars, and I already encouraged you to visit Las Vegas. It's amazing! Bring what you can spend and not a cent more. They do not give it back to you if you lose. Can you afford to lose? Because they can afford to stay there until you do!

Last story: I hate this story, but somebody needs to read it. It's the truth and nothing will change it. Do not become this person.

Back 25 years ago, I was the general manager of a couple of clubs and juke joints in Florida. The company I worked for had probably 12 or so managers and one supervisor and a general managers (me) and a vice president and on and on. In that business, a lot of young people come and go, and we were always looking for good people to become managers. We found that guy. He had recently graduated from a well-known college and happened to have a degree in business. We were very fortunate to get him. He started as a doorman and became the relief manager and then a shift manager and in record time, he was offered the manager's position in one of the clubs. He was sharp as a tack. I liked him, my boss liked him, and everybody up the line liked him.

As I recall, the first little problem was he stayed in the office too much. This was before cell phones, and it seemed like most of times that I called, the phone was either busy or he answered it on the first ring. That phone was getting a lot of use. It was a minor thing about the phone because sales were good; nobody was complaining. I just made a mental note of it.

I also recall the first real problem was one of the bartenders asking to come to my office for a chat. Sure, no problem, come on down, how can I help you? She explained that her manager (the guy we are talking about) was borrowing money from her and one or two of the other bartenders. He always paid them back but after three or four times, it was just not normal. They were kind of afraid to tell him no because was their manager. OK, no problem. We will take care of it.

I waited for a managers meeting and after the meeting asked if I could see him for a minute. How are things, how do you like your job, are you making enough money, etc.? He said he loved his job and like anybody else, he could use more money, hahaha… so I tell him I will see what I can do because he is doing a great job, and one other thing: If he needs a few bucks like we all do until payday, come to see me, don't ask the employees. No problem, only happened once or twice, you know how it is, Porter, just a little short. End of subject? Not quite.

One morning the day manager calls me and says there is no money in the safe. The bank bag to get change is not there. I get the day manager some cash and start calling the guy's pager we were talking about. I wake him up and he can't believe the bank bag is not there. He says he will call me right back. Sure enough, he calls back and reports he found the bank bag in his car, no idea how it got there and he will bring it back at 6:00 p.m. when he comes to work… just a mistake, was a busy night, and when he made the bank deposit, he must have picked up the day bank by mistake etc. I say that's no problem, but I need him to bring it back now. Well, he can't. Why not, I ask. Because he isn't at home, he is .out of town with his girlfriend and won't be back until this afternoon. Remember, this is before cell phones; we had pagers that beeped and you called a service and they told you who was trying to contact you. I had no idea where he was; I do remember he came in that night and had the bank bag and it was just a mistake… wouldn't happen again.

So life goes on for a few days or weeks and I call the club one night and he answers the phone and instead of hello or saying the name of the club or thank you for calling, the first words out of his mouth are, "What's the score?" I said, "Me one, you nothing." He laughs and says he's sorry that he thought it was his brother calling with the score of his college team's basketball game. No. it's me, and we had a short lesson on how to answer the phone. He must have been absent the day they taught that in business school.

The next thing that happened was a $300 IOU note found in a bank bag in the safe. He didn't steal a penny from the club, he took $300 and left a note for us to find at 9 a.m. the next morning. I didn't beep him this time; my boss said for me to have a come to Jesus meeting with him. I did. He explained he couldn't call me at 11 p.m. and wake me up and he had to have the money or his car was getting repossessed and he would have to quit work and his girlfriend had had some medical problems and so on and he would give back every dime on payday. As a matter of fact, he said just keep his paycheck. No, we weren't going to keep his paycheck, but damn it, call me if there ever is a next time. Don't just take the money. Let me or someone know. My boss let him pay back a hundred dollars a paycheck for three paychecks.

Are you seeing some sort of a pattern here? I am. It's always something. Finally, one of the doormen took me aside and told me an interesting story. He reported standing at the door one night when two gentlemen he had never seen came in and asked for the manager. They didn't wait for the doorman to go get him. When they saw the manager, they walked past the door host and took the manager by the arm and walked him into the office. The doorman thought they might be cops or something the way they took charge. He reported the manager went with the two guys into the office and closed and locked the door. He knew the door was locked because he knocked on it and was told everything was all right, he would be out in a minute. Shortly the two guys left and the manager stayed in the office the rest of the shift, about four hours. The two guys didn't say anything to anybody; they walked in, walked the manager to his office, stayed a few minutes, walked out, and never said a word going out the door. End of subject.

Forty eight hours didn't pass and there was a new note in the bank bag... IOU for $1,300. You know what happened next, don't you? We page the manager and tell him to come to the office, now. When he walked in, he looked like he had not slept in days... he was dirty and smelled like old sweat. I almost didn't recognize him. He had been off for two days so to get the money, he had to come to the club after it was closed on his night off and leave the $1,300 IOU.

My boss took him in his office and closed the door. When he left, my boss told me I would be working that club until we found a replacement. The manager was no longer with us. I of course asked about the $1,300, and my boss said if he pays us, he pays us; if he doesn't, we eat it. Naturally, I wanted to know what happened. It was bookies that came to see the manager; he was into them for $1,500 and could only get $200 up. Evidentially, whatever they were going to do to him or our club was not worth $1,300 to my boss.

Here was a good-looking, smart young man with a valuable college education from a well-known school, a guy with a wide-open future waiting on him and because of a gambling addiction, he was going to get hurt real bad by people he didn't even know. The bookies weren't going to beat him up; somebody, somewhere was going to hurt his girlfriend or his family or do something like burn down our club, and he couldn't prevent it from happening. Wait a minute, he certainly could have prevented it from happening… all he had to do was not gamble what he didn't have.

I am sorry to say that sometime later, we read about him in the newspaper. He got mixed up with the wrong people and somehow got arrested and was looking at some serious hard time. I don't know if it had anything to do with gambling, but it had something to do with money. I don't know if he paid us back or not; that was between him and my boss. I do know this young man had everything going for him except his addiction to gambling. It was a case study of one rotten apple ruining his barrel. He couldn't be near money and his education was in business… maybe he should have gotten his degree in English!

Please don't think it is any less an addiction than any of the other things we have listed. It is as powerful as you allow it to be. People max out credit cards in order to gamble, and the more you gamble, the easier casinos or bookies or convenient stores make it for you to gamble.

I am not real sure how to close this chapter. If you have $5 left over after you have paid everything for the week and given to your church and all your family is doing fine and you want to play a lottery ticket, please have a good time and enjoy yourself. I know I will. If you are going on vacation this year and you haven't been to a casino in a few years, man you can't beat seeing Vegas or Atlantic City… they are wonderful. Never been to the Derby in Louisville? You should see that at least once if not more. It is one of my favorite places. Have you gone out on a cruise to the Bahamas and played a few dollars on the ship's slot machines? It's great fun. But when you sell blood to get $10 or steal your children's lunch money or go on welfare so you can put your paycheck on a lotto ticket, you are sick, sick, sick. Get some help, it's available. I bet you can beat this addiction. I'll give you 10 to 1 odds... you can if you want to. You've got to want it.

Like most of this book, I wrote it over a period of three or four years. A couple of things came up that side tracked me, but I have been writing slowly all along. Last week I watched the Kentucky Derby and saw a guy come on and bet what I think was $100,000 on a horse to win. He was on TV with his wife and they were pretty sure they had the winning horse. The announcer said if the guy won, he would get a cool million dollars... WOW! So, they're off and the guy's horse didn't win. For whatever reason, the announcer didn't mention the guy again... wonder why not? They showed him and his pretty wife and the cash in a briefcase when he went to bet it, but didn't bother to chat with him when his money was gone and his horse was in the shower! Friends, that how it is with gambling... whoever wins gets the attention, they get the glory, they get the champagne and cigars and the losers get a broad grin and a "well, maybe next time."

One more time, how much can you afford to lose, not how much can you afford to win... that's how much you can gamble.

Since I finished this chapter, one more excellent example occurred. It cannot be denied. A guy from England made a television documentary about his wanting to come to Vegas and bet a couple hundred thousand dollars on one cut of the deck. I believe it was $250,000 or $500,000 dollars but am not exactly sure. It was something like that. Anyway, the cameras follow him all over the place and he finds a casino that will take his one-time, one-chance, all-or-nothing bet. He goes in with cameras rolling to sit down and work out the very few details (couldn't be that many on one cut of the deck) of the upcoming event.

I'm in complete agreement with this guy. That's the way to do it. Walk in, bet all you have and can afford to lose, either pick up your winnings and walk away or leave your money there and walk away. Short and sweet, right? Not quite...

The manager or owner or whoever he is says the Jokers will stay in the deck and if the fellow betting the money gets a Joker, he loses. Wait a minute, is that fair? The guy betting has 52 cards to cut from. He has 26 chances out of 52 to get a better card then the house. There are 26 chances he won't. But now all of that has changed in favor of the house... don't you get it? From Vegas to eternity and back a million times, the odds are now 28 to 26 in favor of the house. Now there are 54 cards and two of them have a skull and cross bones on them against the bettor. I think they shook hands and called the whole thing off. Smart move on the young man's part. The odds were against him. Smart move on the house part; they are there to make money, not lose it.

If you are having a problem with this, please get the help that is available, please. It has been a year or two since I wrote this and the good news is there are now 48 new tickets to buy and scratch off. In 2012, a Powerball ticket has gone up 100 percent to $2 from $1 dollar in 2011. Now you can play the Morning 3 and the Afternoon 3 and the Evening 3 and on and on and on. I feel sure that someday soon, an enterprising state will come up with the "hourly lotto" where you can stand there and spend at least $12 in a 12-hour day. I can't wait for that to start... I bet it does and never forget, it's all for the children, and if you don't buy tickets and if you think it is the same as the numbers, then you are a communist and hate America and hate children and you are racist and there is nothing wrong and you're homophobic and you drowned kittens when you were a child. Is there anything I've missed? Oh yeah, one other thing...

There was a special on the greyhounds some time back and one of the "secrets" along with steroids and cutting the nails too close so they don't get the same grip etc., was swimming the dog before a race. How would you know if the night before a big race, a dog or a horse was taken out for a swim for a couple of hours? You wouldn't unless you worked there or were told. Now if you did know it, that would sort of give you the edge, wouldn't it? You would better know how to bet when the bell rang. I had heard that unsavory people in the dog business would breed a dog before a big race and then bet against the dog. What would you rather do, breed with some great looking female who was in heat or run your heart out chasing a fake rabbit that you never catch? I know my answer.

Bet what you want to... when you can't stop, it may be too late. I bet I'm right.

Genesis 3:19: By the sweat of your brow you will eat your food until you return to the ground, since from it you were taken; for dust you are and to dust you will return.

I have no idea what the Lord meant by that. If you are sitting at a card table pouring sweat from your brow because you're waiting on the dealer to drop you the ace of spades for a royal straight flush on a $100,000 pot, do you think that's what Genesis 3:19 means? Again, I don't know. There are a lot of "Christians" who hate alcohol and hate smokes and hate porn and hate everybody that uses them. I even heard of some of them that hate sex but feel it is an obligation… oh dear. But get them out on the old golf course or at the neighborhood poker game and well, what the hell, we're just having a little fun, just a friendly wager, it's not really a sin… or is it?

Again, no idea if it is a sin, but I am 100 percent convinced it can be an addiction. Decide for yourself.

Chapter 14

Wade

On November 25, 1970, Wade Cobar came kicking and screaming into this world in Miami, Florida. His parents were from Guatemala, but Wade wasn't going to wait to get back to Guatemala before he appeared. It didn't exactly change his parents' vacation, but it was the highlight of the trip!

The family returned to Guatemala and the next 20 years were pretty much normal for Wade. He went to school, played sports, graduated high school and got a job. On August 20, 1990, Wade packed his worldly belongings and moved to California to begin a new life. He wanted to learn this language and having been born here, he wanted to experience the American dream. He also wanted to improve his limited English.

Step two of the American dream was to get a job at Taco Bell! Ole'... he made the best tacos in all of L.A.! He told me he took so much pride in his work station and the food he prepared, he loved his job and he was learning English. Then one day the inevitable happened. He had met a girl and became very involved with her and all of the sudden, she was going to have to move back home to Chicago. It's the old "sweetheart" story.

Wade packs up all his belongings and here he goes off to Chicago. I'm not exactly sure he knew how cold it can get in Chicago in the winter. He goes there, nonetheless. At 21 years of age, Wade finds himself in Chicago working again at a Taco Bell, making minimum wage. Life is wonderful! He enrolls at St. Augustine University and earns his American GED. He already had a high school diploma from Guatemala, but that one didn't count here. Let's review: He is in Chicago, knows one girl, gets his GED, and is working full time at Taco Bell for minimum wage and loves America.

He continues his education and takes one or two subjects in college each quarter. A new job is available at a 24-hour gas station. This is better because now he can go to school days and work all night. Things are looking up until...

the station closes. Oh dear! He has to move from where he lives and find a new job. Regardless, he never quits going to class.

Wade finds a new job at another all-night service station and finds a new apartment and keeps seeing his girlfriend and keeps going to school and keeps working. At this point, I have to think about some of the people who say life is too hard and they can't find a job, and that's why they drink and boo hoo hoo hoo! Here is a 21-year-old man, thousands of miles from his family, knows one person in Chicago, and is so proud to be working 40 hours a week and going to school and paying his bills and NOT complaining. No cigarettes, no alcohol, no dope, no topless bars, no gambling, no vices whatsoever, and happy to be here.

One night the credit card machine goes berserk at work and Wade is in trouble. He doesn't know how to fix it and nobody is coming out at 2 a.m. in freezing Chicago to fix it and people are pumping gas and yelling about not being able to buy anything and the next day Wade is out of a job. Now the trouble begins.

After looking and looking for work, Wade falls two months behind in his rent. One day after school, he puts the key in the door and it won't turn. You know the rest of the story… he is out on the street with only the clothes on his back. The girlfriend can't help him, she lives at home, and he has no money and no car and can't find work. He has to ride the bus and things are getting tougher and tougher. He does manage to stay in school during the day. It was paid for and he meant to take the courses. There was nothing left to do but bathe in the school gym, sleep in the park, and study on campus either in the library or yard. He wore the same cloths over and over.

He did meet a guy who let him stay on the couch in an over-populated apartment. This didn't work out when he found out he was required to sell dope to pay his share of the rent. "Adios," said Wade. He didn't even smoke cigarettes, much less dope. He had met a new girl at school and finally one freezing day, she told him he could sleep in her car rather than freeze to death… no kidding. He, after months of living in the park, had a place to stay; I believe it was a '78 Chevy! He got another job at another gas station and in 1993 saved enough money to lease a new apartment. By the way… the guy who had the locks changed said someone broke in and stole all Wade's clothes and stick furniture and TV. Wade had next to nothing in his third apartment.

Time passes and he moves to Schaumburg and begins living with his girlfriend. At least they are not sleeping in a car.

This is where the story really gets going. Here we have a young man who came back to America with very limited English, did not know one living human being, worked at minimum-wage jobs, and was happy to get them, learned and improved his English, paid his taxes, stayed out of trouble, refused to sell drugs, and went to school every chance he got, and is most appreciative of America and the opportunities he was given. Then one day he is walking out of a White Hen store in Chicago and his life changed forever.

He had picked up some eggs and bread and when he was leaving, he looked across the street and there in plain view was the combined Armed Forces Recruiting station. Wade wandered across the street and walked in. He was 24 years old. Recruiters have been around for over 200 years... Wade didn't have a chance. He told me he talked to all four branches and listened to what they had to say. They all pretty much offered the same thing with one exception: the Marines had the best dress-blue uniform. That was absolutely the only reason he decided on the Marines. At 5'5", and 145 pounds, Wade thought he would really look sharp in those dress blues. He is the second guy named Wade to tell me that in my life. The first was a Korean War veteran named Jim Wade, who said he went in the Corp because he saw two Marines in their dress blues. Jim never got his. Wade Cobar did.

He told the recruiter he would have to talk it over with his girlfriend and would let him know. The recruiter told Wade it was going to be tough and he better get in the best shape ever and do a lot of running. Wade says the recruiter was very honest about boot camp. The girlfriend agreed and Wade, with some college credits and two languages, scored enough on the test to be guaranteed PFC if he made it through boot camp. Wade signed the papers. A few weeks later he was in sunny, beautiful San Diego, California. That lasted about two minutes.

Wade told me he never really ran other than in sports back in Guatemala... he sure hadn't run in Chicago. He reported the first few days in basic training were unreal... but he tried, and by the time he graduated, he had run a personal record of 21 minutes for a three-mile course. That's three seven-minute miles. Remember, he is 5'5" tall. His best time since in the three miles was 18:36. On a total fitness test he scored a 285 out of a perfect 300. He is still amazed at what the Corp will teach if you are willing to learn and do the work.

Why am I writing about some guy who worked hard to do well in boot camp? Because he would later be asked to give his life for America and he was willing to do it. Keep reading.

Wade loves his uniform and loves the discipline, and the Marine Corp loves him. He continually rates 4.8 out of 5 on his proficiency marks. He learns and memorizes the history and handbook of the Corp. He is what is referred to as a "squared-away Marine." He received Marine of the Month and Marine of the Quarter several times. He is assigned to a transportation unit. He marries his sweetheart from Chicago. Life is good.

In three-and-a-half years, he is promoted to Sergeant. Wade is transferred to Jacksonville, N.C. and makes Platoon Sergeant out of six candidates. He's moving on up! In 1999 he receives orders to the M.E.U. (Mobile Expedition Unit) and is sent for a three-year tour of Okinawa.

In 2003, he finds himself back in Jacksonville, N.C. and unfortunately, separated from his wife. Sometimes the military takes its toll on families. Wade is now assigned to the Tank Battalion. He has also made Staff Sergeant. He gets a TAD (temporary assignment duty) to Columbia, South America. It's perfect for Wade; he speaks fluent Spanish.

In 2006, Wade is back in the states and gets assigned to a whole new Battalion... the LAR (Light Armored Reconnaissance) Battalion. Whew! We have come a long way to get to this point, but here we are. Wade is just back in country and has a new Battalion and guess what? They receive orders for Iraq! On August 17, 2006, Wade puts his boot on the ground in beautiful downtown Aliased. Welcome to Iraq!

The rest of the story gets a little fuzzy. Rather than name some towns that I can't spell and towns that Wade would rather not mention to me or you, we will soon begin calling towns A, B, and C, etc. Let's start with the lovely town of Rawah. This is a city known for housing a lot of Saddam's former military hierarchy. I guess it would be sorta like our Florida and retired U.S. military! You get the picture. Anyway, Wade tells me the first thing he notices is the locals are "pissed."

"Our camp is in the middle of nowhere… it's like living in moon powder… we are in the desert. When we go into town to resupply Marines (Wade supplied food, ammunition, everything), we noticed about 80 to 100 blown-up, burned-out car and truck shells at the edge of town. Not a good sign. Regardless, we rolled past it and moved into town.

"In the center of town," he continues, "Marines are in complete control of all traffic. Nothing moves in the town without Marine inspection. I assume this also created a little friction between us and the retired military. As we get to the center of town, we learn that Marines are being shot at every day and Humvees are being blown up every day. That accounts for the burned out blown-up car shells at the front of the city."

This doesn't slow Wade down. The Marines have to have food and supplies, and there are several other towns on the daily route to reach and Wade and his convoy stop, drop off supplies, and go ahead to the next stop. This happens day in and day out. They try to get back by dark because the trouble doesn't stop when the sun goes down; it just gets harder to see.

So here's the drill: Wade gets up at dawn, loads the trucks, drives to town A, and drops off supplies. He then goes to town B and drops off supplies. Then to town C, drops off supplies, and then to D. Then he backtracks to C, then B, then A, then home to his sand castle in the desert. But soon, things are going to change.

One day, Wade's company is doing a sweep of the nearby river. There is Intel (information) that there might be contraband coming into town by way of the boats and this has to be checked out. So somewhere between towns C and D, Wade and his trucks pull off the main road to travel an unknown route in order to supply a "Quick Reaction Force" that is looking for contraband on the river. This new route takes them through ravines and areas with small hills on both sides. Out of nowhere a white pick-up truck appears and comes along side of them and then shoots past them and is ahead of them.

All of the sudden… BOOM! Gone in a flash… nothing left but the bed of the white truck. Had the truck not passed Wade's group, it would have been one of his five trucks, but the two guys in the truck were in a hurry and it reminds me of the slogan "speed kills" because as they passed the Marines, their weight set off the IED (Improvised Explosive Device). Remember, bullets and bombs don't have eyes, they hit whatever is in their path. This time it was two Iraqis.

After stopping to look for survivors and there was nothing left, Wade's group continued to resupply the troops and completed their mission. They turn around and head home on the same unfamiliar route. There is a radio message that reports to stay off the road, stay to the side, suspicious activity ahead. As they are moving forward, Wade sees another white vehicle (very much like the first one) in the distance watching them. It takes off as they proceed by the road.

Picture five trucks weaving a path, on the side of the road. Each trying as best they can to drive in the tracks of the truck in front of them. If the truck in front of you made it, you should be safe. Stay in the tracks as best you can. Wade is in the last truck because he was in the first truck on the way in. Out of nowhere, truck four gets hit. Boom! Everybody goes into action. They are trained for this. The wounded are taken out and the "less" wounded are put into vehicle five (which, of course, is vehicle four now). So we have six people in a four-person unit. On with the story. The last thing Wade remembers is a transmission to the lead unit saying, "We are trying to keep the same track but…" end of transmission. BOOM, Boom, Boom…

Unit five (now four) is completely destroyed. I don't remember Wade telling me if it was the motor or the front end, but a part of Wade's truck was completely destroyed. I mean it was GONE… never to be seen again. It was a big explosion.

When other Marines came to Wade's vehicle, all six inside were unconscious but alive. Remember, two of them were already wounded from truck four.

No one was dead, yet.

At that moment, Wade was in the most trouble. He had given his seat up to one of the two Marines who came from the first blown-up vehicle and he had been sitting on a little rail edge in the vehicle. No protection.

He had a few obvious wounds: His face was smashed. He had deep gashes in his mouth and forehead. His nose was broken. A few teeth were cracked; his lip was split so bad that his tongue was sticking through it. They thought his tongue had been torn out of his mouth and was resting on his chin. His right wrist was broken and his liver was crushed. In his right leg, the fibula and tibia were shattered and poking through the skin; his left tibia was broken and his ankle was broken. His left knee cap must have said, "I'm getting the hell out of here" because it was completely gone. Vaporized! It wasn't in the truck, it wasn't outside, it wasn't in anybody's clothes, it just wasn't! Wade still wonders what happened to it. Oh yeah, I almost forgot, some of his toes were shattered.

As Wade was telling me this, he got a devilish little grin and said, "Other than that, I felt great, never better." Funny guy that Wade.

He later learned that he had told the Marine working on him that he couldn't breathe and was in some degree of pain. At that moment, they tried to intubate him. He reports the worst part of it was not being able to inhale. He wanted them to cut his throat so he could get a breath of air. Before they could, he threw up vomit and a gush of hot blood. Unfortunately, it went in the face of the man working on him. Wade later apologized.

After a few doses of world-class morphine, Wade woke up while being carried on a litter. He tried to get up, but nothing moved. A couple of guys carrying him yelled, "Don't move."

"Where am I going?" asked Wade.

"To Germany," came the answer.

After a couple of days in Germany, he finally sees his legs. They are wrapped, pins sticking out everywhere. There are rods coming out his hips, stitches everywhere, and for the life of him, he can't remember any loved one's name or phone number. He can see their faces but doesn't know how to call them. More anguish! When he got hit, he weighed 150 pounds, now he hardly weighs 130 pounds. His throat stays sore and he can barely swallow. Too many tubes down his throat all the time. There is about one operation every other day. Pain is his constant companion. His legs get vacuumed out constantly (I understand this is quite painful and it happened all day every other day). It has to be done. The good news is he has a new knee to replace the one that left town. Wade got it from a cadaver. He has bone replacement in his face and more stitches than a North Carolina Quilting Bee.

196

At this point of the story, Wade has made it back to America... he wanted me to especially thank Dr. Kumar from the Navy at Bethesda Naval Hospital and Dr. Andersen from Reed Army Hospital. He has the greatest respect for both these men and what they do and what they did for him and everybody at the hospitals. By now, Wade has been promoted to E-7, a "Gunney" Sergeant. They are like Gods in the NCO ranks. He deserved it.

Probably this is the place Wade Cobar fits into this book. I asked him some point-blank questions and got point-blank answers. If you are addicted to anything that is taking your life, read a different point of view.

Me: Did you ever think of or want to die?

Wade: Never. It never crossed my mind.

Me: What kept you going?

Wade: I can't explain it, but I came real close to losing my legs. I kept saying I wanted to feel sand on the beach under my feet again, both my feet.

Me: Was there anything else?

Wade: Love of life. I had worked so hard to get where I was, I had given so much to get here I didn't want to throw it away. A big part of my desire to survive is what is called the "Espirit de Corp." I was not through being a Marine. I have a new wife, Adriane Cobar, and I wanted to see her again. She was in my heart every minute but in the beginning, I just couldn't remember her phone number. I knew right then I was finished with the painkillers. I was going to feel the pain rather than forget her phone number."

Me: I remember in my life drinking too much liquor so I could forget a woman who was breaking my heart, and Wade Cobar is refusing morphine with two broken legs so he can remember his sweetheart's phone number... I must have been running around with the wrong woman!

Are you clenching your teeth tonight and drowning your sorrows in booze or drugs because your cheating sweetheart is gone? Are you rolling to the refrigerator to get another dose of ice cream because you weigh 300 pounds and nobody loves you? Will you get evicted by the sheriff because you can't pay the rent but you bought a hundred dollars' worth of lottery tickets? Let's compare that with Wade turning down "free" painkillers so his mind would stay clear. I don't know how to go back and undo the stupid, foolish, silly-ass choices I made because I was addicted to crap! Why didn't I have the character of Wade Cobar, who refused pain medication in order to keep a clear head, or Dianne Weeks, who has cried a river of tears from the pain but never ever misses a workout, or Roy Broussard, who said, "They could kill me any time they wanted, but I wasn't going to kill myself."

They were addicted to *living* and were all willing to take the pain of real life-or-death situations! Maybe that's the big difference I am talking about. Me, and millions like me, were killing ourselves one drop or one puff or one kiss or one bet or one whatever at a time, and other people are trying to stay alive, one breath or one heartbeat or one ounce of control at a time. Thank God 15 years ago at age 47, I saw the light… I hope you do before you turn 47; don't wait that long.

I asked Wade what the worst experience has been since this happened.

He reports there were two of them. First, he was in a place that was not handicap friendly. He had two broken legs and was in a wheelchair and could not get a cab to stop and pick him up. Cab after cab after cab went by and just kept going. It didn't take him long to realize that none of them were going to stop. It was just too much trouble getting the person out of the chair, into the cab, putting the chair in the trunk, getting it out again, helping the person out of the cab back into the chair… just too much trouble. Not every cab driver is this way, but where Wade was, they are.

Second, Wade tells me he really had to go to the bathroom, really bad. His bladder was full and there had been a lot of damage to his hips and legs and the entire area. He really had to pee. So he pushes himself along the street until he finds a place to go in and use the restroom. When he gets to the restroom, he can't get the wheelchair in the door. It will not fit. He can't walk, he can't get in the restroom and he can't pee and the pain is slowly increasing. He had no choice but to hold it and go find another bathroom. He told me he would have died rather than pee on himself; he was still a United States Marine.

He did break down once in two years and cried his eyes out. He told me he reported to a hospital for some tests and was put in a room to wait for the doctors. As he lay there, he heard them saying he was going to be tested for Traumatic Brain Injury. Evidently, this hospital was full of veterans with extreme brain trauma. Some of the vets Wade had seen coming in were in much worse shape than he was. It was too much for him and he totally broke down. He says it was more for them, not him. The reality of how fortunate he was to have only lost a knee and teeth and jaw and ribs and internal organs didn't compare to what others had lost. Some of them will never remember any phone numbers or anything else the rest of their lives.

Today, Wade is at Bethesda Hospital in rehab. He trains to regain the use of his legs and has every intention of going on full active duty again. He trains and goes to physical therapy and does his best (remember how he felt about working at Taco Bell) in his recovery. This guy will give them everything they ask for everyday in rehab. He has certainly proven he is willing to take the pain. It will finally be up to the doctors what percent he can do the work. That recommendation will be forwarded to the VA. Then a decision will be made. Wade hopes more than anything to stay in the Marines. He has continued with his classes, earned his AA degree, and is working on a BS in accounting. If he can't stay in the Marines, he said he hopes to work somewhere in the government. He still wants to pay back the United States for the wonderful opportunities he has had.

After his daily therapy, Wade volunteers at the hospital. He sets up visits for the wounded veterans and he travels to military bases and schools and anywhere else he is invited, talking about the Marines and America and veterans. What a guy! I met him in Guantanamo, Cuba, at a Military Appreciation Day with the fine people from Nexcom. They manage the stores on Navy and Marine bases all over the world. A lot of support comes on these trips. The people from Vans are always there and Nike and Adidas and lots of sports figures and talent from all walks of life. I consider it an honor to come and represent EAS and Abbott. There is never a charge for this time or these trips. It's the very least we can do. I am still trying to get to Iraq. I'm going to figure out some way to do it. My friend Bill Marx organizes these trips and he deserves a ton of thanks and credit. He never forgets the troops are out there defending the rest of us!

To wrap it up, I asked for final thoughts. Wade knew what this book was about and wanted to tell anyone reading it, "If you are even thinking about killing yourself through addiction or any other way, think about how much life you are going to miss. Think about how you are hurting the people who love you when you hurt yourself. Just being in America and being an American is worth fighting to stay alive for."

Thank you, Wade, and thank you to all the troops and support groups covering the world. We are safe tonight because of them. Everybody doesn't like us Americans, and that's OK. You can like or dislike whomever you want... you just can't take a bomb and act on that dislike. These men and women in uniform do their best to keep us safe from the idiots that want to hurt us. I wish we didn't want to hurt ourselves.

An afterthought... I wrote this in about 2008, that's four years ago. Today is March 30, 2012. I lost track of Wade, no idea where he might be. His e-mail address changed and that was the only way I had to contact him. I do know he was talking about going to South America if the VA decided he honestly could not continue on active duty. He might be working out of the country, I just don't know.

Regardless of where he is, I want him to know that talking with him and spending a few days with him and the Wounded Warrior group in Guantanamo was one of the highlights of my career at EAS and Abbott. I have given it some serious thought and if I won the lottery, I would want to have a party and invite Jessica and Wade and Dianne and Steve Grossi and Miguel Rivera, Joey, Nick, and Ken and Lisa... all the people I dedicated this book to. I want to be surrounded by these good people who "GET IT." I really don't much care about who can sell the most albums or who can get married the most times in L.A. I don't give a damn about who is wearing the latest fashion... I have my favorite artists and respect great athletic accomplishments, but even some of them don't get it.

Wade Cobar got it. This country is so very fortunate to have Champions like him.

Chapter 15
Religion

The Bible says it rains on the just and the unjust, everybody gets rained on equally. Since we are talking about addiction and since it comes in all shapes and forms and certainly can affect everybody, I am going out on a limb and include religion.

Can you be a fan of religion? Yes. Can you be passionate about religion? Of course. Can you be obsessive about religion? Certainly. So doesn't it stand to reason that you can become addicted to some sort of scheduled religion (or the dealers who sell it)? I don't care if we are talking about Judaism or Voodoo. It can be Catholic, Baptist or Greek Orthodox.

Remember one of our basic rules: "It ain't a problem until it becomes a problem." I think we should find a God that we believe in and then a religion we believe in and then practice it. If you want to be a Hindu or a Buddhist or a Zionist or whatever, have at it. Something has to keep the lights on where you worship and something has to pay for the building. That is done by you and the other members giving part of your hard-earned money to the church of your choice. So far, so good.

That said, here is where it starts getting a little hazy. Some real smart folks have pointed out to me that since the beginning of time, millions of people have been killed in the name of some religion or some God. OK, that's taking your religion a little too far for me. If I believe in God and Jesus (and I do) and you believe in Mohammad and Buddha, is that grounds for us to go buy two AR-15's and 500 rounds and train in combat tactics and try to kill each other in the name of our God? Is there a religion that endorses sneaking into a sleeping household and killing mom and dad and their two or three children because they don't believe in the same God you do? If so, you damn sure better find a different religion with a different ticket for eternity.

Hating anyone because they have a different, but equal, religious belief than you has got to be in the top 10 or maybe top five most stupid things in this world. Maybe in the top two.

Can you imagine dying, getting to eternity, and standing in front of whatever God you believe in and him (or her) saying, "Congratulations, you killed 346 innocent people who didn't believe exactly like you did and you are really going to be rewarded. Outstanding job." It ain't gonna happen... excuse me, I don't think it is going to happen. If it does, then just let me rot in the cold, cold ground. I want no part of a reward like that.

Lighten up on trying to convert everybody you meet. I absolutely know people who start trying to impress others with quoting chapter and verse out of the Bible every time they meet someone. Whoa... not everybody is lost. Not everybody wants to be saved. Not everybody will buy this book. Not every person you ask for a date says yes and everybody doesn't WANT TO HEAR ABOUT THE LORD! I swear, some people memorize chapter after chapter to look brilliant and they couldn't change a flat tire. They might smoke or drink or masturbate when their partner is asleep, but they can quote scripture word for word. I love going to church and I love hearing the "Word," but there is a time and place for it all.

I am a Christian and a lifelong Southern Baptist. I chose the Baptist faith as my avenue to eternity. Right this minute, as I am writing this, I am on an airplane and anything can happen. There is no safety net. I was lost for a long time and for the past 10 to 12 years I have tried to live a better life. I am sorry for all my sins (at least most of them) and try not to commit them again. Please pray for me and maybe with our combined effort, my Lord will allow me into what I think is Heaven. Now, that's it. End of my beliefs. What I don't want to happen is for the pilot and co-pilot to get up in the middle of this flight and come back here to row 14 and start a prayer meeting with me and the other folks in this aisle. Once again, time and place for everything. As a matter of fact, in two weeks I am going to fly from Atlanta to Singapore... that's a long way. I hope the Lord gets me and everyone in that plane there safe. It's a long flight. I am going to see one of the true Champions of that Body-for-LIFE Challenge I talk about. His name is Capt. Russ Pendergrass, USN. I hope that plane doesn't give out or blow a gasket somewhere over the Pacific Ocean. If it does, I will do all the praying, please tell the pilots to stay in the cockpit and get us there safely! See what I mean?

If you are approached by a friend and asked about religion, I urge you to talk about it. If you bring the subject up two or three times and your friends start avoiding you, let it go. Sooner or later they will understand where you stand and will come around only if they want to.

Now, a couple of thoughts on the religion addiction and we will move on. I was in Guam a year or so ago and one of the leading stories in the local paper was about a group of "Missionaries" from a popular religious organization who were FORCING, important word there, forcing a tribe with female islanders to wear tops to their bathing suits. I couldn't believe it! Who in the hell were these people to come 10,000 miles and find this small island off of Guam and try to pass a law for ladies to HAVE to wear a top? What &%$# business was it of theirs? Look, it is about 105 degrees in Guam on a cool day, and it is the second hottest place I have been in my life. The humidity is about 250 percent!

Well, this bunch of do-gooders in the name of some God saw it as their responsibility to try and force the topless issue. There was no reference to rape or sexual assault or teen pregnancy, only that at the beach, girls and boys could be topless. I guess these missionaries got the word straight from God that this sinning had to stop. Dare I say it... the whole issue only addressed the showing of ... here we go... nipples! Forgive me, Father, for I have sinned... I said the N word! Nipples!

I guess this means that all nudists are sinners and are all going to hell... give me a break!

Wouldn't it have been better to take all that energy and effort and hiring of lawyers and deal with education and health and housing and dental issues and anything other than the dress code at the beach? I think the do-gooders are suffering from something far worse than religious addiction... I just don't know the name of it. Maybe it's called meddling in other people's business that doesn't concern you.

Don't send me any letters. I know missionaries who have given their lives trying to save people from death and destruction. Someone in my immediate family does missionary work all over the world and does it willingly and with love for God and with an open checkbook, and asks NOTHING in return. My grandfather was a missionary and Baptist preacher and spent 64 years very calmly teaching people (who wanted to learn) about God and heaven and a better life. So, don't think I believe everybody in the mission fields is misguided, I don't. The religious folks on that island in the Pacific are way off base and have no business, none, trying to FORCE people who have been living there for thousands of years to dress differently! It's crap in the name of religion!

Now, we are going to get down to the real nitty-gritty. On the other side of my family, my precious grandmother, who was in the church until she was too old to attend, bought a television and watched the Christian channel all the time. Great! It was her television and she could have watched the Christian network or boxing, her choice, and she paid the bill. But, my poor old grandmother got taken in by what I think might be the worst addiction; she bought into one of the TV evangelists. Oh my God! She sent him money from her pension and from her Social Security and she cried with him and like in the movie "Rain Man" with Judge Wapner, she had to be in front of the TV when this preacher was coming on. I sat in the other room and gritted my teeth.

Guess what? We later find out that this blubbering, slobbering, balling liar wasn't exactly the man of "God" that he claimed to be. Of course my 90-year-old grandmother bought his "the Devil worked his way into my life and he was so powerful that I couldn't fight him" story. I think the truth is the girl dressed up like the devil and this guy wanted a spanking! I wish an IRS agent had been there instead of the press!

I realize now that she was as addicted to him as I was to partying and booze. Same addiction, different shape. He begged and pleaded for money and she sent all of her spare dollars and she couldn't say no. In my case, the booze begged and pleaded and the girls delivered it and I couldn't say no... same difference. Same church, different pew!

So help me God, my God, this is the truth: There is a professional religious money beggar on TV who flashes an asterisk on the screen that is a disclaimer that reads the following...

"Miracles are from God and results may vary. We cannot be held responsible etc." What the hell are they selling, a *&^ ^%$# diet plan? Then this guy goes on to stare at the camera and tries to sell you a religious lottery ticket. "If you are one of the 300 seed planters who will forward a thousand dollars, God will pay you back over and over and over." This guy must be God's accountant. He goes on to say, "I was in some town (it changes all the time), and somebody who always wants to remain anonymous, came up to me and said, I sowed the thousand dollar seed and today I am a millionaire and want to give you thousands of dollars and for no reason, sticks wads of cash in his suit and no names etc."

Again, I wonder if the IRS was told about this. And, of course, there is another man who gives constantly and reports to this evangelist that all is well, he has made so much money he can't make any more. Yeah, right! Hell no, it's not all right; it is the biggest scam going, because if you disagree with it, you are disagreeing with GOD! If you can please bear with me for just a minute, I am now going to speak in tongues...

Ask yourself this, if the money stops coming in from this seed-sowing scam, what do you think God would tell these people to do? Maybe to put down their worldly possessions and take up the cross and go preach to the world? Funny, I read that somewhere. Back to my grandfather (on my mother's side of the family) for a minute... I knew him for 16 years. He never asks for a dime in the pulpit or tried to sell any anointing oil or tapes or anything else. He devoted 64 years to the church and the Lord. Why didn't God come to him and whisper the 30 wisdom secrets in his ear? Was he not a good enough man to be let in on the secret? Was my grandfather a fake and God, in his wisdom, was waiting on someone smart enough and handsome enough and sharp enough to divulge the secrets to? My grandfather prayed for everyone. He didn't ask people to send money in envelopes and then according to the amount of money in the envelope, it was placed on top of the prayer pile or on the bottom.

Another funny thing, some preachers live in clean, modest, small houses and drive plain economic cars. Others live in gated communities and have Rolls-Royces and airplanes and servants and have their entire family on the payroll. Imagine that. Wonder why they need so much security and off-duty law enforcement around them all the time? Maybe it's to protect them from the Devil. Did God sit down and speak to the entire family? These are the luckiest people in the world. I have looked and can't find the eternity-money connection. How am I missing it?

If you want to give money to the church, do it. Want to give it to a reliable charity, do it. Want to give some money to your community, do it. Go build a bus stop cover so people waiting to go to work don't have to stand in the rain. Buy some wheelchairs; give to the schools for the deaf and/or blind, support a seeing-eye dog or help pay for one of the companion dogs. That way you can see your money at work and it will improve someone's life, not the tax-free pocketbook of a scam preacher who has a choir behind him ooohing and ahhhing. Write me and I will give you a list of the God-fearing, honest places I have found that use 10 percent for administration and 90 percent for cure. Not for jet planes at $7,000 an hour to operate. They will tell you they need the jets to travel around the world and get the "Word" out... what are they doing, writing scripture on the wing for a fly-over?

I watched one guy on TV ask for money 38 times (directly and indirectly) in less than 45 minutes. Funny thing is, I never did hear the message except that you could buy your way into heaven. Oh no you can't. Evidently the Lord picked these few men and women out of millions of us to share "HIS" secrets of success. Why didn't he pick me or you or my granddad? If you send them one dollar, and I have, they will send you a hundred letters asking for more. It's worse than a magazine subscription. They have been anointed, we haven't. They have the keys of wisdom. We don't. They grin in the camera and tell you everything is going to come up daisies and, of course, their entire family is on the payroll; they aren't out of work. Why don't they all go to Detroit and fix the auto industry? Why don't they go to Iraq and share the wisdom with the people trying to kill us? I've got to get off this subject, I'm getting mad.

I looked all over the Bible and tried to find the chapter and verse where the disciples got together and decided to buy Jesus the biggest, fastest Ass in all of Jerusalem to ride around on. Funny thing, I can't find it. Maybe they got together and bought him some alligator sandals? Nope, couldn't find that either.

Imagine a dollar going to the TV evangelist. Wouldn't it be fine to know exactly how that dollar gets divided? Maybe it would go something like this: 47 cents to administration, 33 cents to advertising, 10 cents to the television station, 5 cents to the mission fields and 5 cents to the preacher. Then wouldn't it be interesting to see what exactly administration is? The upkeep of the preacher's house; the salary of the staff, most of which are relatives; the maintenance on the church (owned by a corporation owned by the preacher) might be the answer. Advertising... OK, I'll stop now. You get the picture. Saying the church gave it to you when you can hire and fire everybody in the church is like letting the fox collect the eggs and trusting his total! Maybe it's like letting the rabbit count the lettuce, it's gonna come up short!

Do whatever you want, it's your money. Love whomever you want, give to the church or religion of your choice. Follow whatever "leader" suits you. Remember this, I read somewhere that sin loves darkness. See if you can get an honest statement from any of these money-begging people on TV. Like the lottery, they are doing all they can to separate you from your cash. And like the lottery, there are only one or two BIG winners. Call them and sing a tale of woe and see if they send you any money. Let me know the answer.

Once again, let me repeat: not all of them are crooks. Not all religious people try to force it on you. Not everybody in the pulpit is a money-hungry, two-faced hypocrite. I certainly have my favorite preachers and you know my favorite faith. That said, if you are having a problem with sex or drugs or alcohol or tobacco or a partner or a child or any type of addiction that is killing you and you think sending a lot of money to a scam TV shyster is the answer, you are only getting in deeper, not out quicker.

Funny thing about some of these money preachers, they say you need to be one of the 300. OK, when they get to 300, have you ever heard them say, "OK, we got to 300, don't anybody else send another thousand dollars. We only needed 300, not 310. It ain't ever going to happen. Somehow or the other, God knows exactly when to cut off the number sending a thousand dollars and he waits until next week and tells one of these crooks, OK, the books are balanced, send me 287 more at 5,000 dollars. When you see it on paper it looks a whole lot more silly than when the choir is moaning in the background and eyes are piercing the camera and the anointed ONE is telling you that the Devil is making you hold on to the money. You want to send it, but the Devil is winning as long as you hold out. YOU let the Devil win… aren't you ashamed? Do you want God to lose the fight because of you? Horse$%#@!

Another funny thing about this: If the preacher would sell his million-dollar home and plane and limos and close any off-shore accounts… maybe the Lord wouldn't need our money so bad.

I give up… stay addicted to these people if you want to. You're grown; you know what you're doing.

I was going to write about another group of "religious zealots" who hate Christians and want to kill all of us but, I think I will wait and put that under the chapter on Hate. This bunch isn't asking for money, they want guns. And one more thing, the religious folks leading this bunch are always willing to send some underling to blow him or herself up, funny how "they" never get there on time to strap on a bomb when it's time to blow something up . Maybe we should take up a collection and send these leaders a box of watches... hmm!

Religion is based on two things: love and fear. A God of some kind loved you so much that he either died for you or gave his son for you and you find peace in loving him back and trying to follow his preaching. The other is fear. If you don't do what your God wants you to do, you burn "FOREVER" or come back as a goat or some such other animal... maybe a pig.

Love your God or fear your God... or both. But do not for one minute think that anyone is getting a text message from God or Buddha or Mohammad or Father Moon or King Tut or anybody else telling them God needs 627,589 dollars. If I am wrong, I will pay on Judgment Day. If you are wrong, you will pay every week.

Since I started this chapter, a couple of things have happened. A guy named Trey Smith wrote a book "Thieves." I ordered it but haven't read it as of this date. From all I can gather, he has done a better job at reporting this than I can. He seems to have first- hand knowledge. And the guy he writes about is one of the top four or five of the blessed ones that God has financial chats with on a regular basis.

Please, please, please do whatever you want with this book... tell everyone you know that I am a complete blithering idiot, sue me, gather all the local farmers and villagers and get pitchforks and torches and sign a petition to have me committed to the loony-tunes hospital. I would probably sign the petition and go willingly but DO NOT, I repeat DO NOT send your hard-earned money to a P.O. box.

Here is a small test to try. If you believe in God and think the Bible is the word of the Lord and eternity in heaven is the reward for being good and tithing, just pretend this for me. You are standing in front of the Lord on Judgment Day and he asks you this all-or-nothing question:

208

LORD: Do you (fill in your name) know where the money you mailed in to the televangelist went?

YOU: Yes, Lord, I know exactly where every penny went and I know beyond all doubt how the money was divided, and I sent more because I agreed with every single dime of the way they handled the payout. I wanted to send more because all of it went to do your work. I knew and they told me over and over that the more I sent, the greater my reward was here in heaven and if you hadn't called me home so soon, I was due any day to start receiving my anointing and the cash was going to start pouring in.

Or...

YOU: No, Lord... honestly, I don't have a clue how the money was handled.

Friend, if you answered no, don't send another penny to someplace you have any doubt about. Your heart (like my grandmother's) is probably pure, and you think the money is going to the right place, but are you sure?

Why not keep the money in your community to do some good for people you can see and watch improve their life? I mean, getting the word of the Lord out there is important, but sending someone in a private Gulfstream to get there and ask for more money is not what my Lord had in mind. If you're happy with the way things are going and you're sure where the money goes, keep sending it, they will keep taking it.

Post note: I got the book "Thieves"... what a read. I urge everybody to read it and decide for themselves what's what. Again, suit yourself.

I want you to try this, look up on the Internet "money-begging TV preachers"... there are about 10 of them. They all have the same message, and a couple of them have added some showmanship for extra donations. One guy whips the crowd into frenzy and yanks his coat off and waves it around and people fall out left and right... not from touching the hem of his garment, but from the wind created by the circling of his jacket. I mean, these people have come up on stage and are dropping like flies. It's either one of two things: He really needs a stronger deodorant or it's H*&^%S&^%! I'm going with the second.

Here is an idea and I am serious about this: I put myself forth as a candidate to be this "preacher's" manager... I want 10 percent of the purse and we will start tomorrow. I want him to become a UFC middleweight MMA fighter... hold on, I have a better idea. I want him to fight in the Super-Heavyweights category. This "preacher" looks like he might go 155 or 160, hard to tell with his designer suits on. Anyway, we can make a fortune and give all the money to help spread the word of the Lord. At 160 pounds, he can climb in the ring with some 225-pound, degree black-belt Brazilian ju-jitsu boxing champion who has had 30 or 40 pro-fights. After they touch gloves (of course, the preacher doesn't wear gloves, he doesn't need them), each combatant goes back to his side and gets ready.

The tension mounts and as the ref asks, "Are you ready? Are you ready? Fight..." the preacher waves his jacket at the champion, knocking him into row 7, seat 12B.

The crowd goes wild! Why not? It happened about 50 times on stage, why wouldn't it work in a caged circle? Does God only work on stages? I read somewhere he actually worked in a lion's den. Maybe the preacher could change his name to the Battling Daniel; we will work on that name as soon as he signs a contract with me.

Want to sue me, feel free. As of yesterday I have $384 in my checking account. This book is going to cost me far more than I will ever make selling it, but I promise you this: I will not give one penny to a slick-hair, smooth-talking, guilt-charging "Man of God" who is living the high life on other people's dollar.

As a final note, did you happen to catch that video clip of those preachers who talked everybody in the congregation (I'm sure there were no hooks planted in the audience) into coming up to the steps of the pulpit, don't come on stage, just come to the steps and throw money on the floor? Did you catch that one? Watch it and watch those preachers dance and stomp on that cash. They actually kick the money and wipe their feet on it. So let me see if I got this straight, you work all week and go to church on Sunday and you give an offering to God and the preacher jumps on it and dances on your money (I'm sorry, it's now God's money) and tells you he is going to buy a new car with it and his children are all getting new cars with your money... I'm sorry, tell me again where God comes into the picture, I missed it.

Attention... News Alert: God just spoke to me as I was writing this chapter and gave me two important numbers... he didn't say anything about the IRS or cars or diamonds, all he said was: For the 82,000 chosen seed sewers to send him $649.35 in cash (no checks please) and they will receive a special blessing. He really doesn't want everybody to know where this blessed money is going, so it would be best if you sent it straight to me... as he gave me "Special Instruction" as what to do with this money. Hurry, this is a limited-time offer as I am not sure when God will contact me again. Maybe when I give out of all the money... you think?

I had to get up from this computer and take a break. I put the television on the religion channel for a couple of days and watched for about two hour's total. Ready? Let me give you some of the off-the-wall comments I heard these preachers lay on the faithful watchers. I don't know where they get the gall... oh yeah, I forgot, God tells them to.

"When God gives you the nod, you will receive a miracle within 24 hours."

WHAT? Do you mean to tell me that God, creator of heaven and earth, has to give you a nod?! Why do I think HE could just make it happen? I appreciate so much these preachers explaining how God works... HE nods at the chosen and it happens in 24 hours... probably takes 24 hours because HE is so busy whispering the secrets in the ears of the Anointed Ones. Here's another...

"If 12 obedient watchers will send a thousand dollar seed within the next 30 calls, a Fed-Ex or UPS-size miracle will happen to them within a week."

OK, that explains sooo much. The reason you haven't received your blessing and miracle from God is because God gave you the nod and the drivers at Fed-Ex and UPS don't have your correct address. It's all Fed-Ex's and UPS's fault... give me a break! By the way, what is a Fed-Ex and UPS-size miracle? Don't they both deliver packages as big as an airplane or as small as a diamond? Wonder what size a thousand dollar miracle is?

"Open your hand and HE will open his heaven." I refuse to comment on that one. One more time... YOU CAN NOT BUY A TICKET TO HEAVEN.

"Now this doesn't buy you a miracle… there will be a turnaround and there will be favor, I decree it, there will be favor!"

Hold on, didn't I just hear that you will receive a Fed-Ex or UPS-size miracle? Now all you are getting is a "turnaround and favor"… which one is it? Maybe he meant a "reach around and favor"….I personally hope it's a lady preacher.

One more time, it's not ALL preachers and it's not ALL TV preachers, but you better know which ones are which before you send a dime. And it's not just men…there are and have been a couple of ladies on there that could teach Dolly Parton a thing or two about wigs and make up.

I rant and rave a little more about this at the end of the book but you get the gist of the message here. Don't get hooked on anything or anybody that bases your devotion to them or God, in dollars…… nobody.

No Judge is always right; cases get overturned day after day.

Every Doctor isn't always right, second opinions and malpractice day after day.

No Policeman, no General, no politician, no teacher, no parent is always 100% correct. You will hear this again, no one on this earth is absolutely 100% correct 100% of the time. Albert Einstein made a mistake or two…..but the Television preacher is always right and if you disagree… you are arguing with God's word and you will burn in hell for ever……unless of course you send a special offering requesting forgiveness.

Please don't get hooked. Please keep your money in your community. Local people have needs just like the ones in TV land….see where your money goes…or don't. Remember, God loves you unconditionally….not because of your 401. The shuck and jive preachers should write a book called: The financial secrets to Heaven that God doesn't want you to know……

Chapter 16
The Bird

Have you noticed a lot of chapters named after animals in this book? I think there are four. I certainly didn't plan it that way, it just happened. There is a little story in here about a little bird. It has one hell of a big moral. Read on...

In 2008 I began moving from Colorado to Georgia. My Mom had passed away and left me a small, old wooden house in Augusta. My sister had stayed there off and on but for the most part it was vacant. It's not much of a house, one bathroom and two bedrooms and falling apart. It needs a lot of work, more than I can give it but, it's part mine and here I am. The house isn't worth half of the tax assessment, but so many children need lunch money, the city says it's worth $74,000. If that is a good yardstick to use, this Timex watch I am wearing is worth about $1,250.

It's the sentimental value that keeps me here and that value is priceless. We moved in here in 1961. There is a reason I tell you all this and it has everything to do with addiction. I'm also in Augusta because I want to spend a little time with my step-dad (81years old) and my real dad (86 years old). I love them both.

As with any old house, there are snaps and crackles and pops and creaks and noises of all kinds both day and night. Sorta sounds like I am describing myself. Me and the house are pretty close in age and we both make the same kinds of noises. There are some small woods behind and beside the house and once in a while, I get a stray raccoon or possum or feral cat causing all kinds of noise. Usually a yell or door slam will run them off, usually. What I am about to tell you is completely different.

One bright spring morning I woke up because something was banging like crazy in the backyard. I got up and yelled out the window, slammed the back door, and it got quiet for a few minutes. Then, pop, pop, crackle. Then pop, pop, pop, snap, pop, bang, crack. What the hell?

I got back up, yelled out the window, and slammed the door, didn't hear anything, and lay back down. I don't think my head hit the pillow and here we go again. Pop, pop, crack, snap, pop, on and on and on. That's it, I'm up. On go the shorts and flip-flops, I grab a rake by the backdoor, and in about 2 seconds I am standing in the yard ready to do battle with whatever varmint insists on waking me up. Nothing. No raccoon, no cat, no dog, no nothing, not even a mouse! I'm beginning to think my mother is trying to contact me from beyond.

As I am standing in the yard, the noise starts again. This time it is coming from a car I have parked under the awning beside the house. I approached; rake in hand, at the ready to investigate. Sure enough, the noise was coming from somewhere in or at the car. Either a cat had got stuck under there or Stephen King's Christine was coming to life in my Nissan. Had to be one or the other. Either way, me and the rake were ready.

The closer I got to my car, the stranger the situation became. Here it is: A small brown bird was attacking the side mirror on my parked car. The bird could hardly hang on with its little feet but when it did get its footing, it was hell bent for leather to attack the bird in the side mirror. It pecked and head-butted and flew into and scratched and beat its wings at the other bird. I watched it hit the mirror so hard it knocked itself to the ground. After several of these attacks, it would stay on the ground (kinda like a boxer in the corner) and then fly back up and start a full-frontal attack on the other bird again.

Each and every time the bird pecked, the mirror bird pecked. Each time the bird flew into the mirror, the mirror bird flew into the brown bird. After a few flurries, the brown bird would full-body crash into the mirror bird and knock itself to the ground. It was the most even fight I have ever seen.

The brown bird was probably 6 inches long and 3 inches high. It might have weighed 5 ounces, I don't know. I think it was a mocking bird, again not sure. I am 6-feet tall and at the time weighed about 210 pounds. I think in an even fight I could have taken the bird plus I had the rake. That said, I did not scare, dissuade, influence, or impress that little bird. He was on a mission. Nothing I could do or did do was stopping him from attacking the mirror bird. Every fiber in his body was focused on the other bird. Every smidgen of effort was being spent on defending his territory from mirror bird. I could have had a washboard and kazoo and drum and been playing Alexander's Ragtime Band, the bird would have ignored me.

I must have watched him for a full two to three minutes and I know he saw me. I could have reached down and picked him up the last couple of times he fell, he was that exhausted. He didn't give a damn! He was in the fight of his life and his little bird brain was zeroed in on the mirror bird. How sad it was.

Finally I figured out a way to put an end to this. I didn't have the keys to the car on me but there were some towels and gym clothes on the back porch. I got two towels and with the bird sitting on the ground next to the car, I covered both mirrors. That's all it took. Brown bird did come back for round 37 but the mirror bird was gone, Brown bird had won. The fight was over.

I know there are bird baths because my sister and grandmother had one in their yards. Kinda like a bird swimming pool. I know there are birdhouses, kinda like a bird apartment. What I am not sure of is if there are bird bars where at dusk all the birds of a feather flock together and tell each other stories of cat chases from long ago. Maybe they talk of being conked in the head by a plane prop. They might swap stories of small snakes that almost robbed their nest back in '05. I bet once in a while someone brings up that new rockin' Robin that moved in the old elm tree down off Main Street. Wahoo, she has the prettiest red breast!

At some point the little brown bird hops in and it gets quiet. He tells of the life-or-death fight he had a couple of summers ago. Every time he threw a beak, the other bird threw a beak. Every time he pecked, the other bird pecked. It was a hell of a fight. Every time he gained a foothold, his opponent gained a foothold, tit for tat, a wing flap was answered by a wing flap. Suddenly a monster arrived with a long stick and was watching. Little bird wasn't sure what happened but the monster did something and when he went back for round 37, the mirror bird was gone. The little brown bird will close out the story with a bite of worm and with a faraway look tell the other birds, "It was a hell of a fight and I won but I never want to fight that other bird again, never ever."

We all understand the little bird was fighting himself the entire time. He couldn't win, the mirror bird was far too much of an opponent for him, and he was outmatched. The car wasn't going anywhere. Thank God he got a little help from that monster with the stick. I believe the little bird would have fought itself to death. It couldn't stop. Nature was driving it to go back for more. It would have fought until it died.

Does that sound like addiction to you? It does to me. Are we, you and I or people we know, beating ourselves to death with addiction and refusing help? It doesn't matter who you are, the drive and desire for some stimulation or relief or sedative or put whatever name on it you want, will never be greater than the drive and desire of that little bird to fight the other bird. It could not reason the end result would be death. Quitting just wasn't an option. You're smarter than that bird.

I remember about 40 years ago there was a lot of construction in and around Miami. The site I am thinking of was next to the apartments I lived in. There were a lot of break-ins and stealing of supplies at night. The police came around several times asking if anyone saw anything. The owners put security guards in the place, but sometimes they didn't show up or were sleeping or whatever and the material kept disappearing. Finally the owners had enough and contracted with an "Attack Guard Dog Service"… unless you spoke "dog," you couldn't convince these guys to look the other way. I used to look over my balcony and watch the dogs roam the site and raise hell with anything or anybody that approached. End of problem? Not quite.

Maybe two weeks went by and the owner got rid of the guard dogs. He hired off-duty police to watch the site at night until it was completed enough to have a full-time manager live there.

You see, some smart-ass crook or crooks came by and saw the dogs. No problem, they simply got a couple of female dogs in heat and eased them through the fence. Maybe the police were kidding me, but I think not. I think it really happened. The two male guard dogs had their attention diverted. No amount of training or toys or food or treats or pats on the head or "good boy" could compete or compare with two hot bitches in full-blown heat! Those handlers could have been getting the hell beat out of them and I think the guard dogs would have been thinking, "Gosh, I hope they don't get hurt too badly. Did you see the eyes on that French poodle?"

Same thing as the bird, same thing with the dogs, same old, same old. We choose to make addiction more important than any job or person or responsibility or obligation. We make it our goal and our God. The addiction becomes the mirror (for cocaine users there is no pun intended). The addiction of those guard dogs to the bitches in heat is like addiction to sex and porn and STDs and many partners. The addiction becomes everything while you are in it. There are people and groups and medical personnel and churches that will help you. If you haven't lost your job yet, there are some companies that offer help. Take it. I don't think the desire ends, but it can be controlled.

I have never been to a meeting or any kind concerning addiction in my life. Joey believes completely in them. Remember he is 100 percent clean and sober for well over 30 years. It works for Joey. I didn't need the meetings, I had him and Eric.

I've never been to rehab but there is a bar where I live called "Rehab." If I go back in the bar business, I am going to name my bar "Falling Down Drunk"… business should be great!

Let's stay on the subject of rehab for a page or two. I want you to meet a girl who has been to rehab twice. Evidently, she wasn't "habed" quite enough the first time. Sometimes when I read about a movie star or celebrity going to a rehab place at about $25,000 a month, I'm not sure if that's the thing to do or not. Being old and cynical, I wonder if they really want to quit or what they are doing is for the attention and face time they will earn? If they come out and stay clean and sober then thank God, it worked. If they come out and get booked on the 6'oclock news so they can work in a plug for a new product they are selling, well then maybe they went to rehab just because they could. Whatever… more of this later.

That bird couldn't go to rehab. That bird needed a little free help to get over the mirror bird. I'm glad I was there to help him (or her). Without me, I feel sure the bird would have died. There is a problem with this story. I hate to report it but so far everything in this book is the truth. I would not have been there if there was ever another mirror bird. There was no way to follow that little mocking bird all over the state of Georgia hoping it wouldn't land on another car. If it did, I'm sure it came to a bad end. There is a moral here somewhere.

Everybody don't want fixin! This isn't biscuits we are talking about, it's people. There is a chapter in here about the wrong person in your life and like the bird, if it happens to be someone who will continue hurting themselves over and over, sometimes you have to finally admit you can't fix them. We become the mirror. We fight and peck and fall down and they get right back up for more.

When I review my addictions, it looks so much like that bird I wonder if the Lord moved me back to Georgia for that one-day experience. I have a friend named Shawn Phillips who wrote a couple of good books about health and fitness. In one conversation at EAS, he was talking about "Clarity"… being able to stand outside whatever you are involved in and get a "CLEAR" picture of what is happening and what you want to happen. It is so much more productive and so much less wasted effort when your goals and objective and boundaries are CLEAR!

Are we the bird or the mirror or both? It was and always will be impossible for that bird to step back and watch him kill himself. Here's the good news: we can. We can think and we can see and we can hear other people tell us to quit fighting the mirror. We can get that CLEAR picture of self-inflicted demise. If we don't want to see it, it's called denial.

Are we in denial? For so long I was, years I can't get back. But to quote one of my favorite philosophers; Edgar Allen Poe, "NEVERMORE"….do not be that bird. Do not try to control something that you cannot control. You will lose, if not in the beginning, soon. Real soon…..

Chapter 17

Alcohol

Now we're talking, now we're cooking, now we're getting our groove on! In the bar business, we always had an expression: People drink when times are good because times are good, and people drink when times are bad because times are bad... people just drink. One of the worst fights I saw in my bar career was during a wedding on a Sunday morning... and it was 100 percent due to alcohol. One of the worst sights I witnessed later in life was a man trying to get in the coffin with his dead wife and it was 100 percent because of alcohol. Wedding or funeral, alcohol ruined them both. End of subject.

Prohibition didn't work no more than making small amounts of marijuana illegal works. All that happens is this: Illegal sellers sell to illegal buyers, and otherwise legal people from 16 to 90 go to jail and keep the wheels turning. Let me go on record right this minute saying, I do not use drugs; I do not advocate the use of any type of "street drugs"... I am a police officer (hope to retire pretty soon), and I obey the law. I smoked a joint back in 1970 once or twice because the girl I was with wanted to smoke a joint and I wanted to smoke her... get it? Now I am going to get off the drug subject and deal with the alcohol subject.

Alcohol (which was once used as a bug spray, because it killed bugs hundreds of years ago) has cost more people more sorrow and more grief and more heartache than any other thing I know. Maybe even more than everything else combined. And I love it! I am in love with alcohol. I wish I had a drink right this minute. There used to be a commercial about Ritz crackers that went something like this, "Everything sits better on a Ritz"... my commercial would go something like this, "Everything is better and more fun and exaggerated when you got a good buzz on."

One of the all-time great songs by a lady I love to hear sing talks about sitting in a bar on Santa Monica Boulevard early in the morning having a beer. It is a cool song. One of the best songs written in this century has a line about "slip on down to the Oasis." There is an endless list of songs about alcohol. My all-

219

time favorite singer (I admit I have a couple favorites) Ray Charles sings: Let's go get stoned... everybody, let's go get stoned. I've got a few pennies, I'm gonna get a bottle of Gin." Another song, "Pop another top" and "One whiskey, one scotch, and one beer"... on and on and on.

One of the worst fights I had in my life was with one of my best friends, Duke Dearing. He was way tougher than I was, but I had only been drinking about four hours and he had been drinking since he got back from Vietnam. Regardless, we were and still are best friends, and I wrote about him in my first book, Finally Fit at Fifty. Anyway, Duke and I are sloshed. I was managing a beer joint in Orlando called Rosie O'Grady's and he was manager of Harrigan's in Winter Park, Florida. So this one night he shows up at Rosie's and I had a date and to hell with the date because he and I are going to get serious about drinking and we get to it.

He got there about 7 p.m. and when my bartender (I was the manager) cut us off about 10:30 p.m., we stagger out the door and headed to the parking lot. With the three brain cells I had left, I said, "Duke, you better let my date drive you home because you couldn't find your ass in a phone booth with both hands!" He replied, "F*&% you, Tom!" So I go, "Who's Tom?" And he replies, "F*&% you!" And I say, "Tom?" And he knocks the %$#@ out of me and I jump up looking for this Tom guy who just hit me! And guess what? There is no Tom... Duke clocked me. What? And then he popped me again, and then he and I had an up close and personal dance in the middle of the parking lot.

When the cops got there, my shirt was torn off, my date had long since cussed us both out and left, and I was trying to put Duke (who I think had passed out) in the trunk of my car. If anybody out there reading this can tell me why I was trying to put him in the trunk of my car, please call me. Thank you.

Duke is a former police officer and his brother is a DEA agent and the cops think Duke is still on duty and in an undercover operation and they don't know what in the hell to do. I refuse to press any charges and finally his brother shows up because the cops don't know whether to arrest me or him. By this time, we are both throwing up and they really don't want us in their patrol cars. I have never seen two bigger idiots! Not the cops, me and Duke... his brother takes him home, I get a doorman to drive me home, and I later found out that we both called in sick the next day.

Are you still with me? It wasn't dope, it wasn't porn, it wasn't bets, it wasn't cigarettes, it wasn't welfare, it wasn't the wrong person, and it wasn't any of the other addictions. We had not been standing at the bar for three hours smoking mushrooms out of cow patties. It wasn't ice cream, it wasn't a bold-faced lying preacher, it was LEGAL ALCOHOL that got Duke and I to the point he thought I was some guy named Tom and we beat the hell out of each other. It is LEGAL and it is ADDICTIVE and it can kill you and it can wreck homes and it can kill innocent people who drive the same streets the drunks are driving and it can leave families without a father and it can leave families without a mother and it can make people do and say things they would never do or say sober and the government allows you to buy as much as possible. There is a high tax on alcohol. Party on, Porter.

Where I live in Georgia, we don't sell alcohol (except in restaurants) on Sunday. It's called the Blue Laws. That is changing. A few towns around us have started selling it on Sunday, and you can bet it's coming. That's one full day of alcohol the public is missing and one full day of tax the "gubment" ain't getting. That S*&^ is going to stop. The gubment is gonna get theirs and the alcoholics are going to get theirs... and a good time was had by all. Now, on with some real-life stories. See if you find yourself or anybody you love in these stories. I KNOW I am in here, and I know after 15 years that the addiction hasn't gone away, it lingers under the bar waiting for me to sit down. It will slither around my foot and slowly ease up my leg and wrap it's self around my waist. It's warm and it feels good and like cocaine addicts call it the "white Lady," us drunks call it the "buzz"... just got a little "buzz" on. No big deal. And I take a drink and the drink takes a drink and the drink takes me... and I am right back where I left it 15 years ago. And again the good news is, now I can do it on Sunday. Thank the Lord!

This is a true story, as are all the stories in this pathetic book. I say that because all of them are sad in some way. Innocent people who were dealt bad cards or good people who threw it all away. Fate and addiction don't care; they are just looking for victims. Here we go...

He was a good man. I don't know if he still is a good man because I haven't seen him in 20 years and I think he is dead, but he was a good man. Let's call him X. He started out in the military. He was an average guy, did his job, and made it to Buck Sergeant... that's three stripes. As I remember, he worked on

221

planes and helicopters and was assigned to some aviation branch of the military. Anyway, he was around planes for four years. He gets an Honorable Discharge and used the military service to get his BS degree from a state university. I'm telling you this is every word the truth. Now he goes back in the service (this time a different branch) and goes to helicopter flight school and becomes a Warrant Officer and learns to fly helicopters. This guy has an unblemished record. He makes Chief Warrant in these four years. He is 30 years old when he is discharged the second time with a second Honorable Discharge. He is single, very fit, damn good looking, and is a licensed pilot.

I am running a few bars in Orlando and this guy comes in once in a while and he has girls dripping off him and he always pays his tab, tips, and he is the exact type of customer you want to see coming in the door. He is as cool as the other side of the pillow and he spends a few dollars and everybody wants to talk to him and be around him and I think Carly Simon sang a song about him: "You're So Vain." He's good looking, he's smooth. He's got money and he is a recently discharged military pilot. I wished I were him.

It doesn't take him long until he lands the ultimate job of the universe. I respect his privacy and won't go into much detail here but he gets a job flying a type of aircraft that seats eight for one of the most successful businesses in all of America (for sure they are in the Fortune 500). I will leave it at that. This guy is flying everybody but the President of the United States. He flies all the other presidents of all the biggest companies in America and a few foreign countries. This was when Orlando was BOOMING and people from all over the world were coming to Central Florida to set up a business or invest money or visit one of the attractions… he flew them all.

I don't know what it was about the bars we managed but this guy liked them. You could come in, kick back, have a few brews, feel safe, bulls$#*% with another regular guy, talk to some good-looking girl, nobody bothered you. They were just regular neighborhood bars. I give my staff all the credit. You felt at home. This guy really liked coming to visit us. He was never out of line. He was never a problem and we were always happy to see him. He would have one or two or maybe three beers and wait a while and get up and go home. No problem. I do remember he drove a new Corvette. By the way, he lived in a gorgeous townhouse near the beach. It was about an hour from the bar.

Let's review: He was good looking. He was physically fit and had a head full of natural wavy hair. He was tanned and he drove a new car. He had a "bachelor pad" close to the beach and he was a pilot. Does this sound like some television show? This guy had it all and he had EARNED it. He went into the military and then he went to college. He went back into the military and got his pilot's license and got out. He didn't get married, he didn't have a house full of children, he did it the right way, and he was making a six-figure income in the 1990's in Orlando, Florida. What a success story!

It wasn't in Orlando, it was somewhere in or around Jacksonville that he screwed up BIG TIME. He was headed back to Orlando and he was stopped at a DUI checkpoint. Guess what? He was under the influence of alcohol. You want to know why? Because he didn't think he would be stopped. He had flown a group to Atlanta and was driving back to Orlando and he stopped to get a bite to eat and had a "few" beers and made the life-changing mistake of getting back into the rental car and trying to drive on to Orlando.

Dear God, what was he thinking? You cannot drive if you have been drinking! As I recall, he reported having three or four beers sitting at the bar with dinner in a respectable restaurant in Jacksonville before he got stopped. He wasn't in a dive, he wasn't coming out of a house of ill-repute, he wasn't coming out of a drug house, but he was headed to I-95 and hit a roadblock.

There are strict rules about being a pilot and drinking. It was known the next morning that he was in jail and his license was suspended. The company he worked for was notified. Things were not looking good. I remember him coming in our bar and retelling the entire story. To be completely honest, I thought the authorities would cut him some slack and fine him and give him back his license. He and I were both wrong. There is no double standard for being a good guy when it comes to driving and drinking. There shouldn't be and there wasn't. They suspended his license for 90 days and he lost his world-class job. Did you get that? He LOST... gone forever... his world-class job! It's like trying to call somebody up out of the grave. It was over and done. He wasn't Lazarus. It wasn't coming back.

Thank goodness no one was hurt and he didn't wreck the rental car he was driving. He still had a BS degree and he could reapply at some point for his pilot's license. He just could not keep his "world-class job." Well, worse things

223

happen to folks every day. He hadn't killed anyone. He hadn't wrecked. He hadn't left bodies on the road. He totally cooperated. This wasn't the end of the world, and we were all sure he would rebound and get another job. Wrong!

I think a lot of good people have made the one-time mistake of having one too many beers or one too many glasses of champagne or mixing too little sleep with a few beers or whatever and coming in just over the line on legal and illegal BAC (blood alcohol content). That's a big sentence you just read. It has happened to judges, doctors, police officers, firefighters, mothers, fathers, generals, congressmen, and preachers. I believe someone from each and every walk of life has at one time or another driven a little bit, or a lot, over the legal limit. Some idiots do it all the time. Some people have two or three or 10 Driving Under the Influence convictions on their record. The guy we are reading about had one or maybe two beers over the limit, that's all. But, it turned out to be the most expensive beers he would ever drink. Read on...

Remember, he didn't live near our bars; he lived out of town. We didn't see him too much after that but when we did, he was riding with a buddy or some girl. Keep in mind, he didn't have a license except to go to work and he didn't have a job. Life went on and he would drop by now and then. I did notice he started looking a little rougher, maybe he hadn't shaved in a couple of days or his hair was a little shaggy, but what the hell, he didn't have to get up and go to work, so why spruce up? No big deal. I guess he had some money saved. Are you ready for the other shoe to drop? Here it comes.

One of his pals comes in and reports X has got a second DUI and this time he was driving on a suspended license. WHAT? You have got to be kidding. No, he wasn't kidding and to make matters worse, the bank was looking for his car. Seems he hadn't made any payments in several months. It is important at this point to report that I have not laid eyes on X since before his second DUI. All the information coming was from other friends who lived near him or saw him at different times. I never saw him again. I went looking, but could not find him.

This DUI was a lot more serious; he had more than twice the legal limit of alcohol in his blood. It wasn't a roadblock; they followed him and pulled him and only him over. Now he is in another county in jail with no car. He couldn't bond out for several reasons. He had to just sit there. Good. Maybe he would realize where he was and what was happening. Thank God again that there was no wreck and no one was hurt. If you are keeping score, that's two DUIs within a year.

This had been a good man and there was still some sliver of hope for him but he needed help. It was obvious he had some sort of problem with twisting the cap off a bottle and then twisting a steering wheel. The two don't mix.

A pal of his who lived in the same townhomes as X shows up and starts complaining that he is done with trying to help X. Come to find out, X had been evicted (did you see that coming) and begged his pal to stay with him until he got back on his feet. X swears he has learned his lesson, no more drinking; he's done with all that and is on the straight and narrow. His pal lets him stay in the guest bedroom. "Big F'ing mistake," reports his pal! He says he comes home one evening and, you guessed it, all the liquor is gone and some of this guy's jewelry (or stereo or something, I can't remember) is missing. So is X. I ask if he was going to call the police and he said no. They had been friends but now that was over, done, and finished forever.

That's an important fact to remember… you're going to see it again. In Mr. X's life, the weight of a long, long friendship with a guy who let him stay at his house until he got back on his feet weighed about 5 ounces. The weight of all the alcohol and jewelry was about 4 or 5 pounds. The weight of the addiction was about 100,000 tons. Which one do you think weighed the most?

Maybe a year or so goes by and nothing more is said about any of this. X never walks back in our bars and it is all but forgotten. We all hoped he had straightened up and was doing well. Who knew? Nobody had talked to him. In the bar business, people drift in and stay awhile and drift back out. They find new bars and follow some staff that moves around to other bars. It's just the nature of the business. There was someone new the next day to take X's place at the bar. And then one day, it happened.

One of the bartenders came in and as an afterthought says to me, "You ain't going to believe who I saw today." So I guess… "Judge Crater? He's been missing since 1922." She says, "No, do you remember X?"

"WHAT? That's great, where did you see him, is he doing all right?"

225

No, he wasn't doing all right. She tells me she pulled into a 7-11 or Circle K or one of those stores down by the Orlando Airport and as she is going in, she saw X coming out of a dumpster.

What, are you kidding me?

No, she wasn't. She said she had seen him in that area before today but really didn't have as close a look, as this time. Naturally, I asked what he was doing in the dumpster. And naturally, she answered he was looking for something to eat or drinking out of the empty bottles.

Are you sure it was him?

Of course, she says, I used to date him, I know what he looks like.

I had a bunch of questions: How long has he been there, did you talk to him, was he hurt, did he see you? This girl said, "Porter, we see him around there all the time; I honestly didn't know it was X until today. I got a good look at his face, it's him. The people at the store know he goes in the dumpster. Sometimes in the morning, they leave leftover food they didn't sell in a wrapper so he can get it. I keep questioning her and she tells me to ask one of the doormen who has seen X there also.

The doorman tells me he has not talked to X but he knows X lives in a storm drain in the woods behind some store down off Highway 436 and the B-Line road. I have to give X credit, of all the dumpsters in Orlando, that was a really nice area!

I told my buddy Eric about it, and he asked me if I wanted him to ride down there with me. No, I said, I'll get by there in a day or two and see if can find him. I could not. If he had been there, he was gone or, at the very least, didn't want to be seen. He had two full tours in two branches of the military. He knew how to survive in the jungle. It's just a shame he didn't know how to survive in a bar. The folks in the store said lots of bums and "street people" check the dumpsters all the time. They knew a guy who looked like the one I was asking about, but when people don't wash for days or weeks or months, they tend to all look alike. That was 1993 or 1994 or somewhere in there, and I have never seen or heard of him or spoken of it until today. I hope Mr. X is all right. I really do. He was a good man. He could control a plane and he could control a helicopter. He could control a beautiful high-powered Corvette, but he wasn't able to control the alcohol, it controlled him.

My pal Joey explained it like this: If you have a problem with alcohol, you might start in the penthouse. You might own a skybox at one of the major football or baseball stadiums in a major city. And this is how addiction to alcohol can work. The more you drink, pretty soon you give up the skybox and next season you get VIP season tickets with a thousand other people. You keep drinking and pretty soon another season rolls around and you get reserved seats with 5,000 other fans. Keep on drinking and giving up more control of your life and the next season you are buying general admission (what I usually get) to a few of the games. The more alcohol you take in, pretty soon you are watching all the games on a big color television in your den. As the alcohol takes more of your life, you end up listening to the games on a radio. For some people, they end up in the parking lot near the stadium, washing windshields for quarters, in order to get another drink.

Joey said to me the alcohol elevator only goes down, not up. You're not washing windshields in the parking lot one day and with the consumption of gallons of alcohol, you end up in the skybox a few quick years later. It doesn't work that way. Now, if you own a brewery or a distillery, you might start in the parking lot and work your way up, but that's if you don't abuse the product you sell. I guess the Alcohol Abuse elevator has only one button, it says "Basement."

My friend Mr. X worked his way up. High school, military, college, and four more years in the military learning to fly. The American dream. He did not use alcohol to climb that ladder. When he got to the top, a side effect of alcohol was the elevator down. First he went from the top to the middle, then to the street entrance and then to the basement of the stadium. Then he went to the parking lot and then he vanished. Some people say it was the elevator's fault, some say it was the team's fault, some say it was the way the stadium was built, until you surrender and say, "I need help," it is always going to be someone or something else's fault.

It's like a sparrow that happens to fly in the open door of a parked plane. Let's say the bird is in Florida (about 80 degrees and sunshine) and is fluttering around at the airport and just happens to fly in the door while the plane is being serviced. The bird falls asleep somewhere in the cargo area and wakes up when

227

the plane lands... in Watertown, New York! Now, it's 10 degrees and everything is frozen and there are no insects flying around and the ground is hard as Chinese Algebra and the bird doesn't get it. What the hell just happened? Where am I, where is my other sparrow family and friends? I was only asleep for a few hours... how did this happen? I don't get it!

Same thing with Mr. X... it did happen and it did change and like him, we were there. We simply didn't know it; we were asleep in our addiction. We don't feel the pain going down because we are anesthetized and hadn't hit the basement yet.

My pal Carl Watkins said one of the smartest things I ever heard. I wish I had thought of it but I didn't, he did. Years ago he drank pretty good and then one day he and his heart had a long and painful conversation. Simply put, his heart mentioned it might STOP playing if Carl kept on sending so much alcohol down his throat. Here's what he told me: "I was lost in my own attic." I love that expression, lost in my own attic. It is so different than being lost in a basement. You can fall down a flight of stairs and be lost in a basement but to be lost in an attic? How in the hell can you be lost in your own attic? You can if you're up there drunk. And, there is only two ways down: go back down the same way you came up or go out the window. Down the ladder is always better.

I need to cut these stories short because they begin to resemble each other. Somebody has something and celebrates having it and continues to celebrate and begins to lose it and finally has nothing. It's funny that drinking is about the only thing that you start doing legally and if you don't stop pretty soon, you end up doing illegally, all in the same night. But, it is legal to have a beer and I am going to have one. It is legal to have two or even three. The illegal part is when you get up from the drinking and start to do something else that is illegal to do, if you have already been drinking. That's understandable.

Because I live in America, I am completely aware we sue each other as often as possible hoping to hit the big lawsuit payoff lottery. The phone book is slap full of lawyers who will be thrilled to "WORK FOR YOU"... if you are banged up in a wreck, they will be delighted to stop what they are doing and get up from the dinner table and come to the hospital. Of course, they will bring their standard 35 percent to 40 percent contract (plus cost) for you to sign. I absolutely think there is a time and place for lawyers. I have hired one or two in my life and actually worked for several back in Florida in the 1970s. There is nothing wrong with being a lawyer. I think Abraham Lincoln said, "Time and Knowledge are a lawyer's tool of trade." I think it was Abe who said it. The reason I bring this up is, if you see that I am writing about you, and you are offended, sue me. As of today, I have an eight-year-old car and half of a 66-year-old house (to be honest, it needs more repairs than you are going to be willing to spend), and when we get paid this coming Friday, I will have $988 in my checking account. Enjoy! P.S., what follows is another true story.

It was a holiday weekend, Thursday, Friday, Saturday, and it was over on Sunday. This happened a long time ago, but the truth never changes. It did happen. I am working for a police department somewhere and we get a call about a fire or disturbance or something that ain't cricket at this address. I believe the call came out as an unknown disturbance/fire alert. So, a couple of officers respond and it is a nice house in a clean and well-kept neighborhood. So far no problem. The call had come in from one of the neighbors of the address we were responding to. No answer at the door, nothing on fire, dogs barking in the privacy-fenced area beside and behind the house. Now the neighbors show up and are yelling and pointing around back. Nothing else to do but jump the fence and investigate. There were two people in the backyard we will call them A and B. If they sue me, these are not really their names. Here we go…

There is a barbeque grill going with some huge hunk of meat in it, on fire. Unless A and B wanted their steaks well-done to a charcoaled jet-black color, this grill was out of control (but at least contained in the grill area). It was flaming up, about 2-feet high. The meat was burned to a crisp. That is not against the law unless you are from some chef's school.

"A" was standing on the porch stark naked with a glass in hand. In other words, A was holding a drink (I can testify it wasn't hot cocoa). A wasn't moving, per say, A was swaying and drooling and groaning, and did I mention A was as naked as a jaybird? Still no problem except maybe the grill. That is until A got enough &^%$ together in that alcohol-soaked brain to point to the hot tub. Guess where B was? You got it, B was underwater with just enough face out of the water to barely be able to breathe. At this point, I give my partner all the credit. He got both arms under B and somehow, in a very confined area, held B above water until I could get one arm under B to get B halfway out of the hot tub. It wasn't freezing outside, but it was cool and B was a bright red. The hot tub

229

was on full blast as high as it would go… maybe about 108 or so degrees. I honestly don't know the exact tub temperature, but it was set as high as possible. I do know that because it became evidence.

By now the fire rescue arrived and, thank the Lord, took over. My partner's arms were turning as red as tomatoes. It was real hot water. As our attention turned to A, we all noticed A had a complete bowel movement. A may have moved everything in the intestines, bowels, and colon, but A didn't move either foot. What a stinking mess. A had not moved from where A was standing when we arrived. The fire department did their job and rushed B to the hospital. B had had a massive stroke. B was not responding. Our supervisor arrived and we got A into the house and got the dogs penned up and tried to figure out what happened. I took A to the shower to clean up. It became crystal clear that A just might have had an alcoholic beverage or two. There were seven empty vodka bottles (all of the same brand and all quarts) and half of one and a full one on the coffee table. For a million dollars, I could not tell you the number of empty beer cans… let's just say a lot.

As A came out of the shower (still naked) a towel was wrapped around A. When A was told to get dressed, the shirt was too difficult to manage so a bathrobe was used. When the underwear went on, it went on backwards so there was only one thing to do, A pissed all in this clean underwear. Just stood there and urinated nonstop until the old bladder was empty. Ahhhhh, relief!

A finally got through having every bodily function known to man (wait, I stand corrected, A didn't ejaculate, but I think that's the only one missing) and sat down. It would have been easier for me to recite the Greek alphabet than for A to blow in a portable breathalyzer to measure blood alcohol. A could barely talk. Drunk, drunk, drunk, rotten drunk. I knew what A's problem was, I had been there once in my life but nowhere near this level. A started drinking on Thursday and was going strong on Sunday. I had never gone three full days without eating or sleeping or brushing my teeth. I have no idea what A had been doing, but I knew what A had not been doing. A was too drunk to help B, when B was drowning in a hot tub. Thank God the neighbors saw the meat burning on the grill. That's why they called us. They couldn't see the hot tub.

B was taken to the hospital and the report was "critical." B was not doing well when our shift ended. B had had a stroke. B had gone underwater when the stroke occurred. B took in a large amount of water in both lungs and stomach. B had serious burns all over the body. I'm not positive, but I think, again not sure, but I think B did not recover.

A was too drunk to be taken to jail, and there was some discussion about whether or not a crime had occurred. Is it a crime to get drunk in your own home? It is not. Is it a crime to burn up dinner? It is not. Is it a crime to stand naked in your backyard? It is if you do it on purpose where the neighbors can see you? Is it a crime to be so drunk you can't get your husband or wife or children out of a pressure cooker? I don't think it's a crime, but it's a shame, isn't it? As I recall, A didn't even go to the hospital. They wouldn't take A; too drunk. A did go to a "sober-up" house. A wasn't under arrest but couldn't leave until decisions were made and A was sober enough to give the hospital the necessary information.

How did you spend your holidays? Do you know why so many police and fire and rescue and first responders have to work on Christmas and New Year's and the Fourth of July and Thanksgiving? Well, it's because so many of us celebrate by getting blind-running drunk. I did it for a couple of years. I am guilty. I do not have a wife, and I do not have children. If I got gassed up, it was with another drunk and we never left the house, or hotel, or tree, or whatever we were in, or I was alone. In the bar business, you work most holidays and close the joint, so no hot tubs. On the police departments, fire departments and in the emergency rooms, you have seen enough by the end of shift and just want to go the hell home.

There is nothing wrong with having a drink… nothing. Win the Super Bowl, champagne for everybody. Put in a long, hard day, I say have a cold beer or two fingers of liquor or glass of wine with a great meal. There are millions of people who can and do control alcohol, and there are millions who let alcohol control them. If you don't know which side of the fence you are going to land on, you better not jump. It sneaks up on you. Inhibitions dissolve and you laugh easier and there is a lot to be said about the good times and fun you can have with a small or moderate amount of alcohol. I really think you can. But, when all hell is breaking loose in your life and there is major trouble and you have to face it, I think something in our bodies remembers the fun times associated with alcohol and we get us a dose and we think it helps smooth things out. We THINK it does, but the truth is it doesn't. The problem is still very much there, and we have run back to the bottle, instead of facing whatever it is that is causing all the trouble. I do NOT believe that alcohol has the same effect when times are good as it does when times are bad. We drink both times but for two completely different reasons. Nobody should drink when trouble comes their way. It distorts the reality of the situation and causes us to make poor, poor decisions. We don't have all the facts and information in the correct order, and it simply makes the situation worse, not better. Please God... I never want to go there again. It was a blur.

She was beautiful. She still is beautiful, and she has been to rehab twice, I guess she wasn't "habbed" enough the first time.

Sometimes when I read about movie stars or celebrities going to a $50,000 rehab retreat, I wonder if they are doing it to get well or to get some face time on David Letterman. I mean, if they really stay clean and sober or if they keep the weight off, then it was a wonderful thing. If they are doing it because it's the latest fad and they want everybody to know, then it might be for the wrong reason. I thank heaven for the people who got well. Maybe it's just that I am too old and cynical to believe everybody does it to get well.

One of the best shows on television is Intervention! It's real and for those of us who can identify with addiction, we know these shows aren't scripted. There is no rehearsal. The stars of Intervention are dying their real life... they cover all types of addiction. You remember the expression, "You take a drink, the drink takes a drink, and then the drink takes you"? Here's one, "You eat a gallon of ice cream, the ice cream eats a gallon, and then you gain five more heart-clogging, high-blood pressure, fat-ass pounds to help kill you." Something like that. Maybe we could say, "You smoke a joint, the joint smokes a joint, and then you end up in the joint!" It's a very real show and worth seeing.

So anyway, I have this lady friend who I am extremely fond of who finally came to the realization she needed help. She drank and smoked a lot. It's been a while since I've seen her, but I think it was vodka and Camel Lights, vodka and Camel Lights, vodka and Camel Lights. Yep, that's what it was. I believe she is OK now and I asked her if I could skip over her story and share it with the readers. She said I could, so here goes...

Keep in mind that alcohol does not give one iota if you are male, female, young, old, black or white, gentile, or Jew. Alcohol doesn't mind if you are rich or poor, it doesn't care if you have a Ph.D. or a fifth-grade education. You can be the Jethro Bodine of the neighborhood or the Milburn Drysdale of the community, alcohol just don't care. It didn't care who this girl was. It doesn't care who you are. It didn't care who I was. It just don't care. It's the worst kind of lover, it just don't care!

She did have the "Beaver Cleaver" childhood. Mom and Dad were at home and all needs were met. Really, it was the average middle-class life in a major city. All was good. She played sports in school and was no problem. Her siblings were no problem. And then somewhere along about the grade, she fell in with bad companions. The first problem was skipping school here and there. No big deal... almost every kid skips school at some point. Not the end of the world. Now trouble comes her way. She gets the first F on a report card. The first thing to go is the sports. She is off the team. No reason to practice after school so she might as well hang out at with the bad girls. And then she had her first cigarette.

Now we are in the grade and getting by with Cs. Also, some of the bad companions have boyfriends. She develops a great interest in boys. Unfortunately, he smokes. grade brings a part-time job and along with that brings money. With money she can buy the "beers"... so by the time she graduates, she is smoking and drinking on a regular basis. With no real interest in college, there is a full-time job and a hell of a lot of smoking and drinking. It's the thing to do. Then came the apartment and parties and lots of booze. Then came marriage. Fortunately, or unfortunately (I don't know which), husband likes to throw back a few and now we have two young people working and partying with their friends and everybody is drinking. Are we seeing a pattern here since the grade? Maybe a little too much freedom? Maybe falling in with the wrong type of people when you are 16 years old. Maybe parents too busy making a living trying to keep up with the Jones? Maybe.

The marriage runs its course for a few years and for whatever reason, it doesn't last. There were no children and no real property to speak of and a hell of a lot of marriages don't last for a thousand reasons. Now the real Devil shows up. My friend has two roads she can travel. One is to recover from the disappointment of the marriage and go on with her life, or drown herself in sorrow and really hit the bottle. Let's stop right here and now and remember this is a book about addiction. Addiction: The uncontrolled urge to repeat an action or behavior with NO regard to the positive or negative results of that action! My friend was at that crossroads where a choice needed, demanded, to be made in order to suffer the emotional pain and get over it, or self-medicate the pain so that she never had to really face it. Guess which one she did? Which one are you doing? Which one is your mom or daughter or dad or son doing? As for my friend, every time she sobered up, the reality of the pain appeared and a few belts would smooth it over.

She was and is a good-looking lady. It didn't take her long to find a good-looking, successful man to hook up with. She developed her business and was pretty successful at it. But the drinking didn't stop. There were cocktail parties and dinners with a lot of wine and social events with more wine and these two social butterflies were always on the go and party, party, party... the drinking got worse. Funny thing, there was always a reason to drink. Landing a big job, going to bid on a big job, his firm completed a big job, always something. Get up and go to work. Meet after work for a few cocktails and dinner. Go home and have a couple (of drinks) before bed. Next day, same thing. Weekends: Get up and go to the lake or beach or someplace and swim, boat, meet friends, and drink some more, drink all night. Get up the next day and do the same thing again. With each swallow, the hook was going in deeper.

That relationship ended and mine and hers began. In hindsight, there were never two people on the face of the earth who had no more business being together than me and her. Well, I take that back, maybe Bonnie and Clyde! She liked to drink, and it's my second-favorite thing to do in this world. Our friendship started at a bar and made its way to the liquor store. We did a lot of stuff but it always ended with alcohol. We never started the day off with alcohol but rather somewhere between lunch and about 4 p.m. The rhythm of the evening and night was set. For about a year and a half, we never missed a beat.

Now here's the deal: Somewhere in there we should have taken an inventory of the kitchen cabinet. We didn't live together, but we were together almost every night. We might run out of coffee or run out of food, but we never in 18 months ran out of booze, never. One of us made damn sure there was enough beer or bourbon or vodka. If not, there was a liquor store about a half mile from my house, and we knew the business hours there by heart. I couldn't tell you what day it was, but I knew the liquor store schedule to the second.

I moved and she moved and we stayed in touch and remained friends. I went to see her once or twice, and she came to see me once or twice. She met someone new, and I was happy for her. We should all be with who we love, she was and I really hoped the best for her, still do.

The funny thing about it was when she left, I sorta straightened up. I started dating a lady who was very healthy and would have the occasional drink but not much and when it wasn't there in my face and not a part of my day, I didn't do it often. It wasn't the link that bound us. Listen and listen close. If you or a loved one is in addiction, look at who you or they are around and with, most of the time. People do what they do because they are who they are! I have never walked in a bar and seen my preacher playing beat the clock on two for ones. I have never seen him sitting there during Unhappy Hour because he can't quite get Sunday's sermon just right. I have no idea if he drinks or not, but I do know who he associates with and they are not alcoholics. If I was with her, I willingly got hammered. If I was with someone who might have a glass of wine now and then, I cut my drinking 75 percent. It has nothing to do with which one I miss today, but I don't miss the drinking. (Hell, I miss them both....shhhhh)

One night I call the drinking lady and she tells me she is in trouble. She didn't cut out the booze; if anything it got worse. She has gone days without eating a time or two and is smoking more than ever before. Why, I ask? Because it's free... her boyfriend owns a bar or something and she stays in a state of "glaze." The latest problem is she has fallen and really hurt herself THIS TIME! Well, how many other times were there? She can't remember. She has got to get some help. There it is, the surrender. She finally, after all these years, since the grade, finally she admits it's out of hand. She's going to rehab, finally.

So this rehab is out west somewhere in a beautiful area with great surroundings. I think boyfriend is paying about $30,000 for 45 days at this place. Money well spent if it works. I guess my friend had a note from her mom because she left early. Forty five days without a drink is one thing but without a cigarette, no way, Jose! I don't know how long she stayed, but she didn't get a diploma. I think she was paroled after a few weeks. She had been sneaking a few smokes and probably needed to get to the store for more. I'm not being funny; she told me giving up smokes was far more difficult than giving up alcohol.

A short time later, she visits Las Vegas… what do you think happened? That's right, she is now right back in the saddle or barstool or casino. She takes a drink, the drink takes a drink, and we are off to the races. This is just me, but if I was trying to sober up, there are two places in this world that I wouldn't go: Las Vegas and New Orleans. I can assure you, if you want to go out drinking and either of those places are on your schedule, won't you invite me along, please! I am going to have a couple of cold beers if I go either place. She was in Vegas in a matter of weeks after rehab. Not a good idea.

Don't go where you have an addiction… it will be there waiting, just waiting, either knowing or hoping that you hurry back. It misses you and things will be different this time. You can handle it now and you know when to stop now and you're in charge this time. Oh hell, no you are not. Addiction is in charge, make no mistake about it. Joey told me, "Addiction is a patient lover; it will wait on you to get out of the grave."

After a few months and a few more close calls and a few more falls, she returns to rehab. This time I am so proud to say she completes the program. She still has not quit smoking, and she (like me) has an occasional drink. Not everybody can do that. But she is so much better, and I hope and pray she never goes back to where she was. And one other thing, now she has a family and deeply loves her family enough to give up the booze. I am not telling you to go get married and have babies in order to give up drinking, but it seemed to have worked for her, and I am so very, very proud of her and happy for her.

On one of mine and her episodes, death was only inches away from her. I guess the Lord knew she would and could recover from her addiction because I really think he saved her that night. I know I had nothing to do with it, I was asleep. I thank God for intervening and helping her. She surrendered and a Power greater than her took over. I really cared about her and think of her now and then. She'll be all right.

What I am worried about now, is me and you. Will we be all right? They haven't quit making alcohol, and you can get it most anywhere most anytime. The problem is, it can get you most anywhere and most anytime.

As of August 2011, in America, $57 billion was spent on alcohol products. As of 2011, in America, somewhere between $100 and $175 billion was spent on alcohol-related illness and alcohol-related crime.

I would like to thank everyone who had a hand in helping my friend get re-re-habed. She didn't and probably couldn't have done it alone. I want to thank Joey and Eric again. I noticed when I got over my real addiction, I was drinking less and less. Maybe with me, drinking was a side effect of the real problem. Regardless, the results were the same. Does this girl's story sound familiar to you? Is it like yours? Is it like someone you know and love? Did mine and your addiction start out by creeping along and now it's going 100 miles an hour and slap out of control?

We see it happening and we stand by and put up with it. We tolerate it and we suffer along with them and their sickness. We say things like, well, if it was cancer or a broken leg, everybody would understand. No, they wouldn't. If it was cancer or a broken leg, we would take them to the ER. That's not the case with alcohol and sometimes drugs. We say things like, "Well, I wish Junior would cut back on his drinking or, "Well, I wish Missy would stop whoring and spreading diseases all over town, that devil dope got her. You know she's really a good girl."

NO SHE ISN'T. Junior and Missy are SICK and need help! They are not now who they used to be. That has changed. Obviously they are not getting well on their own, so we have to make a choice. We either have to be part of the problem or part of the solution, there is no gray area.

Let me ask you this: Would you stand by and watch someone you loved cut themselves and bleed a cup full of blood in front of you each day? Hell no you wouldn't. But what we do is let them light up a couple of packs of smokes a day or drink a couple of six packs a day or a fifth of liquor or shoot a few syringes of dope a day. Sometimes we take them to an "all-you-can-possibly-eat-before-your-heart-comes-pounding-through-your-chest" buffet and slap on the old feedbag. Yee-haw!

Nobody, and I mean nobody, came to me and said, "Damn, Porter, you better ease up on the alcohol." Maybe it was because they liked to drink as much (or more) as I did.

237

So the question is: What do you do about it? Here is the only answer I can come up with. You don't own anybody and here in what's left of the good old USA, people are free to do whatever they want that is legal. Knowing that, it makes the rest of this solution simple. They don't have the right to do it in your presence. Here is a good example. I have out-of-town dear friends who are Christians. That's the end of it. He and his wife are devoted to the Lord and the church and it is first in their lives. How wonderful.

I go and visit them once in a while and have always taken whatever girlfriend I had at the time with me. They always welcomed me and her and made us feel at home. That said, let me add this: me and whatever girlfriends always (and still to this day) have to sleep in separate rooms. That's it, end of subject, no room for discussion. It's their house and their rules. I respect that.

If you have someone in your life who is killing themselves and keeping you up nights worried to death or gambling away the children's dentist money, or whatever they are doing that is an addiction and ruining your and their life, here's an idea. Tell them to either get help and quit or leave. No sense in killing both of you.

Remember, Joey's wife said, "Get some help or we are out of here." She was past begging and pleading. That had no effect.

My girlfriend had to hit rock bottom, or almost walk through a plate-glass door, in order to seek help.

I had to step on a scale at Publix grocery store to realize how sick I had become. Nothing anybody said had any effect; they didn't understand. The scales didn't know if it was weighing diamonds or cow chips. It just reported that whatever was standing on it weighed 265 pounds. There are over 100 calories in a beer and that many again in a shot of bourbon. Do the math.

Something else I noticed: after work, people would stop by and have a beer or drink. It was like a signal that the workday was finished. 5o'clock, "let's go grab a beer" It was like a whistle being blown. First it was a habit, than an anchor, than an addiction....it slips up on you.

And my final word on alcohol is this: On that glorious afternoon, Joey Vincent finally said, "She ain't the problem, she's an alcoholic and a drug addict, she's doing her job, you're the problem,   I got it.....thank you.

Proverbs 20:1: Wine is a mocker and beer is a brawler; whoever is led astray by them is not wise.

Proverbs 23:32-35: In the end wine bites like a snake and poisons like a viper. Your eyes will see strange sights and your mind imagine confusing things. You will be like one sleeping on the high sea, lying on top of the rigging. "They hit me," you will say, "but I am not hurt! They beat me, but I don't feel it. When will I wake up so I can find another drink?"

Chapter 18

Quit Stopping or Stop Quitting

I know it's a play on words, but I was trying to understand the difference between stopping an addiction and quitting an addiction. Either way, the addiction won't stop or quit you. Well, maybe it will stop you, dead in your tracks, but it sure won't quit you!

Not only did I talk to successful people, some of whom you have met, but I tried to read as much as I could stomach while writing this book. I read about how addiction works and the different approaches to curing addiction. I read about things I understood and about five times as much as I didn't understand. Here's what I got out of all of it. "Stop" killing yourself and don't "quit" trying to get well.

Let's suppose you are going to drive from Chicago to Denver. You get up one morning, pack a suitcase, lock up the house, and head west on I-88. Before too long you decide to stop for a coffee. After a while, you are going to stop for gas. Then later in the day you are probably going to stop for lunch and to go pee. You might stop down the road and get a hotel room for the night. No sense in rushing the trip, you have all week. The next day, you leave early and stop again for coffee and the next thing you know, you are approaching Denver. Congratulations, you had a safe trip! You never did quit driving toward Denver, but you stopped several times along the way. See the difference? We can stop and start and stop and start, but if we honestly quit, it's over. You wouldn't keep driving to Grand Junction once you got to Denver, you would quit!

Now I am acutely aware of how silly and simple and childish that example seems. Except, not very many addicts can do it. Every addict I know can stop anytime they want to and most of them do. The problem seems to be they can only stop for an hour or two hours or maybe a day or until the next paycheck or in some cases until their jail sentence is served. They do stop; it just ain't for very long. Maybe it's fair to say addicts never quit stopping until they stop quitting. Makes perfect sense to me.

I do not know your story, I know mine. I have a good idea about Joey's and a couple of others' in and out of this book, but I don't know everything about their story. I guess we will have to relive mine for a paragraph or two. How dull!

Without a doubt, I stopped my addiction two or three times a month for several years. I didn't quit it until 1997. That was 15 years ago "thank you very much!" Keep in mind, the addiction didn't quit, I did.

Whatever my problem was, I would get to the end of my rope and swear I was going to quit it. If it was drinking or the wrong women or eating 3,000 calories at one sitting, whatever the problem of the day was, I can't tell you how many times I pledged to "never do it again"… yeah, right. Sometimes I would stop for three or four days and sometimes it was for eight hours. But, I stopped and started and stopped and started. Wonder why I couldn't stop and stay stopped? Well, I couldn't do it because that would be quitting… and I guess I really didn't want to QUIT! Quitting in its purest form is permanent and stopping is just giving yourself enough time to catch your breath.

Another good example is when two fighters are in the ring and one gets knocked out. The commentators say, "The fight was stopped in the fifth round" or "The Champion stopped him with a body shot." They say stopped because the fighters didn't quit; the fight was stopped. If it went the distance, they would say the fight ended or went the distance, however many rounds there were. If they were to say, "Well, the fighters quit," that would mean everybody got off their stools and left the ring. So where does that leave us? When it comes to addiction, I hope and pray I stay quit, and I hope and pray you will one day soon stop and never start again. Then you also will have quit. It's a pretty good feeling.

It is important for me (because this book is part of my sobriety program) to tell you I have slipped a few times since 1997. I have. I am human and I have made some mistakes concerning my addiction in the last 15 years. Not many, but a few. I did on several occasions have an ice-cold beer after work. Sometimes I had two. On the few occasions that I slipped up and had three, I stopped quitting and started stopping. It only happened a few times, but I'm telling the truth here, it did happen. Let's hope it doesn't happen often.

I want to tell you an interesting story. It's kind of sad, but there is something to be learned from it. I've seen it a dozen times, and you probably have also. I would think anyone who has graduated from college has seen it more than I ever will. The starting and stopping part. Here goes:

I go to a couple of gyms here in Richmond County. One is the Live Fit Augusta gym on Washington Road. It's a great place and great people working there and I intend to stay a member as long as they will have me. One of the managers is a young man named Lance Smith. When you meet Lance, it's pretty obvious he knows his business and takes care of himself. He's in good shape. He and I have talked about a lot of things concerning the fitness and health business and when I was writing this chapter, I asked him an important question: Why do people sign up and quit? He has been dealing with this all of his fitness career. He had a pretty smart answer.

Lance told me he sees a lot of good people with good intentions come in the door. He has seen it happen for years and years in each of the gyms he has managed. A good example is the lady who finds that life has caught up with her and between the job and the husband and the kids and everything else she has going on, she has neglected her health and slowly added about 25 or more extra pounds. When she comes to the gym and has the initial interview, she usually reports that a vacation or a reunion or a wedding or New Year's or something has "woke her up" and she has got to get started exercising. Sometimes when the person is completely honest, maybe it was the doctor who alerted her. Sometimes it's the husband or even the absence of the husband that alerted her. We will leave it at that.

So, the lady tours the gym and inspects all the equipment and meets everybody and signs up. (For the record, Live Fit Augusta has a seven-day free-trial period, no contracts… you are free to come and go as you please. If you don't want to be there, you are not obligated.) Now she is ready to go! First she has to go buy some workout clothes. That's understandable, nothing she owns fits anymore. So she goes and buys three matching, latest-style, outfits and two pairs of new athletic shoes. Now she is almost ready… headband, towel, and a subscription to the newest magazine on women's fitness. OK, now we are ready to go. Hang on a minute, doggone it, she can't start this week, something came up at work and it's urgent. Work comes first (everybody understands that), so she calls and tells Lance she will start next Monday for sure.

Go ahead, good reader, and finish the story. That's right, Monday rolls around and she doesn't show up. When Lance calls, she has 47 excuses why she didn't make it but for sure she will be there on Tuesday. Finally on Tuesday she shows up and has a complete workup done. She is the complete and total center of attention. It's her health and life we are talking about and today is the first day of her getting healthy and back in shape and achieving her goals. And she never shows up again... Lance lowers his head and with somewhat of a sad expression tells me this lady is in love with the "idea" of getting healthy, not getting healthy. On more than one occasion, he has enrolled the same person in two different gyms at two different times and they never came back either place. They couldn't stop quitting.

As an afterthought, Lance reported the worst case was the lady who came in (this was at a different gym) and begged and pleaded with one of the trainers to work her into his schedule. I think most personal trainers in most gyms really do want to help people, and this trainer went out of his way to accommodate the lady. He moved a couple of willing clients and rearranged his schedule to be there for her. Without too much detail, she paid over $500 for over three months of personal sessions plus the price of a membership and NEVER came in one time. Are you waiting for the other shoe to fall? She later called back and wanted to sign up again and purchase three more months of personal training. I am very proud of Lance, he politely told her no, he really didn't think she should waste her money. Enough said.

Addiction is a fair and patient lover. It loves you and me and will love anyone who lies down with it. You lie "with" it and it will lie to you! Do you know two guys who started college the same time? One went two quarters and then dropped out a quarter. Then he went back for a quarter and then stopped for six months and toured Europe. Then he went back for two quarters and then got a great job and signed up for night classes and stopped after three weeks. This guy started going to college back in 1983 and hasn't finished yet. He has gone back seven times and hasn't completed one full semester. He can't quit stopping.

Do you know the other guy who signed up in 1983 and went full time and worked after school and weekends and never missed a class? This guy worked all summer and lived at home and saved his money and took a full load each semester. He couldn't quit. I knew a lawyer who did just that very thing. He worked in a grocery store all the way through his undergraduate degree. When he applied and was accepted to law school, the next thing he did was find a bagboy job at a grocery store where the law school was. He quit bagging groceries the year before he graduated. One guy never quit, and one never quit stopping.

I saw on the news last night about a man from some country in war-torn Europe who came to the USA and got a job as a janitor at Columbia University. He has worked a full-night schedule and taken one or two classes a day... 19 years later, he is graduating with honors! He didn't quit. Now he wants to get his Master's degree and someday earn his Ph.D. I bet he gets it.

Look up Dawn Loggins if you really want to see what determination and not stopping looks like. She will quit someday when she has her M.D. or Ph.D. degree, but she won't stop until then. God what a story!

I have a habit of rambling and going on and on and changing subjects in mid-chapter. I am going to write a few more examples about this and move on. I wish I could sit down and talk to you; it's easier to explain face to face. It was for me to understand. It comes to this: If you are addicted to anything, and I mean addicted, I'm talking about where it controls a part of your life, I want you to know there is a way out. I'm sure of it because I have met far too many people who stopped their addiction (with and without help) and never went back to it. Some of them exchanged addictions until they weaned themselves off of all of them. Others went cold turkey and still others work at it every day. However they did it, they did it. The results are all the same; we are getting well.

I have a friend in California for whom I have a great deal of respect. This guy is a Champion on several levels and although I know him well enough to contact him, in truth, I am just one of thousands and thousands of his fans. His name is Don "the Dragon" Wilson and I want to give you a quick background before I relay our recent short conversation.

Please feel free to look Don up on his website. It's pretty impressive. If my statistics are correct, he began fighting full-contact kickboxing back in 1974 in Florida. The kickboxing back then had a huge influence on today's Mixed Martial Arts competitions. There were several sanctioning bodies, and it was honestly a sport in its infancy. I would say it grew up fast and became real popular, wouldn't you? Today the MMA matches have sold millions of tickets at the event and on PPV. Don was one of the first television commentators when MMA came on the scene.

He has held 11 world champion titles! He won those titles in three weight categories and has literally fought all over the world. In my humble opinion, the most impressive record he has is his first pro fight was in 1974 and his last pro fight was in 2002. That's 28 years of training, dieting, running, sparring (I know a couple of his sparring partners, and they didn't take it easy on him), sit-ups, focus, dedication, and during those 28 years, he was a father, a husband, and a movie star who would rehearse, study his lines, travel, act on the set, and train for an upcoming world title fight! Whew!

So what in the whole wide world could that have to do with addiction? *Everything.* I had a couple of questions for Don: Why didn't he quit? What drove him to keep getting back in the ring? He was a successful movie star, why put yourself through that pain and torture for nearly 30 years? He said it was simple, he couldn't quit. It would have hurt more to not train and not accomplish as much as he did then to quit and perhaps wonder about what may have been.

Wonder why the simplest things seem to be the most profound? Imagine getting up tomorrow morning and being more willing to face the pain of freedom than living in the pain of addiction. Don made a choice to run five miles and do hundreds of kicks and punches and spar with several partners for a couple of hours and diet and not drink alcohol and not smoke and no matter how many trips to Las Vegas, he didn't gamble away his home and family. Now I'm not just singing Don's praises; there are a lot of people, male and female, who have done the same thing. Maybe they didn't win 11 championships and maybe they aren't movie stars, but they live normal, healthy, productive lives because they quit stopping until they reached their goal. What's your goal?

Stop! Stop right this instant and review your life, and I will mine. Are we where we want to be? If the answer is NO, then let's spend tomorrow working on getting there. If you want to be a professional gambler and do it for a living, great, go do it. Read all the books you can on statistics and probability and study great players and maybe go to work in a casino. I wish you nothing but success. But, if you haven't been to the dentist in 15 years and you're $150,000 in debt and your children need braces, and the utility company is coming to shut off your power, try not to spend more than $2 on the lotto this week.

I believe we can get addicted to quitting just as easily, if not easier, than any other vice known to man. We quit playing little league because we aren't real good at it. We quit the Scouts because we don't want to sell cookies once a year. We quit the team because practice interferes with cartoons after school. We quit the band because we can't play as well as someone else. The list is endless. And the little habits start adding up and it's like adding another rubber band and another rubber band and another rubber band and after you have quit enough times, that rubber band is so strong, it will stretch but it won't break. We get in that habit of quitting, of starting to do something (like a college education), but we don't stop, we quit. We never go back and we never will. That's quitting... when you set out to do something, you don't do it, and you never will. If your addiction is beating your ass, stop it until you can say you have quit. If you are in addiction of any kind, quit "inviting" it into your life and it will stop coming around.

One of my addictions stopped calling me and I stopped calling my addiction. My addiction quit showing up at 3 a.m. drunk and I quit driving around looking for my addiction at 3 a.m. Guess what? That solved the problem! No more addiction. Yippee! Here's the good news, you can do it too. You can, you will. If you want it.

I have had one beer so far in 2012. I have wanted about 688. I like to drink. There has never been a secret about that. I spent the second 20 years of my life working in bars and restaurants. I really like to drink. If I lose this job I have now, I will have to go on welfare or just drop out of sight because I hope I never work in another bar as long as I live. I hope I don't. Why? Because it gets to be a little too much of a temptation. All the customers are there laughing and having a good time and saying things like, "Want to have a drink" and "This rounds on me" and "Buy Porter one." I would be saying "OK, great" and "No thanks" all in the same sentence. So, as much as I want to, I don't work in bars anymore. If you are in addiction and you are going to be surrounded by it in the morning... if you can't get out now, start planning your escape. It doesn't matter what the addiction is, you can get away from it. If you weigh 350 pounds, you might not want to be the night watchman at the donut store.

Remember somewhere in a previous chapter we read, the most powerful thing in the world is an idea, followed by an action. We tell ourselves we are going to get well and we are through with our addiction and then what happens?

246

Nothing if the appropriate action isn't taken, nothing happens at all. My friend Rena Reese (Body-*for*-LIFE Champion) is a pretty sharp lady. She has written books, has an online health program, and has helped a countless number of people with their lives. She's helped me whether she knows it or not. Anyway, we were talking about this very subject, the quitting and stopping, and once again she made the answers more clear. This is sort of what she said.

"People have an illusion of what "action" really is. Someone comes to me and wants my help to get healthy and they have no problem with signing a check for a gym membership. We learn to sign our names in the first grade (incidentally, Rena is also a school teacher) and signing a contract or signing a check is painless. It's easily done. Signing their name makes some people feel as if they have done something. In reality, they haven't done anything yet. Then life gets in the way when it's time to get down to doing the work."

Where have we heard that before? Maybe Lance?

Rena reported one lady who signed up and bought all the workout gear and naturally couldn't make it to the classes. When the lady finally showed up one day, her hair was perfect and as always she had perfect acrylic nails done to a high gloss. The lady reported she just didn't have time to attend the exercise sessions, just wasn't enough time to work it in. So Rena asked a couple of simple questions, "How many hours do you spend a month getting your hair done? How many hours do you sit and pay a high price to have acrylic nails put on? How much time do you spend a week shopping and window shopping? Couldn't you take some of that time and devote it to your health, your heart, and your blood pressure?"

Of course, the client had no answer. This lady was overweight but she wore beautiful clothes and her hair and nails were perfect. Funny thing about this lady that Rena pointed out to me, she wore expensive, beautiful shoes. Her feet were the normal size even if she was 100 pounds overweight. So, she would spend $1,000 on designer shoes that drew people's attention away from the rest of her, down to her normal-size feet. I had never thought of that but Rena is absolutely, 100 percent right. Wouldn't it have been easier to get in shape and leave the junk food and the $250 outfits at home? The gym ain't a fashion show! I guess not, it was easier and more rewarding to chew a chocolate bar than to be free. You can't just sign up; you have to do your part of the bargain and do the work.

Back to Joey. He took Rena's brilliant example a step further. Once you sign up to get well, then the trouble starts. The first thing you or me or this lady or anybody who wants out of addiction has to do is "BE HONEST WITH YOURSELF." You can lie to the rest of the world and to heaven (that won't do you much good, but feel free to try), but after you sign up to get well, you have to take an honest inventory of YOU! You have to face you… you have to admit, here I am and this isn't where I want to be. It does not matter what the addiction is, getting well involves some pain, but it gets better. Like learning to sign your name in the first grade, you lean to write a sentence in the second and then a paragraph in the third and a chapter in the fourth grade and by the time you graduate, you are writing term papers and applications for work or more school. It starts with some pain but it gets better.

And now I go back to Don. He had 70-plus wins in his career and only lost five. That is amazing. After his fights, he went back to the gym and threw more punches and threw more kicks and did hundreds of down blocks and upper blocks and he sparred more and got hit less and less. The more he trained, the more he won and the less he got tagged. There was less pain because he practiced more. The same is true of the addict. If you will just start and not stop, you will get better and better and better and then you might have to keep practicing all your life, but you will have quit your addiction. Trust me, it's worth it.

Have you ever been blind-running drunk and sick and hung-over and the Marine Corp Band was playing a medley of marches in your head the next morning? Have you ever done a few too many lines of cocaine and you found yourself trying to paint the bedroom a new color at 4 a.m.? Have you ever once gone to a casino and maxed out your ATM card because you had a good feeling about where the 8 of clubs was going to show up on the next hand? Did the 8 not show up and you had to pawn your watch to get bus fare home? Have you just once in your life argued and cried and shown your ass because of another person and cried or drank yourself to sleep? Did any of the above hurt? Now here comes the big question… did you swear you would NEVER do it again? I swear I am through.

And then the reality sets in, the reality that a huge part of your life is not going to be there anymore. Those three or four drinks after work are now gone. That triple-pancake breakfast and four sausages side plate are a thing of the past. That 8 ball on the big weekend is forever in the side pocket. Those smokes are not going to be there with the morning coffee or after lunch today. And this one is really a wakeup call… someone else is going to be getting the goody from your now ex-sweetheart. But you are strong and you swear, "I'm really going to do it this time, I mean it. I can beat this, I can." This is the truth as I know it; it ain't ever going to be easy. I would be typing a lie if I said it was.

I wrote in a previous chapter that I drive a 2006 automobile. It's paid for and I really like that about my car. Here is the truth: I wish I had a new Mercedes Benz 550. That is a beautiful automobile. I think they cost about $70,000. Anyway, no matter what they cost, I want one. The problem is, I can't make the payment and eat and have electricity and have cable and a cell phone and car insurance and the basic necessities of life if my monthly car payment is 96 percent of what I bring home. OK, let's review: I want a new Mercedes, but I do not want the payments. I suppose I can't have the car. I can either keep my car and make my bills month to month or… get the new car and lose everything else I have and eventually lose the new car because I won't have clean clothes to wear to work. I can't afford a washing machine or detergent and I have to have a clean uniform or I will get fired. Tell me that's any different than addiction. Your addiction may be affordable today, but it will outsell you in the long run. Remember Jack from the beginning of the book? A pack of smokes back in the early '80s was maybe $2. Unfortunately for me and Jack and everybody who knew him, the price of his addiction was far too high.

Get out of your comfort zone; you are going to have to. There is no way around it that I know of. Nobody on the face of the earth can do it for you, nobody. It is your cross to bear or to set down and walk away from. It can be done. I didn't do it by myself, and I have to work my own little program every day. Writing this book is part of it. I don't know what I'll do when this book is finished? I'll get to thinking about that in another chapter or two. Anyway, my pal Eric trains people for a living. He spends his entire day coaching and planning and guiding folks to a healthier life. He doesn't eat for them and he doesn't exercise for them and he doesn't live for them. He shows them (and me) the path to take to freedom. We have to do the work. I love that story in the Bible about how the Lord provides food for all the little sparrows, but he doesn't come down here and spoon feed them. They have to make some sort of effort in order to eat.

Eric tells me, "You have to be the champion before anything happens." It has to be inside you wanting to get out, and our own wrong choices, keep it locked up. It makes me think there is another contract you have to sign before you can really get well, the one you sign with yourself. Now we are back to Shawn Phillips, prepare to succeed, get ready to get well. Get your house in order. It's starting to look like all these successful people are doing and saying some of the same things. 1. Are you a champion, are you bigger than the addiction, do you have more character than the addiction does? 2. Are you signing, on the dotted line, a contract with yourself to get well and are you (like the car payments) going to HONOR it? 3. This is where we separate the wheat from the chaff… are you going to do a little "uncomfortable work" for a greater reward the minute you start getting well? That's it. There is help available. In 1997 with a hell of a lot of help from places you will never know and some you will, I asked and answered those three questions: yes, yes and yes. If any of those three questions had been answered "maybe" or "not sure" or "no," I would have stopped and you know what happens when you stop.

Somewhere I read an article that I am not sure happened. I would like to think it is true, but if it did happen, nobody there is still alive to swear to it. Whether it's true or not, I like the story and want to share it with you.

Supposedly, someone asked Michelangelo how did he carve such a magnificent statue of David? I hope at the end of this chapter, you look up a picture of that statue, it is beyond words. Remember, back then there were no drills or sanders or machines, it was all done by hand. Anyway, a student asked, how Michelangelo had created such a magnificent statue, and Michelangelo replied, "I didn't create the statue of David, he was always in the block of marble. I simple wiped away the excess marble and let him out."

Thank the Lord Michelangelo didn't quit halfway through. I hope you and I don't. There is a beautiful work of art in all of us created by a creator a thousand times more brilliant than Michelangelo. Every time we fool with our addiction, we put more marble back on when we should be keeping it off. I pray you bring out the David or Venus de Milo in you.

Chapter 19
The Wrong Person

They own you. They know it and you know it and sooner or later, usually sooner, all your friends know it. You are helpless and all the wrong person has to do is tug your strings and like a puppet, you dance. Just like Howdy Doody could not help but dance when Buffalo Bob pulled his strings, it never changes and it never will, unless you cut or untie the strings. You know I'm right, and I know I'm right, and if you have never been hopelessly addicted to someone, God bless and keep you. I hope you never are.

When you refuse to QUIT the relationship—did we just read about QUITTING?—when you refuse to quit, it doesn't take the other person long to learn they are in charge. They laugh and their friends laugh and you ache and live in pain and misery. You gnash your teeth and swear you are through and you will never go back and then the phone rings and your heart starts pounding and you try and act and sound tough but they see right straight through it. Their voice might break or they might sound like they are fighting back tears. In truth, they are fighting back a snicker—not the candy bar; *you're* the candy bar, and they're fighting back the overwhelming urge to laugh out loud.

Do those two paragraphs sound like I am talking about a lover? I am. Does it sound like I am talking about a husband or a wife? I am. Are those two paragraphs about a son or a daughter, maybe a mom or dad? They are. Could they be about a boss or a coworker? Yes, they absolutely can. There are too many examples, including a spiritual or political leader.

Somewhere in this book, I believe I wrote the worst addiction is the one where you really love someone, you can't leave them for whatever reason and you have to stand by and watch them wreck their (and then your) life. Let's start with what may be hell on this earth beyond description: addiction to helping a family member. I have been told another word for it is codependence. You are as addicted to them as they are to their addiction, and unfortunately, your blood is in their veins, and theirs in yours.

Maybe it's a child who has become addicted to drugs. Each and every night, you lay awake wondering if they are getting the hell beat out of them in an alley somewhere. You don't hear from your child and you have to wonder if a drug deal went bad and they are dead. All sorts of morbid thoughts race through your head and sleep don't come. Finally, you hear a car door slam and you run to the window hoping and praying it isn't the police or the coroner. Finally, finally, they are home. When you open the door and ask where have they been and why didn't they call, you are told to mind you own *&^ % # business. Somehow, they turn and twist the truth to make it appear that "you are the problem," it's all, your fault.

At least you can go back to bed now and cry for a while. You lay there remembering when Junior was a precious little bundle of joy, and you fall asleep. Next day, same old, same old. Junior can be a son or a daughter. One more time, addiction is an equal-opportunity employer. All you can do is watch your bank account dry up and watch all your family possessions disappear. You can watch money disappear from your wallet or purse. In the deep recesses of your heart, you silently wish he or she would get arrested and maybe get some state-funded help. If nothing else, you would know they were in jail and not somewhere dead, to maybe never be found.

I talked to a lady whose son was in and out and in and out and in and out of lockup for drugs. She always paid his bail and always got him a lawyer and always felt it was all her fault. So here was my question to her… if she knew where there was a bank that opened at 8 a.m., and she could walk in there and open a cash drawer and take whatever money was lying there, would she do it? Remember, there are NO CONSEQUENCES to taking the cash. It's there and all she had to do was walk in and get it. Of course she would. So the question becomes, why wouldn't the child steal from her wallet or purse or credit card? There are no police reports, nothing except yelling, screaming, crying, and prayer. She is the child's free bank. Good luck with the prayer thing. Go to court and tell the judge that instead of Junior going to jail for selling a pound of cocaine, you are going to make him (or her) stay at home and pray for a year… prayer don't always work! Hold on a minute, dear Lord, please let this book sell 5,000,000 copies. I'll tell you how that works out.

This lady didn't get it. Her love for her child was not in question. The problem was, she believed it was safer to enable the child to continue his drug abuse with her money than to rob and steal from someone who might call the police and put a stop to it. Maybe it's a mother/child thing; I just don't get it. If the child loved his mom as much as she did him, why would he cause her such pain and misery? I guess he loved the dope more.

Let me remind you I have NO education in addiction counseling. I have NO education at all. I am not a family planner (I damn sure don't plan to have a family), and when it comes to children, I think the answer is door three. What I do know and what I have seen is when a child tears a family apart. I have witnessed a grown son and daughter go through their parent's life savings and all they had to show for it was a straw. Of course, the parents blamed that mean old devil dope. Dope caused all the trouble! No, hell no, it didn't. The children caused all the trouble and the parents did nothing about it. Dope just happened to be the avenue the children took.

For better or worse, I promise. OK, how's this for worse... one fellow I knew lost everything he had because his precious wife, who never cheated in their marriage, who never left a dirty dish anywhere or neglected his children or missed church or nothing, snuck $25,000 out of their checking account to BUY LOTTERY AND SCRATCH-OFF TICKETS! He had no idea she put gambling ahead of their trust and vows and family. He didn't discover it until his bank was bought out by a different bank and although she handled the money, the account was in his name. Hello! The bank statement came addressed to him from the new bank. He opened it by sheer luck.

Well, you marry people for better or worse, so he got her some help and she cried and they had been together for 15 years and the children and etc. OK, it happened and nothing was going to change that, so let's move on with our lives. You don't get divorced; you try and work through it because we are all human and everybody reading this and everybody you know has made a mistake somewhere in life. We are probably going to make more. One small problem... the seed of deceit had been planted and now the husband began to worry. Everything seemed cool and the counseling seemed to have worked. But the first blow had been so devastating; the husband knew another one would be the knockout punch. Telling you this makes me a little nervous. Makes me wonder how many times I have been lied to... probably thousands.

Since this story was repeated to me from a relative (of his), I am not sure of the event, but here goes. As quickly as I heard the first sentence, I knew the rest of the story. So will you.

I think it was a wedding or some function at the church, but they both were dressed to the nines. He had on his best suit, and she got dolled up to beat the band. While they were standing in a line to eat or shake hands with the lucky couple, a lady with them says, "Oh no, Beverly (not the real name), you lost the diamond in your earring!" Everybody stopped and looked all around the floor and in the ladies room and since she had put them on in the car, he ran back and thanks to the Lord, he found the diamond on the floorboard of the car. Happy days! They weren't real expensive diamonds, but they were diamonds and he saved the day. Whew! She would get it reset as soon as possible. Do I need to even finish the story? OK, I will.

All the jewelry he had bought and seen in her jewelry box over the years had somehow changed from the real McCoy to costume jewelry. He didn't know or care about the few things from her grandmother, he hadn't paid for those. It was the gifts since they got married that concerned him. Where was the money? It was with the trust he had for her... it was gone.

This wife and children's mother was no longer the woman he married; now she was the wrong person. Like those children who steal and rob from the very people who love them more than anyone else on this earth have become the wrong people, they have changed; they are no longer the "same person" you knew in the beginning. People do change. Unless they return to the person you knew in the beginning, you are now in love with "what used to be, not what is now."

We are not talking about Dianne getting her leg torn off or Nelson having his throat opened from ear to ear or Jessica having cancer. Those horrible things happened and none of that changed who they were or their character. The people who loved them stayed right there every step of the way. The subject in this chapter is like the giant snake epidemic in the Florida Everglades. Cool people went out and bought little baby boa constrictors and anacondas and put them in glass cages in their homes and apartments in south Florida. God only knows why. Guess what happened? They grew up from 1 foot and a great conversation piece into something entirely different. Now they are 12- or 14- or

254

16-feet long and weigh a couple of hundred pounds and have eaten the family dog and are no longer the cute, cool conversation piece in the pet store! We are in no way comparing a living human being with a snake (they did it in the Bible, but I'm not); it's just an example of how things change.

You can't flush them down the toilet; they won't go down the sink and you can't afford a dozen live rabbits to feed them every three weeks. The neighbors are complaining about the smell, and your homeowners insurance has gone up 600 percent. Things change... the love and affection for a cute 1-foot snake doesn't work when it is 200 pounds and 15-feet long! Things have changed and you have to act accordingly. The same rings true when people change regardless of who they are or what they mean to you. When addiction takes the lead, the addict follows and sometimes we become victims. That changes everything!

We cannot help who our family is. Neither you nor I asked to be born. It is not a perfect world. You cannot select your parents. If one of your parents is a drunk and the other one is in jail, it is not your fault. What is your fault is when you continue to enable them. Are you helping a family member by buying their street drugs? Are you carrying them to the store to buy cigarettes? Are you contributing somehow to helping kill them because they cry and tell you they fed you and raised you and you owe them? You don't! You do not owe anyone, family or not, a debt so grand that you need to assist them in their addiction. If you tell them no and they never speak to you again, they love the addiction more than they love you. Help them quit by all means, do all you can to get them professional help, but if they refuse or relapse time after time after time, or just flat out don't want to be saved, save yourself. No sense in both of you dying.

I think I can come up with a better example than the anaconda. This one everybody should understand. Did you ever go to the pet store or the dog pound and see the most adorable little fat 5-pound bundle of fur in the world? Its little puppy breath and tongue sticking out and it hops from your left foot to your right and when you start to leave, it yaps and tugs on your shoestring? Well, nothing will do but you take "fluffy" home with you and take about a thousand pictures of him. Life is good.

Maybe six months go by and "Fluffy" weighs a cool 35 pounds. He is still a bundle of joy but a much bigger bundle of joy. A year goes by and now

"Fluffy" weighs 70 pounds and is eating 25 pounds of dog food every two weeks. Within two years, "Fluffy" weighs 110 pounds and his name should be changed to "Satan." You can no longer let him in the house because you only have two pairs of shoes left. Satan really seems to enjoy chewing on your shoes. The neighbors complain that one of their cats is missing and the people who live three doors down on the other side of the street, well, their dog recently gave birth to a litter that vaguely resemble "Satan"... hmmm!

You see where we are going with this? The puppy started out innocent and a precious bundle of fur. It needed you for every bite of food and drink of water. Not anymore. In two short years it has come to dominate the house and yard and now, try to reach down and take its food away, go ahead and try. It will snap and sometimes bite you. In addition, the same thing sometimes happens with a family member. You know it and I've seen it. At some point in the past, the family member was a loving, caring brother or sister. Maybe it was a son or daughter or even a mom or dad. It could certainly be a husband or wife. But, they changed and in their addiction, you and the rest of the family become the victims. Reminds me of that old song, "You always hurt the ones you love."

My last word on the family "wrong person"... there was a program on television about a parent and her son who were both waist deep in meth addiction. I don't know much about meth but have been told if cocaine addiction has 100 hooks, meth has 1,000. It is deadly addictive. Anyway, mom and son are living together and she gets high and he gets high and her and some of his friends get high and the interviewer asks if mom ever gets high with her son?

"No, mom says, "I don't get high with my son because meth makes you want sex and I wouldn't trust myself around him." I'm thinking that might be the wrong person in that family... I thank God I had loving parents and this was never an issue for me. I wouldn't trade them for anything and even though my mom didn't last, her love has. Enough about family.

Go back and read the first two paragraphs of this chapter again... I just did. The part about they own you and they tug and pull on your strings is my favorite. There is as much truth to that as there is in DNA. They own you as long as you let them. They have the title to your soul, and every time you see them or make love to them or give in to the special little way they reel you in, the payment on that title increases; it never gets smaller. Keep on paying it. I did and found out the hard way; they own the bank!

I wrote in the sex addiction chapter (or one of them) about a song that covers Wrong Person addiction better than the rest: Whipping Post by the Allman Brothers. If you find yourself in a no-win love affair, please pull that song up and hear the words. Listen closely to it. Listen to Janis Joplin sing about a love that is killing her in Ball and Chain. Another more modern song is Feels So Good by Armin Van Buuren on Mirage. A much sadder version of love gone wrong but you can't get over it is How Much I Feel by Ambrosia. Maybe the payoff is Cry Me a River by Joe Cocker or Susan Boyle.

In my opinion (and you certainly have yours), the saddest song about a love that never ended is That's How Much I Feel by Ambrosia. Years later, this dude is married and has a family and he and his wife are going strong... but late at night he sometimes see's "her" face when he and the wife make love. One more time, addiction NEVER goes away. We do or we don't but the addiction is always there. You ought to listen to it. I'm sure there are hundreds, if not thousands, of songs dealing with love addiction. What we are going to talk about is that same addiction but with the wrong person. Hell, if it's with the right person, it probably wouldn't be addiction, it would be bliss!

Some people in this book you know, and this next story is about a guy you won't know. If you did know him, then you'd know it is absolutely the truth. It may be the most difficult, sad story I ever write. There has got to be a lesson here because there is nothing else left.

This guy was some kind of good looking. He could have walked on the stage at the Mr. America and placed in the top 10 in his weight class. His mom was from the Philippines and his dad was Italian and American. They met when dad was in the military, got married, and came back to live in the good old USA. I think he was one of three children. I can't tell you too much about him, except I met him in the gym and he came to see me once or twice in the nightclubs. He was just a hell of a nice guy, and the girls went nuts when he walked in. It's been a long time ago, but I think he ran a tanning spa and had a suntan lotion wholesale business.

If you talked to him, he had a smile and great memory for names. Being a mixture of Filipino and Italian-American, he looked like he tanned about five hours a day, but he didn't. I was running a beer joint called Rosie O' Grady's and we had about 400 employees. It's a small and round world, and on one of the occasions when he came to visit, one of my waitresses asked me if I was going to hire him? I told her no, he didn't ask me for a job. Good, she said, because she would have to quit... she used to be his sweetheart. Naturally, I wanted to know what the problem was and a long story short, he was way too jealous and far too possessive. She almost had to call the cops. Now there were friends, but it took a while.

I accepted her story with a grain of salt but believed her regardless. She was cute and had a great personality, and I had never heard her say she would quit. The waitresses made a lot of money at Rosie's. She told me this guy had a control problem. He didn't look out of control to me. Life went on.

I can't tell you how much later it was, maybe six months or a year, but one night she gets a phone call and goes berserk. She is gagging and crying and I get her off the floor and out the back door. There is a lot of action that goes on at the back door to bars, but this time it was off the scale. I truly believed her mom or dad had been in a wreck. We got her a glass of water and she sat down beside a dumpster, a full stinking dumpster, and to hell with her uniform. I just stood there and let her get it out. She finally calmed down and now for the rest of the story:

This was a little before cell phones and the call came to the waitress station at work. The call was from the good-looking guy's family. He was dead. I remember it like it was this afternoon; it is one of those frozen moments in time. She repeated the story she had just heard. The call came from his mom or sister; I never really made out which one.

Mr. good-looking had gone over to his girlfriend's house and, according to my waitress, had argued with his girlfriend. During this story, she is reminding me of how possessive he was and reminded me he had a problem with control. The story she got was the present girlfriend couldn't take it anymore and weeks earlier had broken up with him. He came back again and again and it was going to be different but it never was. Nothing ever changed and the new girlfriend for the first time that night weighed her sanity against his good looks. It was a 49 to

51 decision, but the girlfriend had had enough; he had to go or she was calling the cops.

I wasn't there, my waitress wasn't there, but the story she got on the phone was when good-looking realized his girlfriend meant business and was going to call the cops, he said, "I'll give you something to call them about. You aren't ever going to forget me." At that point he got between the girlfriend and the phone. He was a big strong man and had no trouble throwing her on the couch. Then he handcuffed his wrist to the girlfriend's wrist, pulled out a .38 caliber pistol and blew his brains out.

Let that sink in for a minute. He didn't shoot her; he handcuffed his wrist to her wrist and shot himself in the head. There she is attached to him with no handcuff key and can't get him off of her in order to get to the phone, or leave. Not only is she in shock, he weighs about 200 pounds of dead-weight muscle. Needless to say, her screams led to a neighbor coming to beat on the door and call 911. After the police got there she was finally free, at least physically.

Do you remember when I wrote about Oprah Winfrey saying, "If someone tells you they can't live without you, you need to get away from them"? That's not an exact quote, but that's pretty much what she said. Truer words were never spoken. If that girl had it to do over, she should have packed up and moved. She was single and if she had to move to rural Mongolia, it would have been worth it. She simply didn't know how bad it was going to end. Do you? The cops will do everything in their power to protect you, but it can't always be done. This man was the WRONG PERSON. Look for signs and set boundaries BEFORE it gets too involved. PEOPLE CHANGE... folks date, then they go steady, then they say the "love" word, then they say they don't want to be with anyone else, and they usually add, do you? Then we get the old one-two punch: where were you? When did you get home? I called you at 8:30 like you told me, where were you? Why did you tell me to call if you weren't going to be there? Who was that person you were talking to?

If you find yourself at that point, it may already be too late.

If I were a woman, I wouldn't date me on a bet. I used to be the world's worst at trying to save everybody that didn't want to be saved. It wasn't another woman, it was the lost woman. Was it caused by my grandfather standing in the

259

pulpit for 64 years telling people there was a better life and a way out of sin and death and destruction here on earth? All they had to do was surrender and put their heart in the capable hands of the Lord. Some of that had to rub off on me. I hope so.

Was it my mother being an RN and working in the emergency room for years and years and hearing her stories of alcohol and drugs and senseless death that made me want to "save" everybody? When I was a winner in the Body-*for*-LIFE Challenge and was blessed to move to Denver and be the director of that Challenge, I was thrilled when we announced the Champions, but I was more concerned with the thousands who quit or dropped out or were unsuccessful. I wanted to go back and call all of those people and try to help save them! What the hell was wrong with me? Not all of them wanted to be saved!

I believe I have a handle on it now. It took me a hell of a long time to learn this but here it is: You cannot love somebody enough to get them well. You can love them good and you can love them often, but you cannot love them well. When the wrong person builds a nest in your heart, whether by accident or by written invitation, it is as hard to quit as alcohol or drugs or gambling or cigarettes or anything you can come up with. Forget about adding sex, that makes it a thousand times worse.

All right, here's the truth, I'm getting loaded. I just went and poured about 3 ounces of bourbon and drank it. Here I am writing about one of the two things that almost ruined my life and I get to thinking about people from my past and I get the urge to call them. It's a damn good thing I don't have their number or their phone would be ringing at 11:00 at night. I am off the next two days, so there will be no problem there. I wouldn't drink the night before I went to work; I have too much respect for my job and co-workers. But Lord have mercy, that ache and that pain never goes away, not when it lives in your heart. It might be dead in every other part of your body, but late at night it still has a heartbeat somewhere deep inside you. I'm not sure it ever goes away. That and the fact that Facebook makes knowing where somebody is very easy.

So under the influence of alcohol, let's try and wrap this up, and then only a few more chapters to go. You were not born and brought on this earth to be hit. About three out of 10 calls for domestic violence are for females hitting males. Women wanted and deserved equal rights and they are finally getting them. They have the right to be arrested just as much as a man does. Congratulations. You have come a long way, baby! Whether it is a man beating on a woman or vice versa, somebody is going to jail. Please tell me why you would stay with someone, anyone, who is hurting you?

Well, I love him. Well, he didn't mean it. Well, I made him mad and he didn't really hurt me that bad. Well, the children... trust me on this;, the children wish you would leave so they could get a little sleep! Well... he didn't really mean it; he's under a lot of pressure. Bull$%&#... it has happened before and it will probably happen again. If you are one of the few men or women in America who has had one big level playing field fight, maybe you are in the .01 percent that it only happens to once and never again... but most likely, it has happened more than once. Get out. Get out as soon as you can. You have hitched your wagon to the wrong mule!

I teach a women's self-defense class as part of my community-service responsibilities. You would not believe the stories I have heard and witnessed in some of those classes. I always ask, "Why didn't you leave"? And they always give me one of the same answers: I had nowhere to go. I loved him. The children. And I think to myself, "Is that why you are here in this Safe House self-defense class?

Listen close, he was the wrong person! He may have been the right man, but he was and will always be the wrong person. And you think you can't live without him.

This works both ways.

She is beautiful and she smells good and she is funny and she makes you smile. She might or might not be a great cook... in the beginning, that doesn't matter much. Her kitchen ain't the room you want to get in. You meet her some kind of which way, and you hope and pray that you see her again. You ask her friends who she is and you try to know everything about her. You may not be on fire yet, but you are smoldering. Maybe because she's so hot!

At work, you think about her and you watch the clock. You still think about sundown and payday but now it's Friday that holds your attention. Have I hit on a nerve yet? Stay tuned. The weekend rolls around and her friends overnight have become your new best friends. You call them up and ask what they are doing this weekend and innocently ask if so and so might be there, just wondering, no real interest, just curious. And then you see her again.

You know, I'm going to throw this in because I think it's the truth. If you're a drunk and she's a drunk, it's a match made in heaven. You both have the same interest and I can testify from experience, the more you drink, the more interesting the other person becomes. It might work that way with drugs, I couldn't tell you about that one. But everybody isn't a drunk, so back to the story.

You ask her for a date and another date and another date and pretty soon, you and her are a couple. Sometimes this is the beginning of a beautiful friendship. Sometimes this is exactly how life and love is supposed to work, I suppose. In addiction, it doesn't quite go so smoothly. I'm not sure how you can want somebody so much and not expect other people to want them also. That stands to reason. But, God forbid someone else talks to them or smiles at them or asks them to dance or does anything to jab that green-eyed monster "jealously" that has moved in where our brain used to live. I'm telling you, that's ownership, not love. Addiction fits in there somewhere.

Another example: If you fall madly in love with someone who is madly in love with drugs (cocaine, meth, heroin, sometimes pot, or any of the hundreds of pharmacy prescription drugs out there), you would be better off falling in love with a prostitute or pimp. What? What did I just say? You heard me. If you fall for a prostitute or a pimp, you know damn good and well what you are in for. There is no lying about another woman or another man. There is always going to be another somebody else. That's the business they are in.

But… when you fall for a hardcore drug addict, you will never know where they have been or who with. They will lie and steal and cheat and look you right straight in the eyes and say "yes" when the answer is no—and "no" when the answer is yes. I wonder why it is so hard to realize that addicts love their addiction more than they love us. Is it because we want to be number one in their lives and we can't. There isn't enough time or paper to relate some of the bar-business stories I have seen and heard. Little Miss Sunshine turned out to be a midnight tsunami when it came to dope. She became the wrong person when her dope went missing and she wanted me to search 200 peoples' bags and wallets for her "products"… you can't imagine the scene that caused.

It's not just drugs that makes a person the wrong one... it can sure be sex. Some folks need now and will need tomorrow and have always needed multiple partners. I'm not sure what is missing in their life, but "one's nothing and two's one." They have to be wanted, and there will never be enough compliments and never be enough attention and whatever it is that is lacking, you alone are not going to be able to fill the hole in their chest. Some folks are big flirts, and when it gets down to the real nitty-gritty, maybe they won't go through with it. But trust me, there are some who will. If you are giving 100 percent and expect 100 percent in return and you don't get it, find someone who will give you 100 percent. You might be able to love somebody so much they leave their addiction, but the question comes up: How much time and how much heart do you have to lose? 'Cause you are going to lose for a long time before they come around. It ain't going to happen overnight.

With the wrong person, sometimes they stay because they don't want to hurt you. OK... what hurts worse, hearing someone say I don't love you anymore or I was at my sister's when you watched them leave the hotel? Maybe it's a close family. Anybody who lies to you, in my opinion, is the wrong person. Get out and find someone who doesn't lie to you. Anybody you are lying to is the wrong person, so why do it? Why hurt someone who really cares for you just because you can. To what end? Don't do it anymore. It ain't worth it.

My mother told me not to fall in love with a movie star; they were already in love with the lights! My grandmother told me to "go with someone as good as you, or go alone." I wish I had listened to that last one.

I'm going to get off this subject because like all addiction, it doesn't end. I will never believe that you can be addicted to someone and then fall in love with them; I believe you fall in love with someone and then become addicted to them. One more time: You lose your heart, then you lose your hips, and then you lose your mind!

The examples of the wrong person listed above are true. So is this one. I have lived in four major cities that had several pro sports teams in each city. You will never know which city we are talking about. That's how it should be. Anyway, this lady I knew (25 years ago) liked to do a line of coke once in a while. She's as cool as they come and everybody likes her. I liked her too. Anyway, her boyfriend gets invited to a party one night and she gets to meet a couple of the pro athletes at the party. How cool is that? She comes back to work and tells us all about it and all the other girls want to go to the next party. Hell, I wanted to go. I guess a few phone numbers got passed around or whatever and lo and behold, one of the very famous pro athletes comes walking into our work one night. He shows up with his posse and the crowd goes wild. This was a hell of a nice guy and he tips like Diamond Jim Brady and he is buying Dom like it's tap water. What a great night, the bartenders made money, the waitress made money, the house made money, and everybody there got to meet a big-shot pro ball player. I hoped he came back. She hoped he came back that night.

He did show up a few more times but didn't become a regular. She did. A couple of the other employees started talking about how strung out this girl was becoming. The first thing I noticed was the same thing I had noticed in a few other employees over the years… she just began to look unkempt and a little dirty. It's hard to explain. Maybe a fingernail wasn't painted or maybe her hair was a little dirty, I don't know… it's the little things you notice. Remember, this was a little before cell phones and her boyfriend was calling looking for her more often. We were calling looking for her more often. Now stay with me… remember, this is about someone you might be in love with becoming the wrong person to be in love with. It happens and if you are hooked on that guy or gal, their addiction becomes your addiction. That is not a good thing.

A friend of mine, who was a professional gambler, comes in the bars pretty regularly and in general conversation tells me the lady we are talking about is getting in a little too deep. He reports she is seeing the sports star on a semi-regular basis. Well, that happens and the boyfriend should move on with his life, right? Boyfriend can't seem to let go. He is calling and showing up and here we go. Pretty soon, we are going to be at the "she gets fired or he can't come in while she is working point."

One of the other girls who worked there gave me the whole story. You might want to sit down for this one. You can believe it or not believe it, it doesn't matter. I didn't see it but I did see her and I believe it's true.

The first night my employee and her boyfriend went to Mr. Sport's house, there was a tray of "blow" floating around and if you were in the click and real cool, you got a free line or two. It seems the whole place was mellow and after a while everybody went home. Remember, I said phone numbers were passed around and after a few days, the girl gets a call and is invited to another party and to drop by after work and bring a couple of your girlfriends. There will be plenty of refreshments. As I understand it, this became a regular event when Mr. Sport was in town. The only thing different was boyfriend was not invited.

The girl telling me this said she went to one party and never went back. It was a little too much for her but the other girl was going over there all the time. She was showing up when he was in town and out of town. She was looking for Mr. Sport to try and get an advance on the dope to hold her over till he got back and then they could party, party, party! This whole time she is telling her boyfriend that she is working late, going out with some of the other girls, etc. He keeps calling and she keeps going over to Mr. Sport's house.

A couple of other employees tell me they have been to this house and our girl has lost her *&^%$# mind. Come to find out, Mr. Sport had given her free cocaine on the first few trips. She's really hooked on this high-quality drug and doesn't give a damn about the guy, she wants the drugs. His thing is he wants to see her (and I understand other girls) beg and be degraded in order to get the dope. Ass or gas, nobody rides for free... I often wonder if that was his intention from the beginning? 1. Hi, have some good dope, there is no cost. 2. Hi, have some more good dope; there is plenty to go around. 3. Hi, you say you like this good dope, well, you know, sooner or later, you're going to have to give me something in return. 4. Hi, you want some dope? I don't want your money, here's what you got to do. That's how the deal worked. No telling how many girls got hooked. I only know of this one.

Here is what I was told happened. You think it over and tell me what you would have done if you were the boyfriend. I am well aware of the fact that it is easy to be brave in someone else's shoes. I know we all say we would leave in a heartbeat, but when your heart beats for that other person, how can you walk away from your own heart? It ain't always that easy.

This girl had become so addicted to the high-quality drugs she was willing to do anything to get them. Mr. Sport would only give her the drugs if she snorted them off a "special" part of his body. He would get undressed in front of a few of his pals and put a line of cocaine on his (you can figure out where he put it), and he didn't make her snort it, but if she wanted it, she had to take ALL of her clothes off and kneel in front of him with whoever was there watching and get the drugs off him. I understand after the first night this happened, it became easier and easier for her to do. She was addicted to the drugs. Mr. Sport was addicted to degrading women in general, and the boyfriend was addicted to her. What a threesome they made.

Do you think boyfriend should have moved on? Do you think he should have left this girl and started dating someone who had a smidgen more self-respect? I have no idea what happened to any of them. The last time I saw her, she was leaving work early and never came back. The last time I heard from him, he was calling looking for her. I hope he found her or at the very least, I hope he found himself. Mr. Sport retired.

In this day and age with e-mails and texting, there is a whole lot of shaking going on. People are fools to send a note or picture that can be forwarded or downloaded or seen by other people. It doesn't have to include drugs, it can just be lies and X-rated language. It can be your sweetheart telling you he or she has to go do something and then you find a text about meeting so and so at the club or hotel or whatever. People make mistakes and people are human. But how many times does it have to happen before you draw the line? People think they are slick… they get a different phone or a different laptop and go right on lying to each other. Just remember this: Nobody is so slick that they don't need one more greasing.

Do we need to set each and every finger, one at a time, on the burner to find out the stove is hot? Some of us do. Some of us have. Why? Why would anybody stay or continue to go back, time after time, to another person who hurts us? I've done it and if you are doing it, you really need to quit. If you say you can't live without him or her, then you are the problem, not them. You can live without anybody. It will hurt but life will go on. Please, please let them take their lies and deceit and addiction and walk, or better yet run, out of your life. You will get through it. It hurts, but staying never gets better and ending the relationship will finally get better. It will. It has. Quit being addicted to them until they quit being addicted to whatever it is that is making a fool out of you. Easier said than done.

I want to end this on a happier note. Not everybody is cheating. Not everybody is in love with an addict. Sometimes you can't help who you fall in love with but you can help how long you stay. My grandmother and grandfather

266

were married in the church, loved the Lord all their life, and were together for 64 years. He was holding her hand when she died, and six months later, he went to be with her in eternity forever. They loved each other more in one hour than I have ever loved anybody in a year. That's not really saying anything but you know what I mean. I have a couple of wonderful friends who adore their husbands and wives. I have friends who are in a relationship and appear to be on top of the world. How wonderful!

I asked my pal who has been married for 40 years how he did it. He said he always wanted to go home. When work was over, he couldn't wait to be with that woman. He always wanted to go home to her, and she always wanted him to hurry home. Now that's the right person. Nothing wrong with being addicted to someone like that.

I don't know how you find that person, unless you are that person and you find each other. But I damn sure do know when it's the wrong person. If you can't spot it, one of your true friends will point it out to you.

My mother and father got married right after he came home from WWII. I don't think young people really lived together so much back then, it was a different time and people got married. So, they did. It didn't last. Then they both remarried and each marriage has lasted over 35 years. They both got the right person the second time around. I'm glad they didn't stay in a wrong relationship. I'm glad they came to the realization that they both wanted to go a different direction. Yippee! They were happy, I am happy for them, and the people they remarried had both been divorced. It means we can make a mistake and we probably will. It means we don't have to stay in that mistake all our lives. It means that life is difficult enough without having your partner pulling you in a completely different direction. For the average person, there will be rent and car payments and insurance and dentists and food to buy and maybe children and jobs and sometimes working two jobs and in-laws and older parents who have to be looked after and on and on and on. On the average, all of that and more will come into your life. Don't waste too much time trying to save yourself plus everybody else and especially someone who is trying to hold you down. Remember what my grandmother said, "Go with someone good as you or go alone."

"Oh the grapevine is jumping, there's talk all over town."

"Yeah, the grapevine is jumping, there's talk all over town."

"The higher I try to lift you up, the further you drag me down." —Ms. Alberta Hunter.

Be ye not unequally yoked, be not yoked with unbelievers. 2 Corinthians 6:17.

As usual, life has handed me another example of exactly what we are writing about in this chapter. This morning in 2012, the headlines in our local paper report that yesterday a man went to argue with his ex-wife and the argument went south. How else can an argument go? From the story, they were separated or completely divorced or about to be when they began to at least talk and be civil. That's not what happened. Now she is dead and he is dead and he knew it when he went over there because he took his gun. Maybe he was scared of her? Right. I think not. He was scared of being without her or her being with someone else, or he was just eaten up with the fact that she didn't want him anymore. Either way, there are about 6,000,000,000 people on this earth. Don't you think there is a chance that somebody, anybody, somewhere else would have wanted him?

I'm telling you I understand it. I have been slap-dab, out-of-my-mind nuts at 3 a.m. looking for some woman who was where she wanted to be and it wasn't with me. Never again! Never ever! Maybe if Sophia Loren decides she wants to date me and someone else at the same time, I will lose control and go crazy with jealously. Other than that, it ain't going to happen. Don't let it happen to you with anybody.

I am so sorry that lady and her estranged husband are dead. They didn't need to die because one of them was the wrong person. Don't you dare let this happen to you?

Stoney Grimes wrote on his Facebook: Sometimes giving the wrong person a second chance is like offering them another bullet because they missed you the first time……Outstanding!

Chapter 20
Let's Eat

Lord only knows how many times we have heard that in our lives! It seems like we eat at births and at funerals and for every imaginable reason in between. Of course we do, we have to eat to live. If not, we would starve to death.

Unfortunately, the other side of the pancake is this: Some people are eating themselves to death. I guess food can kill you either way... the lack of it or too much of it. We already talked about the people in some third-world countries who are starving and their children are starving. It is a horrible situation, but those people keep on having more children and less food and keep on starving. Let's talk about the other folks (with or without children) who are eating like a bunch of - century Vikings pillaging half of Europe.

I am convinced there is nothing I can write or say or recommend that hasn't been said or written or recommended by people far smarter than me. If you can read this book, you can read any one of a thousand books that teach proper nutrition, proper exercise, proper self-control, and anything else you can think of to know about food. There are thousands of personal trainers and gyms and surgeries and chefs and nutritionists and DVDs and pieces of exercise equipment and on and on and on. Go get as many of those books as you'd like and read every one of them. Join three or four gyms and weight-loss clinics and get all the home gyms and DVDs on the market. Watch all the Most Pounds Lost programs on the television and if you don't do the work, it will all be in vain, it will be useless. Reading and watching and preparing might get you ready, but it won't shed one pound. You have to do the work! The most powerful thing in the world is "an idea followed by an action", It must be followed by an action... thank you, Master Kim.

Here is a test I like to use when I'm getting a little out of shape: I ask myself if I think the dog enjoys watching me get naked in front of him? I like my dog and I hate it when he would rather run outside in an electrical storm than watch me take my clothes off. Not only that, he stinks when he's wet. Let's just say I am going to try and stay in shape for the dog! He has to live here too.

Since I do not believe I can come up with ANY motivation or catchy expression or reason for us to quit stuffing and cramming food down our throats, I will only report the addiction to food I have witnessed or received letters concerning. Try to keep in mind that from 1998 until 2008, I was in the letter-receiving business at Body-*for*-LIFE. No names, no identifiers, no exposure. Just what good people wrote me or told me that I knew was true. I had been there; I knew they were telling the truth. I know I am. Read the Abyss chapter in Body-*for*-LIFE by Bill Phillips. I can't improve on that.

So, without further adieu, I will try and be a man of my word. No begging, no pleading, no Do It for Your Family or Children. I wrote enough about getting fit in the other book, Finally Fit at 50. Read that one, it will give you lots of reasons to get well. I want to tell the reader something and then we are going to Las Vegas. When the doctors took one of my friend Jack's lungs (we read about him at the beginning of the book), when they told him part of the other lung would probably have to come out, that's when he quit smoking. He could have always quit smoking; he hadn't wanted to until it was too late. I hate that, I honestly hate that. So this is all you need to know... make some changes in your diet, drop some unwanted, unnecessary fat or your heart is going to send you a Western Union Telegram up your left arm that reads "I Quit." Maybe it will be your blood pressure that sends a Telegram reading, "I am going on vacation, I will be through the roof." Want to see your future? Look at the last plate of food you ate.

January 2009 and here I am in beautiful Las Vegas. I was thinking about the gambling thing when another addiction became blatantly obvious. Here it is; I know in my heart that some people come here, not to gamble, but to eat. If you gamble here, it's hit and miss. If you come here to EAT, you are the WINNER!

I have never seen so much food in one place (tons) except maybe on an ocean cruise. There are people who don't own a bathing suit who go on cruises just to eat. Go for whatever reason you want to; if it's legal, you can do it. Unfortunately, if everybody ate as much as some people, the ship would sink. And that's the truth and you know it.

I am staying in a really nice hotel and I got up early and strolled up to the breakfast buffet. I never saw so many people lined up to gorge themselves in my life. They weren't gambling (well, maybe with their health), but they were as excited about the buffet as the guy holding four waiting on an ace-high flush. These people were going to have a high flush, but it was going to be later in their rooms. Some should have had a wheelbarrow instead of the skimpy little 12-inch plate.

I won't bore you with all the types of breakfast food available but will report there were 17 kinds of pastries and donuts, not including cookies. And it looked like there were thousands of each kind. There was one big pot of oatmeal and 12 brands of sugar-coated cereal. There was milk and chocolate milk and strawberry milk and eggs by the hundreds. The chickens were working overtime. I can't tell you how many ways they made pancakes and waffles. There were eight types of fruit preserves and gallons of syrup. They had fried everything from a pig but the squeal! I had some of all of it.

When I set down, I watched people coming in that were obese. A few of the overweight were using walkers and some were on oxygen. One or two were in wheelchairs. I wondered how they could sit in a smoke filled casino and be on oxygen at the same time. They did.

Some of these people had difficulty getting to their table and were allowed ahead of the line. I'm not talking about people who were in wheelchairs because of an injury or someone crippled, I mean people who couldn't go through the turnstile and had to go around. You know exactly what I mean. Yet some of the huge 300-plus pounders looked like Jesse Owens getting a plate and covering the distance to the pastry station. Some had one egg, one biscuit, one piece of toast, and a cool dozen donuts. One guy had no eggs, no oatmeal, no cereal, but rather a plate of cheese blintzes that were swimming in strawberry goo. He didn't go near the fruit! The really good news is it was all you could cram down your throat for $8. I swear there was a sign that read "Don't go away Hungry." It should have read "Just Go Away."

I have no idea what happened at lunch, I wasn't there. There was a card in my room advertising an $11 lunch buffet special. I hate I missed it. It was dinner that got me!

When dinner rolled around, the entire 1,000-pound four-member family showed up. I am not sure what parents are thinking when innocent children are allowed (if not encouraged) to be 30 or 40 or 50 percent overweight. How can that happen? Is it because the parents are fat and they want company? It shouldn't, but it drives me crazy. It's NONE of my business, I don't have any children but I was one. When you are a fat-body child, you get made fun of and you get hurt and you don't get invited to the parties and words like "husky" and big boned and "will grow out of it" are used. "Plump" is a good one. The day a person becomes 18, the law says they can do (only legally) and be anything they want, earlier in some cases. At 18, if you want to buy two dozen coconut, chocolate, peanut butter, cream-filled, lemon-glazed, maple-frosted, cashew-covered treats, have at it, you can. Happy eating. You can't buy a beer but you are welcome to 30,000 calories! Wait a minute… it just dawned on me… you can buy all those donuts at 12 or 13 or any age if you have the money. Yes you can.

Here comes dad to dinner. He probably hasn't seen his groin in 20 years, but I guess mom had because they have two large children I would guess 12 and 14 or so. Dad was dressed nice and looked clean and probably worked hard for 50 weeks and brought his family to Vegas for a vacation. Good for him. He might have been a doctor or policeman or schoolteacher or plumber, I have no idea. I would guess he went an easy 300 pounds, maybe 325. Stomach was hanging so far over his belt, once in a while it peeped out from underneath his shirt.

This guy had not done one thing wrong. He might have been a deacon in his church. He acted like he loved his family and they loved him. He could have been a veteran and a pillar of his community; he certainly was big enough to be. This is America and you, dad, and I can look how we want to. If he had 27 tattoos, it was OK. If he had three rings in his nose, it was OK. If he and the Mrs. wanted to dress up like Santa and a reindeer and play hide the Christmas Cane, it was OK. He could have any hairdo or mildew he wanted, it's America. He was obviously concerned about his family being well fed; he was leading the charge of the heavy artillery brigade into the Valley of the CARBOHYDRATES! CHARGE….

The Mrs. has two children and since breakfast, is now carrying a little bitty baby. Way to go, dad! I think maybe the baby was asleep at breakfast, I didn't see it. I will tell you she was a pretty woman. The children were clean as a whistle and well dressed. I am convinced mom and dad loved those children and took care of them. They did not appear abused in any way or mistreated. I feel sure both parents would protect those three children with their lives. That said, the parents were feeding the kids to death.

Mom was probably 5'5" and went 215 pounds. I should work for the carnival; I can guess weight pretty good. The young man was probably 175 (he looked like he could anchor Notre Dame's front line), and the girl, probably 150. No idea what the baby weighed. Mom had her hands full because she was alone with the kids; dad had shot like a rifle to the mashed potatoes display on the buffet. Mother sat down exactly three tables from me. She didn't get up again until after I left. Or maybe she is still sitting there three years later, I have no idea.

Here is the whole point to this true story: They weren't there to gamble; they may have taken in a show, but I guarantee children are not allowed in smoke-filled, alcohol-drenched casinos. They were there to eat. Plates of pizza and bowls of spaghetti and hamburgers and hotdogs and whatever they were drinking, I don't know. It could have been water or milkshakes, the glasses were too dark to see into. They had slabs of barbeque ribs and plates of fried chicken. There were mashed potatoes and French fries. There were knives and forks flying all over the place. The kids would take two or three bites out of a slice of pizza and then start gnawing on a cheeseburger. Back to the buffet. More food, more hotdogs. It was a damn eat-a-thon! All the time mom and dad are shoveling food in their mouths and grinning. You could have found Noah's Ark sooner than you would have found a vegetable on that table. What were those parents thinking about?

Now come the desserts. Oh my God! All I will tell you is this: One full line of the buffet was devoted to dessert. Dad was the first to jump in the dessert pool. When he came back from his first trip, I quit looking, I had seen enough. I swear to whatever you hold sacred, other people were watching this family just like I was. It was awful. I really felt sorry for the children. I wish every child born was loved by two parents. I wish every child had new, clean clothes. I hope every child gets to go on vacation and have fun in Vegas. But, I bet you three years later, if someone didn't intercede, those two children are both well over 200 pounds. And it was fat, not muscle. It was rolls of jellied fat on those children. Somebody ought to alert mom and dad to the fact they are killing their children because the two parents like to bulk up. Whatever... those two children were given a death sentence because the parents were out of control, addicted to food.

Have you been on an ocean cruise? It was wonderful... lying by the pool and the motion of the ship and the view... it was great. My pal Jerry Braam (one of the Body-*for*-LIFE Champions) took the responsibility of getting all the work done to have a cruise each and every year. I got my schedule worked out so I could go in 2003 or 2004, somewhere in there. Anyway, I give Jerry all the credit for putting the entire operation together and it was worth every cent. I don't think I have slept that well in years. The boat rocked me to sleep without fail; I want to go again soon!

Now let me tell you the downside. It had nothing to do with Jerry and it had nothing to do with the ship or the trip. It had everything to do with food addiction.

Don't get mad at me. Don't say I'm a party pooper, and don't say I'm hard-hearted and have no consideration for other people's feelings. You would be 100 percent wrong. If they are killing themselves and you are standing by grinning, then I love them more than you do. You have no idea what I would give to go back and ask John to "cut back" on the smokes. All I ever asked him was to not smoke in my car. That's the only discussion we had in 15 years about what eventually killed him.

I refuse to get into the argument about what ifs. What if the person doesn't want to quit? What if the person refuses to quit? What if they get mad at me for nagging? Well, what if bullfrogs had wings, they wouldn't bounce around on their ass all day. I think in the book of Revelations bullfrogs are going to have wings one day, but that's another subject.

Here is the only answer I have to the "what ifs": tell that person you love them but you refuse to let them kill themselves in front of you; you have that right. Tell them you will NOT contribute one dime to them killing themselves. Tell them you love them and they are free to do what they want but there is no law anywhere on any book that demands you ENABLE, FINANCE, APPROVE, or CONDONE what they are doing. Simple, isn't it? Remember, I tried to get someone off cocaine and it didn't work. All it did was wreck my health.

274

Remember, someone tried to get me to slow down my drinking and all it did was make me not be around that person anymore. I loved the liquor more than I did her. Again, simple, isn't it? If people do not want to get well and you cannot make them get well, all you can do is take the necessary steps to NOT be involved in their suicide.

A former roommate of mine hanged himself in the shower with a belt. He had a couple of addictions he couldn't handle. Nothing I or anyone else could say or do made him quit his addictions before it was too late. He had been in and out of every program known to man and he went back to his addiction. You tell me what we could have done to save him. A bunch of other people and I tried the "we love you approach" to no end. We tried the "come to Jesus approach" to no end. We tried the "come stay with us" approach to no end. His mom tried the "I gave you life and love you" approach to no end. So in the end, all we had left were two choices: We could stick around and contribute to his end, or we could tell him we loved him but we had to save ourselves from his life choices.

Since this is about food addiction, let me point out two small differences in his failure and the food addict. His tools of choice were a shot glass, a straw, and rolling papers. With the food addict, it's a knife and a fork and a spoon and sometimes a vending machine! If you put a chair at the head of the table at Ruth Chris's Steak House or a half a joint in a trash dumpster, he would go dumpster diving every time. It's the same thing with food addiction. Put a dozen people at the pool having fun, playing volleyball, laughing and swimming, and enjoying the day, or sitting on the couch eating six glazed donuts... the donuts win every time.

I got off on a little tangent there, didn't I?

Do I think it is more difficult to overcome a food addiction than a drug addiction? Maybe so. Food is perfectly legal, dope is complete illegal, and alcohol (my favorite) is somewhere in the middle. We have to eat. If we get hurt, and we have to have medicine and drugs to help us get well. I think the difficulty of the addiction is simply how far in the hook is. Stay with me. If there were a cruise ship that went out of Miami called the USS High and it was filled with crack and cocaine and alcohol and an all-you-can-smoke opium den and when you got on board, the captain handed you a bag of reefer and a souvenir lighter, drug addicts would be lined up trying to buy a ticket. Maybe their slogan would be "Stay High on the High Seas." Sounds ridiculous, doesn't it?

Now imagine you are extremely out of shape and about 35 percent body fat. Imagine you have high blood pressure and are borderline diabetic. Imagine you don't exercise and have no interest in gambling, don't drink alcohol, and your doctor has "warned" you that you are getting dangerously close to heart problems. Now imagine there is a sea cruise where you can go and eat from the time you get up until the time you go to bed. Suppose on this cruise there is a 24-hour pizza and burger/hotdog shack. Imagine on this cruise there is a midnight dessert buffet each and every night. Imagine breakfast is served from 6 a.m. to 10 a.m. and lunch is from 11 a.m. until 2 p.m. and dinner is from 5 p.m. until 9 p.m. Just for one minute imagine there is a cruise like that!

There is never going to be an all-you-can-shoot, smoke, or snort "Drug Cruise"… that is completely nuts. As a matter of fact, you better not ever take any illegal drugs in or out of a cruise ship. But… if you are a food addict, I just described damn near every cruise that leaves America every day out of every port. You know it and I know it and you can call it tough love or being mean or whatever the hell you want to. People who cannot control their eating have every right and no business on a 24-hour all-you-can-eat sea cruise… food is everywhere and you can't get off the ship. Don't go. At least, don't go just yet.

I'm going to get off the sea cruise after this thought. I had a ball. That was so much fun, and it was wonderful to see old friends and meet new ones. I can't thank Jerry enough for putting the whole thing together and all the work he did. Thank you again. That said, I am now going to reveal the lie I lived on that entire cruise. Here goes. I got up every morning and ate breakfast and worked out and went swimming. That's the truth. At lunch, I ate pretty healthy and enjoyed everybody's companionship. I was all over the ship and went on the shopping trips into the different ports. About 6 or 7 p.m., I would get dressed for dinner and absolutely had the time of my life. I tried to sit next to people I knew and some I didn't know. New friends and old friends. I loved it.

After dinner, I went and played the slot machines for a little while and mixed and mingled with the whole ship. If you didn't know me you would have thought I was the Events Director for the cruise line. Now comes the lie…

276

About 9 p.m. or 10 p.m., people started drifting off to the different shows and lounges and adult areas of the ship. There is some great talent on board and everybody was asking which show and where was I going to go and we will meet up at this lounge or that place and on and on. Great, it sounded fabulous to me. I did the lie four out of five nights on that cruise. I would tell them I had to go to the bathroom and I would meet them here or there or see them in the casino or whatever and save me a seat, be there in a minute... yippee!

With God as my witness on my mother's grave, all five nights, I went back to my little single-occupancy room, got undressed, read a couple of chapters out of two or three books and went to sleep, alone. One night I fell asleep on a lounge chair by the pool, woke up, and then went to my room.

The next morning a dozen people would ask me, "Where the hell were you, you should have been there, so and so threw up in a trash can he was so drunk, and A and B got thrown out of the bar on deck, and what's her name started taking off all her clothes, and you missed a good one!" Yes, I did. Somewhere in the day, a few guys would slide up to me and ask, "Who in the hell were you shacked up with all night?" Then they would start the guessing game about who it was. I would just grin and look away and try to change the subject and they would say things like, "You dog" and "That damn Freeman, you gotta watch him every minute," etc.

They meant well, but they didn't get it... I couldn't go in those bars and lounges. I know my addiction real well. You get me in a bar with my pals and different people buying me drinks and a bunch of single girls laughing and getting drunk and no limits and people trying to get it all in on vacation and more drinks and more people letting their boundaries slip and more drinks and more and more and I am right back where I was in 1997 and I can't stop. I don't want to stop. In that environment, I couldn't have one or two drinks and then start ordering soda; I want to get serious about drinking along about drink number three. So, you know what? I went back to my room and got a good night's sleep. It's not that I am stronger than you, I'm not. Here is why I didn't go when I said I would: I would still be there seven or eight years later and you would be gone.

One night Joey and I went to dinner at Charlie's Steak House in Orlando. It's become sort of a ritual when I get back to town now and then. So this night we are sitting there and laughing and talking and I am having a glass of wine and ask Joey what would happen if he just once had a drink. He again explained it so dumb me would get it. He said, "Porter, if I had one drink, just one, there isn't enough liquor in here to satisfy me, and so I don't have the one." I got it.

So the truth is, nobody ever came back to my room on that cruise. I never went to a different room and all the guys can think what they want. At my age, I appreciate the thought! I didn't do anything spectacular or anything that deserves any kind of credit. All I did was survive the night. Me 5, my addiction 0.

Now, tell me how you do it when liquor isn't the problem, fattening food is? Tell me how you get past the addiction when 50 or 60 percent of the event is based on eating? How do you make it five or six days up to your ass in the one thing that is killing you and everybody else is doing it and you shouldn't? When food and overeating is your kink, and you have to eat or die, what do you do? We don't have to have sex, drugs, porn, credit cards, gambling, smokes, alcohol, or a list of other stuff to live. We do have to have shelter, water, and food. You don't even have to have teeth to chew, but you have to have food.

What did you eat for breakfast? Did you have a couple of egg whites and a piece of whole-wheat toast with fruit spread? Or, did you skip breakfast and at work you will grab a cinnamon latte with whole milk and a jelly roll around 10 a.m.?

At lunch, somebody in the office is running to a fast-food joint so if they will, just grab you a ham and cheese with mustard and mayo and a bag of chips. By the way, Betty Lou's son is selling cookies for his softball team, so you will grab a box of the peanut butter and jam, double icing, and knock out about five of them after lunch. It's for a good cause. You really don't like sliced turkey and fat-free mayo on whole wheat with an apple. Yuk, who can eat that?

Now we are home for dinner, assuming we didn't stop off and have a quick beer or two after work. Here we can get comfy and take a load off. Got to do the chores and get ready for the same old grind tomorrow. So, a quick frozen meal in the microwave (some of these are actually healthy) and then catch the news and sit down for a few minutes. News then watch a rerun of Mayberry and now American Idol comes on. Dear God, I hope Frank and Beverly don't get voted off! Let's see who is on Dancing with the Stars... one and a two and a one and a two. You know what would be great right now, a bowl of ice cream and

I've still got some of the peanut and double jam cookies left from work. Yum yum!

That's what can happen five days a week and thank God the weekend rolls around and we can honestly reward ourselves and get something to eat we really like. I mean, what the hell? We have worked all week and we deserve a little something. You can't expect me to work all week and do house work and take care of everybody and not have a little something for myself. I believe I'll have the deep, double, all-meat, two-layer, all-for-me, none-for-you pizza! And two diet drinks please.

I repeat, there have been thousands of books written by far smarter people than me about food addiction. There have been millions of words published, there are hundreds if not thousands of programs and interventions available for food addiction. There are places that will measure the food, cook the food, freeze the food, and deliver it to your front door. All you have to do is heat it or eat it frozen, whatever you like. Try them all until you find the one that fits. I am not the answer, nothing I write or say is the answer. The answer is in you. I heard an expression that I believe covers it better than any other. I'm sure you've heard it, if not, here it is: "It's not what you're eating; it's what's eating you."

The only way in the world anybody would know me or of me is because in 1997, I read an article in my roommate's magazine about a get-fit challenge in Colorado. I won't waste your time with the details, but I did pretty good in the challenge and was absolutely blessed to get to move to Colorado and go to work for the outfit that started the Body-*for*-LIFE explosion. What an adventure that turned out to be... thank you, Jesus!

Anyway, one of the most fit people I met and got to work with was Shawn Phillips. We didn't hang out together or become best buddies, but he was in the building and in the gym and I would see him and talk to him at different times. He was a big part of the EAS and Body-*for*-LIFE success. Hell, he's on the cover of the movie Body of Work. I guess you could say he had a part in it.

One day I am sitting in his mom's office and Shawn walks in and sits down. There happened to be a box of Christmas cookies on her desk and as people came and went, they would get a cookie and go on about their business. Great. Merry Christmas!

There is a point to this story and I am getting to it. This guy wasn't the biggest or strongest person at EAS but without question, he was the most cut, lean, shredded human being I had ever seen. He didn't have enough fat on him to cook a single French fry. I have my favorite bodybuilders, athletes, and my favorite sports teams and have been lucky enough to attend the Arnold Classic in Columbus, Ohio, about 10 times, the Mr. Olympia three times, and countless fitness and health expos all over the world. When the subject gets around to best abs, Shawn Phillips' name always pops up. This guy knows abs. To know abdominal muscles and to have the kind Shawn does, it goes without saying you have to know diet, nutrition, and exercise. Look him up, you'll see what I mean.

Back to the story. I'm in Mrs. Klein's office; Shawn comes in, sits down, and reaches over to get a cookie. Then he gets another cookie and another and another and he finishes off all the cookies in the box. When he was through, he tossed the box in the trash can, burped, got up, said something, and left. I'm sitting there looking at the empty box in the trash can and realized Shawn just ate about 2,000 calories, 100 carbohydrates, and maybe 200 grams of sugar. I had had one of the cookies and suffered a sugar rush for about 15 minutes! Nothing was ever said about the cookies.

A few months later, we all went to Las Vegas for the Mr. Olympia or something and on the way out of town, they took me to a place I had never been. At the time, I think there was only one of these, but regardless, it was the "In-N-Out Burger." We go in and Shawn gets a double-double. What the hell is a double-double? It's a double cheeseburger with everything, a large fry, and the thickest milkshake known to man. That milkshake was like drinking a cup of chocolate butter! Shawn polishes his off and is eyeing the menu again.

I was eating as clean as a whistle back then and there was no way possible I was ever going to get abs like Shawn. What was the deal? How did he eat like that and stay at about 8 percent body fat? The answer was again, real simple… he wasn't addicted to cookies or double-doubles. I asked him how he did it.

"I don't do it all the time," he said. "I haven't eaten a cookie since Christmas and this is the first time this year we have been out to Vegas. I won't eat like that again until we come back out here or Christmas rolls around again."

The more I asked him about his diet, it became more and more simple. It was the same thing Eric had been telling me since February of 1997. Eric and Shawn were on the same sheet of music. You CAN have some donuts, you can have a plate of barbeque, you can have a milkshake, and you CAN eat whatever you want ONCE IN A WHILE. Shawn and Eric both told me you cannot reward yourself day in and day out and expect anything other than what you're getting.

If the addiction to food is slapping roll after roll of fat on you, trade it for one of those world-class workouts with the trainer of your choice. Now suppose you are eating like Christmas and Vegas every day and NOT exercising... then what? Then you can have a double... a double bypass, a double hernia, a double chin, a double dose of diabetes medicine. STOP... stop right now and make food work for you, not like something it's not supposed to be. It is not a lover, it is not pain medication, it is food. We attach an emotion or reward to it and that is wrong. We have simply moved the hole in our chest down to our stomach.

Get Shawn's book "Strength for Life." The first thing he talks about is "GETTING READY TO IMPROVE." Get the book, get ready, and get busy living.

Some people are addicted to success and choose bodybuilding and health as their avenue to success. If you are eating your blues away or if your addiction is food, then like me in 1996, you are addicted to failure, and food (or whatever) is the avenue we chose in order to keep succeeding at failure.

Stand out in the street with a bag of dope and eventually you will get arrested. Stand out in the street with an open fifth of liquor and eventually you will get arrested. Stand out in the street with stolen property and eventually you will get arrested. Stand out in the street with someone else's husband or wife and chances are you might get shot. Stand out in the street with a television showing porn and you will get arrested. Now, stand out there with a sack full of double cheeseburgers and two boxes of donuts and fried cheese and opinion rings and it is perfectly legal and perfectly all right. The only one that suffers is you. It doesn't get one bit better, life just keeps getting worse. I have never known

281

anyone whose life improved because they gained 20 or 30 or 40 pounds of lard on their body. It just gets worse.

Wait a minute, I just thought of something. There are a few times gaining 30 or 40 pounds of fat can improve your life: if you are a movie star! In one of the best movies ever, Robert De Niro gained a ton of weight to play the retired Raging Bull, Jake Lamotta. After the movie, he lost the weight. In the movie In the Heat of the Night, Rod Steiger gained a lot of weight to play the town police chief. I read somewhere he ate loads of pecan pie and ice cream to accomplish the weight gain. Keep in mind, they were acting… it was real acting (I think they both won Oscars), but it wasn't real life. If you and I are 30 or 40 pounds overweight and we are not preparing to star as Jabba the Hutt in a remake of Star Wars, then it "IS" real life and we are crazy for staying addicted to fat. I don't know about you, but Hollywood hasn't called me lately. I have no excuse to be 20 or 30 or more pounds overweight!

Let me go back to the cruise for a minute, I forgot something. One of the guys that went on that cruise was Marc Bennett. Marc was a judge for the Body-for-LIFE Challenge and one of the best men I have ever known. He was fit as a fiddle. This guy biked and skied and took advantage of all Colorado had to offer winter and summer. He hiked and mountain climbed and lifted weights and was very healthy. On the cruise he checked in at about 9 or 10 percent body fat. Everybody wants to look good on a sea cruise!

I would have to rent a warehouse to hold all the food he ate in those five days. This young man was not afraid of a knife and fork. He took full advantage of the buffet! Why not, he paid for it. He ate pancakes and donuts and syrup and hamburgers and pizza and chips and pasta and on and on and on. He drank more on that cruise then he did all year. He got every dime out of his ticket.

When we all got back to EAS and to work the following Monday, everybody was in the gym at lunch and I asked Marc how much weight he had gained the previous week? Are you ready for this… drum roll please… he gained a whooping ONE pound and 8 OUNCES! No way… I had watched him knock out about five pounds of chocolate goo at the midnight madness dessert-a-thon. Something must be wrong with the scales. No, the scales were exactly right. He had gained one and a half pounds.

282

Remember, this is about addiction, not cruises or anything else. The point is we now have living, breathing proof (Marc) that if you maintain a healthy lifestyle and you put healthy, intelligent, nourishing food in your mouth 90 percent of the time, you can do a full-court body slam on the buffet once in a while. What we can't do is eat like we are on vacation or eat like it's Thanksgiving or Christmas, every day ALL YEAR LONG. Food becomes an addiction and being healthy one day a month becomes our body's Christmas. We get it backwards. I am telling you that Marc and a few other guys and gals I know could leave tomorrow for a five-day cruise and come home weighing within four or five pounds of what they left weighing. So can you... so can I. We just can't go on a cruise day in and day out.

A short story by Porter: She got dressed. Today, she did all her shopping for the week. Between the fulltime job and the part-time job and church and everything else she had to do, there didn't seem to ever be enough time. Rush, rush, rush. Today was going to be extra stressful; her best friend in the world was flying in for a visit.

Everything was ready... the guest bedroom was perfect, all the towels had been washed and folded, and the apartment was spotless. Hurry, hurry, hurry. She had to be ready because they only had the two days together. Both she and her best friend had to be back at work on Monday. She couldn't remember exactly when the last time they visited, maybe two and a half to three years ago. They talked every week and stayed in touch since college, but this new job had put 500 miles between them. It was going to be so good to catch up and laugh and talk and revisit old times.

OK, out the door by 8 a.m., get to the grocery store, stop by the liquor store and grab a couple bottles of wine and some snacks, be sure and check the flight arrival time, home by 10 a.m. Get a quick shower, a little makeup, and head for the airport. Her best friend and college roommate was due in at 12:15 p.m. She made it to the airport at 11:30 a.m. Did she take the time to eat breakfast? She couldn't remember but she did have 45 minutes before the plane landed. That was enough time to catch her breath and grab a soda and a pack of chips. Whew!

It was 12:20 p.m. and her best friend is walking into the terminal, YIPEE! Hugs and kisses and you look great and you look great and how was the flight and I am so glad to see you, do you have any luggage and giggles and did you eat yet? And did you eat yet? And did you have a chance to get a bite?

I'm so glad you're here and we have so much to talk about but first let's go to this adorable little bistro they just opened. You are going to love the sandwiches. After lunch, I want to go across the street to my favorite coffee shop and let you try their double mocha caramel with whipped cream, you're not going to believe how good it is. They have these little cookie snaps that are fruit filled and I just love them. We'll get some to take home.

So after lunch and coffee and cookies, they get home and have a glass of wine and relax and laugh and talk and have a few snacks and it is a wonderful day. About 4 p.m. the hostess announces she has made reservations at one of the best restaurants in town. On Friday night they offer a seafood buffet and the girls need to be there by 6 p.m. It gets real busy by 7 p.m. They both hurry and get ready.

They are in the door of the "No Scales Needed" fish house at 6:05 p.m. Hmmm, what an interesting name. The car parker knows the young lady by her first name. She is a regular. They hit the bar and then the buffet. Fried shrimp and fried calamari and buttered pasta and scampi. Those are the appetizers. For the main meal, it's the fried catfish and it is out of this world. The chefs have added a drop of hot sauce to the batter and the catfish is to die for. Oh my God! Did you taste those hushpuppies, oh my God! I can't eat another bite, it was soooo good. I really couldn't get any dessert, I'm stuffed. But, could we go back by the coffee shop, I wanted to try one of those cinnamon espresso whips. For $3 more you can get the 24 ounce! OK, why don't we get a half-dozen of these fresh-baked lemon macaroons just in case you want something to nibble on later tonight.

The macaroons are gone by 11 p.m.

The next morning starts off with a visit to the Hungry Bear family-style breakfast buffet. Wait till you see how they do the pancakes. I don't know their secret, but I bet it's why they are so popular. I bet so too. They mix fresh bacon bits in with the pancake batter and they have real maple syrup. If you eat here four times in a month on Saturday morning, you get a free breakfast on the fifth trip. You can't beat it. It saves you $8!

What do you want for lunch?

Are you getting the drift here? It wasn't about seeing a dear old friend, it was about an excuse to go out and eat instead of hiding at home and eating. In this make-believe (some truth) story, the bigger thrill was in planning the menu, not in catching up. You know it and I know it, and if food is your addiction, as it was one of mine, everything revolves around what's next to eat. Before some of us can get up from the table, we are dreaming of, fantasizing about, planning and plotting our next feeding. There will never be enough food and the stomach will never be full.

I watch a particular preacher on the television raise hell with addicts and people in sin. He gives them "down the country" about letting God in their life and then, all will be fine. He knows the devil is behind all the dope these folks can't seem to do without. He knows the devil is making people watch porn. There is probably some truth to that, 'cause the devil sho'nuff knows your weakness. But there is some truth in this also. This fat-ass preacher is as addicted to food as the dope addict is to dope. One can't put the needle down and the other can't let go of the fork. One is legal and one isn't.

I'll bet the farm on this: If the government was to outlaw cake and pie and donuts tomorrow morning and attach the same jail time to desserts as to drugs, about half the people pointing fingers and raising hell and telling folks to "just pray" and quit their addiction would be living in San Quentin. They can't stop their addiction one bit easier than the guy who gambles his paycheck away. They are addicts just like everybody else. They're just real good at pointing out everybody else's weakness.

Get that sugar in your mouth and chew it up quick. It gets in the blood and the little receptors fire off some "dopamine" and your brain says, "Ahhhh." The preacher and the mayor and the fat policeman and the fat fireman and the soldiers who are barely passing the minimum PPST test are as addicted as anyone. And it's me... that's right, I would like to shut down this laptop and go get a cheeseburger and about six beers. I'm telling you, I want a plate of pork ribs and cornbread and some collards with white steak (fatback) in them. I could wash that down with a pony keg of cold beer. Don't you for one minute think I am above slipping back to my old "used to be." I am very capable of it. Each and every day I have to "work on Porter" to keep from being back in 1996!

I would love to eat whatever I wanted, I would love to be able to stay at 210 pounds and not sweat for an hour at the gym. I want to be LAZY... but on a 51 to 49 scale, I can't go back to that death style. It ain't a lifestyle, it's a slow, miserable, self-inflicted illness. That jumbo bag of salt-drenched, cheese-flavored, fried chips and that 70-carbohydrate, 300-calorie, 45- gram-of-sugar soda is taking the place of something, and I think I finally figured out what it is.

This is just me and I would love to know what you think. I will buy your book when you write it, but I think back to the lowest point in my life, something was violently missing. I say violently because the effect of whatever was missing was wrecking my life. Finally it dawned on me, it was life itself. I was substituting bad food choices at 3 a.m. for life. I was having parties and cookouts and Oktoberfest every Saturday, instead of really being alive. I love my friends (like the girl at the airport) and would celebrate any excuse or reason to cook out and party, party, party. Often, I didn't need a reason. Just cook and eat and eat and drink and drink and watch life go by wishing I were living it. I wasn't. Are you?

Tomorrow morning or afternoon or evening or whenever you get up, plan on eating four or five times. Try eating small meals throughout the day. Try to cut out the full-bore sodas. Try to cut back on too many dairy products (whole milk, ice cream, full-fat yogurt). Try to get in a little more water. And here comes the big one... try, just try, to hold off on the salt- and/or sugar-soaked treats. You know what they are. Go easy on the fried foods and lighten up on the red meats. I am a big steak fan, once in a while. Go easy on the alcohol. It sure goes easy on you; return the favor. Reward yourself after six or seven days and then start back again. You can, you will, just do it, if at all possible.

If you find that the health, family, and life results of horrible food choices don't dissuade you from making some changes, if people begging you is doing absolutely no good, if you live to put on 45 more pounds of fat, if nothing yet has influenced you, please get some professional help. Not everybody can do it alone. Some people have gone to college and learned how to help food addicts. Of course they will charge you for the help, but that's how they buy their food and pay their rent and sometimes it's well worth it. If you are broke, ask your local health department for free advice and free group sessions. Help is out there and available if you really want it. Oh yeah, one other thing... pray. There is nothing wrong with prayer when the task is too difficult for us to face it alone.

Pray for help when the temptation is always at the corner store waiting on you to come get it. Don't be afraid to pray; I wasn't and it's been helping me for the last 15 years. As a matter of fact, while we are on the subject, please pray for me, I need all the help I can get!

Chapter 21

You're Toast

It's all about addiction. Something we can't make it through the day without. Obsession is thinking about something all day long and addiction is acting on those thoughts. With so much going on in the world and with it becoming more and more difficult to get by, obsession and addiction seem like such a waste of time. Remember, Time DOESN'T go by, we do.

I'll try to be brief. I have been told I have the habit of starting to talk about one subject and end up rambling on and on and going all over the place. I'm sure that's true. One thought leads to another and then another and it reminds me of the old expression: It's hard to remember why you drained the pond when you are up to your ass in alligators. You have my solemn promise that won't happen this time. I am going to try and stay on the subject.

Hopefully this is the last chapter in this book. We are going to have a review, but this will be the end for me. I don't want to dwell on death but certainly, death brings a close to all addictions. As a matter of fact, it brings an end to all everything. You have read about a few people who chose it over rehabilitation. I can't help but remember Joey saying, "What if you die and nothing changes?" What a thought.

Since 1997, I have tried (along with quite a few others) to live a somewhat healthy lifestyle. The Body-*for*-LIFE program keeps on working if you keep on working it. I have changed it around a little bit but for the most part, I still get in the gym and still eat pretty healthy and only slip once in a great while. Healthy is better, end of subject.

I gained 5 or 10 pounds so many times because of schedule or travel or school or whatever, but for the most part tried to stay pretty close to 210 and sober. I have done really well up until recently, then the bottom fell out. Remember I started this book in the Magnolia Cemetery on Street and Walton Way in Augusta, Georgia. I am finishing it at University Hospital on Street and

Walton Way; I've gone 10 blocks up the street from the cemetery to the hospital. Looks like I am doing this backwards.

So here is the deal. I have had a birthmark on my back for 61 years. My mother had the same exact mark on her leg, same color, same size, same everything except the location. I knew it was there, but where it was located, I couldn't see it without a couple of mirrors. At my age, there is really no need for a bunch of mirrors in the bedroom. It was just one of those things and each year when I got a physical, the doctor would check it and say everything was fine. Life goes on.

This is important, so listen close because it's not about me, it's about you. There was a lot going on in 2010 and somehow life got in the way and I missed my annual physical. I felt fine and was on my new job and had moved completely home from Colorado and intended to spend a few years here and retire. That was the plan. I heard an expression once that said, "Want to see God laugh? Make plans."

Being on a police department, we all usually get a haircut about every two weeks. I go to the same place and most times to the same guy. He does a fine job. In April of 2011 while he is chopping my hair off, he mentions I have a small mole near my sideburn that looks like it might be changing color. He has been cutting my hair for about a year or so and he has noticed a slight change in this little mole. He sees this mole more than I do, so I take his word for it and make an appointment to see what's going on here. By the way... when did you have a dermatologist give you a complete going over? How long has it been? Unless you are married to one, you ought to think about it. On with the story.

The good doctor says it doesn't look like much of anything but to be on the safe side, we will snip it off and he will let me know. Almost as an afterthought the doctor says you're here, we might as well check your whole body, slip that shirt off. He checks my chest, stomach, legs, and head. He says for me to turn around. He checks my shoulders and arms, my back and stops dead in his tracks, "Ut-oh."

"Ut-oh what," I answer.

He says this doesn't look good and asks how long have I had this mark on my back?

"What mark?"

So he gets three or four mirrors and gets me positioned so I can see this dark-brown birthmark... DARK BROWN! What the hell happened? A year ago it was light tan, now it's almost black. It went south. Some time back a lady had told me it looked odd. How strange was that? I just blew it off.

The doctor says we need to get this biopsied. The mark meets all five characteristics for cancer. Cancer? I ain't got time for no cancer. Where have we heard that before? I make another appointment and the guy cuts a hole in my back and puts four or five stitches in there and I figure "ouch" and that's it and I'm glad it's over with. Not so fast, buddy roll.

Ring, ring... "Hello? Yes, Mr. Freeman, this is Dr. Skin Cancer's office and we have the results of the biopsy. How soon can you be in here?

Well, I'm off next Friday, will that be OK?

Can you be here any sooner?

No, I work 12-hour shifts and you haven't opened when I go to work and you're closed when I get off.

All right, Mr. Freeman, be here at 8:00 on Friday morning, we are going to see you first thing that morning. Mr. Freeman, be sure you are here. Good bye.

If you have read this far in the book, you know how this ends. See, there are no surprises with the truth. It was a malignant melanoma. It was the worst kind of skin cancer you can have. Two more cuttings and about 20 more stitches and they think they got it. Thank God, that was close. Whew! It made me think, my mother brought me into this world and now she was taking me out!

I waited a couple of days and go to the gym for a very light workout. Damn, there was a lot of pain in my back. Hmmm? I go see my chiropractor so he can adjust my back, and I thought I heard angles singing when he made the adjustment. It hurt and felt better at the same time. A couple of days go by and I am in the most physical pain of my life. It was like I had about three abscessed teeth in my back. It felt like I had a half-dozen broken razor blades inside my skin. My back was killing me.

I had to go to my regular doctor and when he sees me he knows something is bad wrong. He asks me to sit in a chair and I couldn't get up. The pain was off the chart. Off I go immediately to get 12 X-rays. The next day he calls me and tells me I have two broken ribs. Where did they come from? What has that got to do with so much back pain? I have got to get some relief somewhere. I can honestly say I would have done damn near any kind of painkiller that he prescribed. I wouldn't have cared what it was. It sorta helps me understand how people in a different world of pain will look anywhere to find a little relief. Some of the addicts we have read about and have known may have been running from a pain that the doctors couldn't see or diagnose. Maybe they didn't have insurance and couldn't go to the doctor. Maybe the corner drug dealer was their doctor. Maybe the lady behind the counter at the liquor store had the only prescription they could afford. I know I had to have some relief, and I suppose they had to have some too.

At this point I can't get my breath, sleep is out of the question, and all my hopes and dreams of joining the Great Wallenda's trapeze act are out the window… I can hardly walk. My doctor sends me to see a lung specialist.

The lung doctor is the third guy I have seen. Thank the Lord he had an elevator… he would have had to examine me in the lobby 'cause I couldn't have made the stairs. He listens to me try to breathe, asks how I got two broken ribs, and asks me to take a good old-fashioned deep breath. I took the deep breath, then I took a chair and then I almost took the floor. He saw it and I felt it. He scheduled me for a PET scan. Hell, I don't even own a dog.

In a PET scan, they shoot you full of a radioactive material that gets in your blood and roams around for a couple of hours. It goes all over the place, in your brain, in your toes, anywhere blood goes, this sugar-coated radioactive goo goes with it for the ride. Then you go through a huge donut machine for about an hour. It takes pictures of your entire body. The theory is, cancer loves sugar and the sugar will clot around the cancer and since it is radioactive, it shows up on the pictures the donut is taking. There, I have passed my medical school entrance exam. I plan to start a practice soon.

Waiting, waiting, waiting for a couple of days. Ring, ring… "Mr. Freeman, could you come by and see the lung doctor as soon as possible? Could you be here tomorrow morning at 10:00 a.m.?"

Don't know why he needs to see me to tell me I am all right? Maybe he just wants to charge me for another office visit, I bet that's it. Not so fast, Mr. Know it All...

I show up and I get another basic medical lecture about sugar and how the radioactive material and cancer loves sugar, and you did have the most serious type of skin cancer and if it did breakaway in your blood system, it can be set up all over your body and on and on and on. And we don't know why your ribs are cracked and they are in direct line with your melanoma and let's review your film.

All the pictures are in black and white. For what it costs to have a PET scan done, I wanted color and wallet sized. He didn't see the humor in that. We review the photos and there it is, a small spot on my esophagus. There is a gray cloud around it and although small, it is definitely there. It is directly in front of the incision in my back. He tells me it is not 100 percent exact, but to be on the safe side, I need to have a tube put down my throat with a camera or at the very least a CAT scan done. PET scans, CAT scans, and I think I am at the vet's office. He doesn't laugh at that either. This guy must have worked his way through medical school as an undertaker. Hold on a minute, maybe I shouldn't associate him with undertakers, I take it back.

OK, if it is this type of cancer and if I do have it, it isn't only in my esophagus, it can be anywhere, right? He says yes. If I did have it there or in my lung and I do take all the radiation and chemo and it is going to cost my insurance hundreds of thousands of dollars, and there is no guarantee of remission, correct? Yes, that's right. And if we get it under control in my esophagus, it could already be somewhere else by the time I am done with the first treatments? If, if, if, if frogs had wings.

I am sitting there thinking all this over and looking at those black and white pictures when I ask, "OK, doctor, let's say I do have it, it's pretty much terminal isn't it? Well, yes it can be. He reports it can be in two or three or five or more places at once. Again, if it is in the blood, it can set up housekeeping anywhere. He tells me there really isn't a lot of hope for patients if it is this cancer and it has advanced.

OK, now it's my turn to talk, how about this: I don't go through all the radiation, I don't go through all the chemo, I don't lose all my hair. I don't run up thousands and thousands of dollars in medical bills, I don't become a burden on my sister, I sell everything I own (which isn't much) and go live in New Orleans and party for whatever life I have left, then what?

OK, the doctor says, if you have this type of cancer and you don't get the CAT scan to be sure, if you don't take the prescribed medications, if you don't do anything at all about it, "You're Toast!" A few times in my life I have had someone say something to me I will never forget. Think about your life and things people have said to you, I can remember what I was wearing, what time it was, and what kind of baseball hat I had on… "You're Toast!"

There is a funny story about W.C. Fields when he was sick and on his deathbed. Supposedly, one of Fields' friends came in his room and found him reading the Bible. Since it was widely known that Fields wasn't a religious fellow, the friend asked Bill what in the world are you doing with a Bible? Fields replied, "Looking for loopholes"… that's what I was doing at the doctor's office, looking for loopholes. There were none.

I did go on and have the other test done and they came back negative. They couldn't exactly explain the spot or the cloudy area or the broken ribs but without surgery we will never know. It could be several things, but right now it isn't cancer. It may show up some day, but as of today the entire experience was simply a wakeup call. By the way, I want to publically thank all three doctors. They each have a different personality but they all had a common goal and that was to get me well. I'll never forget "You're Toast"… he knew how to shut me up and stop all my "what ifs." I'm glad I took the other test. Thanks, doctor.

When did you have a physical exam? When did you stop and examine your health and life? When did you last say, "I ain't got time for no whatever?" Somewhere in my tired, abused mind, I see a direct relationship between the cancer story and ADDICTION. Something (or somebody) can be slowly or quickly killing us. We may know it's there, but we ignore the signs. We don't have time to deal with it or we are smarter than it is and we will outthink it. No we won't. If Jessica had not gone and had the annual test, she would very probably be dead today. If Dianna had not been in such good heath, she may not have held on while she was bleeding to death. If Nelson Reyes had not gone at the insistence of his doctor to get that looked into, he very well might not be here today. You know my story. Since last year I have had two cysts taken out of my wrist, but there is no connection to the skin cancer, thank goodness. But we all had to stop and discover that the direction our lives were headed was a dead-end street. Maybe not with Dianna, but thank the Lord she was healthy and her body could withstand that shock. Are you ready for one? Am I?

This last paragraph is absolutely personal. I'm writing it so maybe my pals read it and at the very least consider my idea. I have two friends who I do not want to bury. I want them to bury me. They have accomplished more in the first 25 years of their lives than I will in all 62 of mine. I wrote about both of them in my first book. They are Duke Dearing and Jim Schneeberger. One was a Recon Marine in Vietnam and the other, a Selous Scout in Rhodesia. These have got to be two of the toughest men I have ever met. I'm not talking about MMA or the World Heavyweight Boxing Title, I'm talking about lying in grass 1 inch tall and having the enemy shooting at you and you are outnumbered and you fight back like a lion and go toward the enemy, not away from it. There are a lot of men and a few ladies I know, Leslie Hamblin and Luz Hendricks comes to mind, who I would want with me if I had to go to war. Remember, I said if I had to go down a dark alley, I would want Nelson Reyes with me? He's been down several dark alleys and always come out alive. That says a lot.

My pals Jim and Duke mean the world to me. Who means the world to you? Is it your son or daughter? Is it your dad? Is it your husband or wife? Who do you love and respect and admire and want to be around for a long time? I want a lot of people to be here for me to call and talk to, but I know it will eventually end. The thing about it is, I don't want to aggravate them and I damn sure don't want to waste the time I have with them talking about bad stuff. I want every minute with them to be fun and lighthearted and exciting and I wouldn't do anything to disrupt that. Now, I beg them to go back and read Jack's chapter again. Duke actually knew him.

I plan on drinking a lot more alcohol before I die. I plan on going to a couple more countries before I die. I want to see the Great Wall of China; I plan on having a few more dates before I die. I plan on figuring out where I want to be and who with as I grow old and rock on the front porch and hold hands with and slowly fade off into the sunset. I plan on maybe writing one more book with Eric Shrieves about getting healthy before I die. What I don't plan on is standing by the bed when they take out one of Duke's or Jim's lungs because they didn't CUT DOWN on their smokes. I didn't say quit... I didn't say start an exercise routine. I said CUT BACK on their smokes.

I am going to love these two guys if they smoke or if they don't. That has nothing to do with it. What I want is for them to think about what they have been through and if the unreal terror of their youth (that they survived) should end as they cough up blood and lung parts in a hospital bed 50 years later because of choices they make day to day. The enemy wasn't clever enough, or mean enough, to kill them, so he has waited for them to kill themselves. I am not asking them to quit, I am asking them to slow down. Ask whomever you love or care about to slow down on their addiction. Nobody else needs to hear, "You're Toast."

Chapter 22
Recovery

Killing time murders opportunity; don't miss another opportunity.

There is no shortcut to any place worth going.

A lie can take care of the present but it has no future.

Two things that are constantly with you, God and your body.

You don't have to live this life; you can sit on the couch or sideline if you wish. But you are going to actively participate and be the star player in your death.

First and foremost, the desire for wrong has to die in your heart.

You can't think yourself into right acting; you have to act yourself into right thinking.

There is this great expression: "You keep feeding the alligator hoping that it will eat you last." In addition, every time you feed the alligator, it eats a little piece of you. The more you feed it, the more it eats. In the jaws of addiction, you are your own alligator. No more feeding time!

Joey told me, "You can get in the 'House of Addiction' from the backdoor, the window, the attic, the sliding-glass door, the chimney, the side door, or a hole in the wall. But, there ain't but one way out. You have to stand up and walk out the front door. There is no side door to rehab!"

Feelings are not fads… they are not here today and gone tomorrow. They live in us until we really read them, readdress them, and mail them somewhere else.

People tell us stuff and we own it: parents, teachers, husband and wives, grandparents, boyfriends and girlfriends, friends and friends in sheep's clothing.

People with an agenda or a false witness and we attach a value to it and it dictates our lives. And then, we own it.

Addiction is something is missing in your life; rehab is finding whatever it is that is missing and replacing the addiction with it.

There is tremendous power in the draw created by addiction, but it pales in the power of forgiveness created by God. Addiction will give you up, God will never give up on you.

Power is not where we think it is… it is where we have not yet gone.

Rehab is getting the message out of your eyes and into your heart.

You be the author of your life on this earth.

Remember: You are dust and to dust you shall return. But, you are not now, nor have you ever been, dirt!

You were not created to come on this earth and die; you were created to come on this earth and live! Read that one again, please.

We have no say-so on being born. We have very little say-so on our childhood. Today, right this minute, if all things are equal, we have "ALL" the say-so in our future.

STOP! I want you to. The people who love you want you to. The Lord wants you to. Most importantly, you want to. You can and you will. Want it and act on that desire instead of the desire of the flesh. You are forgiven. God will be here to receive you. All is forgiven.

In the martial arts, there is an expression that says: The danger isn't straddling a sleeping tiger; the danger becomes evident when you try to get off. Now, almost 20 years later, I look back at my addictions and finally see how easy it was to slip into (or onto) them. At that time I wanted to be where they were. With Jesus listening this morning as I write this, I can tell you, even when the addiction no longer wanted me, I still didn't give it up. It had me. The sleeping tiger tore me up, would then walk away to lay down somewhere else, and stupid me followed it. Every time I straddled it, it tore me up again. This is as simple as

297

my GED-trained brain can make it... "Quit getting on the tiger, and it will quit tearing you up."

No idea who she is, but a lady wrote that every morning she got up determined to be a success and every night she went to bed a failure. Somewhere in her day the addiction got to her. She gave in to it. She didn't have to but for whatever reason, it started pulling on the hook and that began to hurt. The only pain medication was a bowl of ice cream or cookies or cake or candy or pie or sweets. She didn't want liquor or cocaine or porn or anything else except that chocolate bar in her desk drawer. I have said that line to myself every day since I heard it. "I get up every morning determined to be a success and I go to bed every night a failure." It does not have to be that way. Somewhere along the 16-hour ride, the hook began to hurt and NO wasn't an option. It certainly can be. You can change, you can get well. If you can't do it alone, there IS help available. You can recover from the pain of that hook. Tomorrow wake up and say, "Today I am going to be a success," and tomorrow night go to bed saying, "Today I was a success." We only have so many days left.

Once again we revisit Joey Vincent. He came to the absolute truth that his way wasn't working. Regardless of the program he found or the person he found or the religion he found, he had to stop drinking and do something else. Again, his way wasn't working. Is your way working? Mine wasn't, I had to stop what I was doing and try something and somebody different. If you are addicted and that addiction is killing you, or at the very least making you wish you were dead, before you completely surrender to the addiction, try a different surrender. Start by saying, "OK, I give up. I cannot beat this alone. I need help." If a guy as rough and tough as Joey Vincent can do it, so can you. I did and thousands of others have. It isn't always easy but neither is dying one drink or toke or snort or puff or needle at a time. That's the great thing about forgiveness; you get to start over from a new beginning.

PSALM 51: 1-2: Have mercy on me, O God, according to your unfailing love; according to your great compassion blot out my transgressions. Wash away all my iniquity and cleanse me from my sin.

MATTHEW 19: 26: Jesus looked at them and said, "With man this is impossible, but with God all things are possible."

Chapter 23
Reviews, Ramblings, and Opinions

Every day, something else happens that absolutely floors me. The list is too long and far too boring to write or read. I spared you the trouble. There are some things that didn't exactly fit in this book yet demand to be, at the very least, heard. Also, I started this book in 2008 and today it is 2012. I want to revisit some of the chapters and perhaps make a final plea to some of my friends and some of yours, in the sincere hope that we can all get a handle on whichever addiction is holding us to the fire.

Try not to forget, "the Devil don't always look like the Devil." He can look like a she and he can be warm and tender and exciting and we need him and we want him around all the time. That is right up until the hook is set and the Devil starts reeling us in. Then it's too late. Trust me, the Devil is always fishing. Keeping all this in mind and the fact that I can't spell "catt" nor have any formal, semi-formal, or casual training in addiction or recovery, I would take all this with a grain of salt, unless, of course, you are addicted to salt.

So many people in this book probably don't want to be. I can certainly understand that. Not everybody thinks like I do and far fewer have the "I don't give a damn attitude" I have cultivated over the last 63 years. As of today, I do not owe anybody one red cent, have never declared bankruptcy, have no children, and my entire family consists of three people: my step-dad, my real dad, and my sister. None of them can help being related to me, so please don't hold it against them. If I move to rural Mongolia, my three relatives will simply tell folks I am there doing a Body-*for*-LIFE presentation. All that said, let's get started.

Remember the chapter about smoking and my pal Jack? A friend of ours wasn't sure Jack played all four years of college ball. Maybe he did and maybe he didn't. We couldn't remember. The problem is, Jack has been dead about 20 years. That's 20 years we didn't have him here. We can't ask him about his college basketball teams or anything else. Wish we could, we can't. We CAN still talk to you.

Nothing has changed since I wrote the chapter about addiction to tobacco, except that probably more people have been diagnosed with some sort of tobacco-related illness. In my life, at some point I have dipped (Cheyenne Saloon) or chewed or smoked tobacco. I didn't do it for long, and I don't do it at all now. But I sure do understand how it calms you. I sure do. I do NOT object to having a smoke once in a while. I do NOT object to having a smoke once or twice a day, just not the first thing in the morning before you pee! It ain't my thing, but if you like a smoke after lunch and or dinner, have at it. It's America and you can smoke all you want. It's just this simple: Probably somebody loves you more than you will ever know and they wish you would at least cut down. Nobody said quit... you won't hear me say you can't get well from tobacco-related illness, you might. My last word here will be this: Imagine every time you smoke a cigarette, it's like tying a knot in a fishing line. For those of us who have been fishing, you know what that's like. Now suppose your life depends on you untying all those knots. Do you want to have two or three knots a day or 30 to 40 knots a day to untie? We hope it's two or three but you suit yourself.

June 2012. Concerning Jessica Brasington, I spoke to her this week. It was wonderful to talk to her and she sounded in great spirits. When I asked her how she was doing, she again put me in my place. Remember when I asked her why she was smiling and she had replied, "I was alive"? She did it again. She told me "To the best of my knowledge, at this time I am cancer free." Halleluiah!

Jessica lives in Charlotte, N.C., and is a business-develop manager, whatever that is. Her business card reads: "It's my business to connect businesses." More than likely, Jessica goes to a lot of business meetings and corporate lunches and dinners. I understand she has an occasional glass of wine at one of these functions. Here's what else I understand, she don't smoke at any of these events. She don't shove fattening, unhealthy, chemically-filled foods on her plate no matter how big the buffet. She makes the effort each and every day to exercise and get healthy, nutritious food in her body. And she gets her rest. You remember she had a slow dance with death, twice. Today, Jessica is acutely aware of the importance of good health. She has two daughters and three grandchildren and she WANTS to stay around for a while. Why play roulette with cancer? Like the gambling house, the odds are on cancer's side.

Remember Carl (not his name)? He was the good old boy that liked his cold beer until his "BUDDIES" got him started on the cocaine. They didn't force it on him; it was just there time after time after time. And the cocaine led to something else and that led to something else and he was smoking crack when it finally caught up with him. Please tell me when a 15-minute high is worth two years in jail? I don't believe I can get that high. It reminds me of a true story involving another buddy of mine. He will damn sure remain nameless.

This second guy was flying to a construction job out of state; he and another fellow were real knowledgeable about electric-cable connections and they had hired on for a two-month job paying a ton of money. I wasn't there but my pal was and he told this story. It seems like on the flight out of Florida, they were seated about two rows behind a loud-mouth drunk. That's a deadly combination: bad attitude and alcohol. It was a long flight and this guy had a few too many. This was way before September and security wasn't an issue. Anyway, the jerk keeps saying MF this and MF that and SOB and shit and damn were like every other word. Nobody said anything. Finally, finally out of the clear blue, my buddy gets up and walks up the two rows and sits on the armrest on the aisle seat. Do you know what's coming?

My buddy says, "Excuse me, but me and everybody else in hearing distance are sick and tired of your filthy mouth. If you say Mother F----- one more time, I am going to hit you so hard that whatever amount of time I spend in jail, it's going to be worth it. Every morning when I get up with those thousand other convicts and march to breakfast and go work on the chain gang all day, when I go back to my cell at night and sleep in the heat with some other sweaty convict, I am going to think about how good I drove my fist into your mouth and down your throat. I'm going to make that one punch worth it. Now go ahead and say something else."

It was a nice, quiet flight the rest of the way. Now, I repeat, I wasn't there, but my friend was and I believe him. The other fellow would have done it. I'm sure of it.

I know a female police officer who was driving home one night when she had to stop for a stop sign and let the traffic pass. She's a pretty good-looking lady and sitting in an unmarked car, looked like anybody else going home. According to her, there were three "thugs" waiting on the corner to cross the street. Again, I know you know what's coming. One of the "thugs" tries to open the rear door as they walk in front of and behind her car. Thug can't get the door

301

open and the policewoman puts the car in park, steps out, blue light on the dash and .40 caliber semi-automatic pistol in her right hand, takes aim and pleasantly asks the "thug" (in the most polite language you ever heard) if he would like to try and open her car door again? The funniest thing happened, all three thugs skipped away like little roaches do when someone turns on the kitchen light! Amazing, isn't it?

In those two simple examples, we learn: The consequences of our actions are sometimes NOT worth the thrill of showing off or breaking the law or making a poor decision. Whatever high and whatever addiction Carl was going to get that night was not worth the time in jail. Time lost is gone forever! The loudmouth and the thugs decided it wasn't worth it. Is the dope worth it? No, never...

If you are in addiction by way of drugs, you can get off addiction by way of drugs. If you are dancing with the devil, you can quit and start dancing with the Lord. If you are with the wrong person, you can leave and get with the right person. You can turn drug addiction around. It is probably difficult to do but hundreds of thousands of people have done it. I know this much... the dealer won't be there to bond you out. They are sellers, not buyers. If they don't sell to you because you are doing a nickel in lockup, do you think they are going out of business? They want you, but they don't need you. Remember this, you trust them to give you the good stuff to put in your body, but they can give you whatever they want to. They get it, cut it, take their taste, cut it again, and sell it on down the line. They are not coming to bond you out of jail and nobody can come bond you out of the morgue. Have you noticed there ain't any lawyers' offices near the morgue... think about it.

Happy to report my pal Carl is like Jessica, so far, so good. He is 100 percent drug free and working full time. I wish you could talk to him; he went from having to have dope in order to start the day to not touching it in several years. Please God, help him stay well, and if you are in that addiction, hurry and get well, there is a great big new-and-improved life waiting for you. Come on before it's too late.

I have no idea what happened to the other drug people I reported on; I never heard from them again. I hope they left the drugs and Orlando behind... or at least Orlando, because the drugs are everywhere. If they want them, they will find them. I knew a girl real well (hint, hint) who could have found Bin Laden if she thought he had an ounce of blow on him. Hell, we could have saved millions of tax dollars. She should be working for the CIA… I'm not being funny, it was sad. She could find drugs and she could find excuses; unfortunately, she couldn't find her way. God bless and keep her. If she is reading this, I hope she found a little peace. I hope you do.

Concerning Joey Vincent: I mean this with all my heart; he is one of the smartest people I have met in my life. Not because of his education, not because of his job today, not because of his boxing record, but because of his ability to do something that thousands, if not hundreds of thousands, of educated, beautiful, wealthy/poor people can't do… stay clean and sober. He wouldn't want me to say this, but that makes him a little smarter or, at the very least, a lot more in control than they are. How can a tough guy like him with a high school education be smarter than the bank executive or the doctor or the school superintendent or the mayor who can't give up their addiction? I guess it's simple… he is stronger than them, he wanted out, and he surrendered and he worked his program. One time a fighter named Pinklon Thomas told me, "If you work the program, it works for you."

I guess that's like a college education: If you work to get it, it will work for you the rest of your life. I am admitting here and now that I couldn't sit in class for four years and get a college education if it were at Harvard and my teachers were all Playboy Bunnies. The answer is NO. I don't want to go to school; I hate school, screw college. And I have paid for it a thousand times. Do you have a college education? Some jobs are completely out of bounds without an education. Some aren't. Any job I ever get will have to be less than college level. If you get one, it will work for you (maybe not in this economy, but someday). Joey got clean and sober and he works his college-level life program every day. Why can't you? Why didn't I for so many years? Because we choose to be addicted instead of graduating. Joey gets his Ph.D. every night when he goes to bed clean and sober. I sometimes continue to fail the grade.

If by chance you are dying in your addiction, you should look Joey up… you do the work to find him; I did and I am alive today because of it. He's in Orlando.

I haven't talked to Dianne Weeks in a month or two. I don't have to. I know where she is and I know every day she is exercising and doing all she can to improve her severed leg. A lot of people get hurt in auto accidents and some get hurt worse than Dianne Weeks. Wonder why I chose her to write about? A couple of reasons but one for sure was how hard and determined she is in the gym. Also because her life was as close to perfect as a life can get and then it went to hell. It can and might happen to us. That's the redeeming value about her story. She and her husband, Carl, had worked for 30-plus years to ease into a mild, comfortable retirement and to enjoy their grandchildren and to enjoy their friends, and after years and years of hard work, relax and rejoice and recuperate!

Not so fast there, buddy boy! Life reminded Dianne and her husband and her children that very much like a candle, it can be blown out in one breath. What in God's name could that have to do with addiction? Simply this: Dianne was in great health. She exercised every day and she didn't smoke and she didn't drink to excess and she ate healthy and she was in good enough health that when fate knocked the %$#@ out of her, she survived. Don't you get it? I do. If she had not been in great health, when her leg was gushing blood and the pain was off the chart, she would not have made it. Don't you see, she wasn't hollering for a cigarette when they were carrying her up the elevator, she wasn't yelling for a line of cocaine, she wasn't screaming for a drink of liquor (I probably would have been), she wasn't concerned about what movie star was dating what movie star, she was telling the surgeons, "Do Not take my leg. I am going to walk again. Do not take my leg." On a personal note, I wonder who George Clooney was dating that week and if Kim Kardashian was in love with a new boyfriend and if some rap artist was in jail for a drive-by and if Loretta had caught Moonie with some bar floozy? I guess when they were attaching what was left of Diana's leg, all that other crap didn't really matter, did it? That's why I chose her. She's real, and if not for her dedication to a healthy lifestyle, she would be on crutches today, maybe worse. What an amazing Lady!

Today, July 3, 2012 is a sad day for me and probably quite a few other folks. According to the local paper and cable news, three important things happened in the last 24 hours. The newspaper and TV didn't put them in order or list them alphabetically; they deemed them all newsworthy and reported them. First: Anderson Cooper is gay! OK, now what? How in the hell that made national news is beyond me. They might as well have said World War II was over. I want to announce here and now today, I am not gay... now what? Is there a party? Will it be in the paper tomorrow? Am I going to be asked to be in a parade? I don't know; I just don't get it. I think everybody in America should announce that they are gay, everybody. Then we wouldn't have to hear about somebody's sex life when nobody cares. I'm going to make an announcement concerning goat farm legislation I want passed. We have rights like everybody else!

Come to think of it, I hope some gay man runs for and gets elected president. We could have the first First Guy in the White House (as opposed to First Lady). Wouldn't that be great? We could hire the Queer Eye for the Straight Guy gang to come in and put some color in that place. It really needs some pastels and earth tones in those drab rooms. And the Lincoln bedroom, it screams for gold. Abe was no slave to fashion... and the pool, whoa dude... think of the parties. The Secret Service would really be secret.

I think here and now we need to apologize to Wilbur Mills. He was the Democratic Congressman from Arkansas who got caught drunk in Washington, D.C. in the Tidal Basin with a stripper named Fanne Foxe. You've got to watch those boys from Arkansas... I like that about them. Anyway, Wilbur is riding around gassed up with a firecracker babe from Argentina and gets caught. Eventually, it cost him his job. I wish he were still alive so he could have attended the Barney Frank and Jim Ready wedding. Barney wore a beautiful black tux and was stunning as the blushing bride or groom or whatever. We have come a long way as a nation, haven't we? You have the right to be whatever you want and love whomever you want and live two or three or four to a house. It ain't nobody's business. Go do what you want to do. Do two things for the rest of us, please: 1) be safe, I'm reading where they are hoping for a new HIV drug called Truvada, a combination of Emtriva and Viread. I honestly pray it works. But you still need to wear some protection! There ain't a piece of ass on this planet worth dying for; 2) if someone you know doesn't want to be as sexually active as you and if someone you know is a Christian, please show them the same respect you want. Everybody doesn't want or need to know about your lifestyle or wild weekends. Have some respect for yourself; it's your business, not everybody else's. Thanks. If you disagree with me on this, you are a homophobic, double-racist, race hater bater, conservative, liberal, right- and left-wing, commie, pinko , redneck, abortionist, klan, two-faced, people hater! Be sure if you "respectfully disagree" with anyone about anything they say or think, that you include at least two of the previous adjectives. Remember, as long as they are not hurting anyone, it's OK. That includes man goat love! I will be looking for contributions in the near future... watch the mail on how to join.

The next item reported Tom Cruise was getting divorced. It was on the news for 20 minutes; I was breathless watching it. I just don't know how I am going to deal with his breakup... it might be too much to handle. How about this: If our last name isn't Cruise and we are not kin to Cruise or his wife, it's none of our business. I'll bet there will be 500 photographers and news reporters at the courthouse when the divorce is final. Honestly, the world might stop for a minute or two. Let's hope not. That's just half the bet. Here is the other half: I bet when the next Solider or Sailor or Airman or Marine comes back from the war, there won't be five photographers to meet the plane. That's not Tom's fault; it's simply the way it is. As a country, I think our priorities are a little out of whack!

The last thing that happened was Andy Griffith died. My friend Kelly Jones sent me a photo of a Mayberry Sheriff Badge with the black mourning band around it. There isn't much I can add to that.

Mayberry was a lot like granddaddy's farm... it was innocent and you didn't hear a lot of ladies being called bitc&#s, you didn't have a lot of people getting killed over who used the last needle and lost the spoon. I know it wasn't real and I know that not enough minorities were represented in those episodes. Maybe the one Japanese guy who taught Barney judo could win a class-action suit? Let's look into it. I know they didn't have enough pregnant high school girls taking Barney and Opie to court for child support. My favorite episode was when they had the food stamp party and the mayor won and passed out because he drank too much. Lord, that was a good one. Remember the episode when they had the drive-by shooting at Mayberry High? Who can forget when Barney and Floyd and Gomer started that swinger's men's choir at the church and Otis sobered up and they won second place in Mount Pilot at the state contest? Remember? Who could ever forget when Andy told Barney to "Pop a cap in that mutha f*&^ %! I think we all know what was going on with Aunt Bee and Floyd....it was nobody's business.

So long, Sheriff Taylor. Thank you and Barney and Aunt Bee and all the decent characters that created a 30-minute vacation each day. I don't know if all those people are going to heaven, but I hope so. It would be that much more reason to try and live a decent life… maybe we will get to see them again.

The way I see it, Anderson Cooper and Tom Cruise were the lucky ones; their names were in the paper the same day that Andy Griffith was.

Back to the book…

What the hell, let's review the addiction to sex chapter and get it over with. Just like my pitiful sex life, this review will be quicker than you think. Unfortunately the sad news is, nothing much has changed since I wrote addiction to sex last year. More people (some innocent, some not) have died because of AIDS. That might be the worst news of all. There are grown men and women who know unprotected sex with several partners or with a new partner might reward them with a slow, horrible, deadly disease, yet while you are reading this book, it has already happened. Now they have the virus because they didn't take any precaution. Why didn't they listen? Was the attraction so strong that it couldn't wait long enough to get to the drugstore or for the test results to come back? I guess so, and that is one of the saddest things I know. Gay, straight, one partner, two partners, three partners, whatever, not one person should die because of an intercourse. Please be careful.

If you are a drug addict and shooting up with community-property needles, why not pick up some cans along the side of the road and buy a clean needle that no one uses but you? If you are hell bent on drugs and needles, don't you know that the other folks around you (except the dealer) are doing anything and everything, including sex, to get money for dope? Their blood might be infected and now you and he or she are using the same blood-infected needle. Whatever they picked up in an alley or front seat of a car or hotel room is now wandering around in your blood looking for a place to set up housekeeping. Don't do it. If nobody else is begging you, I will: Please don't sleep around with different people in order to get a few free drinks or a line of coke or a balloon of heroin or anything else. You and your body are worth more than that.

Are you determined to shoot dope? OK, just don't use dirty needles. Why kill everybody else and yourself just because you want to get high? It don't balance.

307

Back to the sex addiction… I think most everybody that has tried sex, probably understands the draw. Hell, sometimes it's so good we learn to do it by ourselves! Being in the bar business and hanging around gyms for years, I have probably heard every story about sex ever told. I know one couple and the guy complains his wife never wants sex and I know another couple where the guy complains his wife wants sex all the time. I should introduce them to each other and see if they can work something out! The kind of sex we are talking about doesn't fit in any of those categories. We are talking about addiction that is hurting you and your life, like addiction to porn. It's still there and more of it every day. Addiction to different partners as often as possible, even if you have to pay for them, hasn't gone anywhere. Remember, you either pay with money or with character, but one way or the other, you pay.

I can't speak for you, but I don't really care what kind of or with whom or why or any other reason somebody is having sex. In all honesty, I don't care what Elton John is shoving down his throat as long as it doesn't hurt his vocal chords! When some fool comes on TV and announces to the audience that they are gay or queer or lesbians or bisexual or trisexual or swingers or bull dykes (all words I have heard on national TV shows) or virgins or they are in love with small farm animals (now there's a show I would watch), please tell me what the hell difference it makes? Why would you think me or anybody else would care or give a damn about your sex life? We don't! If you can't get enough of sex, believe me, the people with you already know it. Nobody else cares.

Please put a high, high price on your body and on your character. It was paid for by the blood on Calvary. Have a little respect for it, or don't… suit yourself, it's your ass. I know they didn't film Calvary like they do porn, but I still believe it happened and we are all going to get to watch "Jesus comes Back" at a theater near you soon… it has to compete with 1,000,040,000 websites under "all girl videos"… good luck.

Listen, I was as guilty as anybody. I was addicted to the wrong person, and the amazing sex just added to the addiction. It can be so powerful that we seem to forget… if the person you're with now left somebody else because sex with you is so good, what makes you think they won't leave you if better sex comes along. Wonder if your sweetie is still in touch with his or her old flame? Wonder whose calling (or texting) who late at night? It ain't love; it's addiction to being wanted and being desired by all, and getting what they want for a little "sumptin' sumptin'." People can't seem to keep their damn mouth shut. I don't mean sexually, thank goodness, I mean talking. I don't care who you are, read that again, I don't care who you are, when you get to shaking your tail feathers around town, people talk. The more important you are, the more people they tell.

Some men never say a kind word. They drink a few beers, fart, smoke a cigarette, and go to bed. Three minutes later the lady has to get up and wash and then come back to what sounds like a McCulloch chainsaw cutting through three cords of wood. Then there is the guy who holds and kisses and looks deep into her eyes and says the right things and makes her feel like the Queen of Sheba. He gets up and gets a wash cloth and he sleeps on the wet spot and he adores you until you go to sleep... whoa, what you talking about.

That works both ways... she puts rollers in her hair, no makeup, burps, and has on a nightgown that never comes off, it stops at her waist. You hear sweet things like "Hurry up. Ouch that hurt, or sometimes.... get off me, you fat pig." A blowjob is completely out of the question. How romantic! Then there is the lady that about once a week puts on high heels and stockings, wears them (in the bed) and nothing else. She smells good and has on makeup and has this low guttural moan that seems to start from just below her naval... it finally works its way up her throat. Hold on for a minute, I got to stretch my legs...

I sort of see why the partner in both cases would become addicted to some other sort of stimuli if you are the first person in either example. Don't drive your partner to addiction... if you're getting at home what you're longing for, you won't be looking somewhere else. If you ain't, you just might.

Let's save some of this rambling for the religion review... but here's a few things to think about: Want out of any addiction, including sex addiction? Try some light reading this evening: EXODUS: 20 numbers 7 and 10. Having a little problem with who you are and not sure what the Lord might think of it, try: DEUTERONOMY: 22.5 then read HABAKKUK: 2.15... MATTHEW: 5.28 is a good one and ACTS: 15.29, ROMANS 1: 26-28, this can go on and on. I appreciate all the brave people who stand up for their rights and tell the world they are sinners living in sin and nobody can do anything about it. It is the way it is. I am very proud of them and enjoy going to their national conventions and seeing their parades. This is America and right now, you can still look and act and dress and live anyway you want to. Amen.

There is one small, slight problem... nowhere in the Bible does it say you can be both saved and lost at the same time. It's like being a little bit dead or a little bit pregnant... there ain't no such thing. You either are or you're not, no in-between. The word of God isn't Bud's International Food Buffet; you can't take some of the salad, skip the beets because you hate beets, then get some of the steak, but you really don't care for the fish so you don't get any. We don't get to open the Bible and say I think I will keep this Commandant but not those two... it doesn't work that way. If we surrender and say OK, enough, there will be a time and place for sex and it is a blessing. HEBREWS: 13.4.

I wish I could go back and undo some of the harm and sins I've done, but I can't. All I can do is ask forgiveness and try not to repeat them. But... I am human and so are you. All we can do is try. Pray for me... I will for you. As an after-thought, I was fiddling with a crossword puzzle the other day and 36 down was "breaking a Commandment"... it was a three-letter word and "n" was already there. I put SIN. I got it right. Then I thought about the people who want to eliminate three of the 10 Commandments because "they are outdated." I'm being serious. So, I guess pretty soon the crossword can't have that 36 down anymore, it won't be a sin anymore. Lord help us.

No need to rehash welfare. Damn few have got off the welfare train since I started this book and more have gotten on. Why would anybody get off? Have sex, have a baby, get a check. Have sex, have a baby, get a check. Sex, baby, check. See, my teachers were right... I do need algebra. S+B=C. Sex plus baby equals check. No sex, no baby, no check. And all of God's people said "well" and started singing Kumbaya.

Some idiot actually said that all children were a blessing from God and it wasn't our place to question a wonderful gift from heaven. Let me go get a trash can, I am going to throw up. If you and your husband or wife are working and you can afford a baby and you are in love and in a church and you are ready for children, what a blessing from the Lord. Some of my friends have convinced me that their children are the BEST thing that happened in their life. God knows what he is doing. Even my friends who are divorced both still love and adore their children. They quit loving each other yet they kept right on loving their children.

But... everybody doesn't love their partner. Everybody ain't married. Everybody doesn't love their children. Everybody who gets their love thing on doesn't have an aunt or grandmother or mom to keep, watch, bath, raise, love, and educate their children. I know you are not going to believe this but some people squirt out kids with different partners or the same partner and never give it a second thought. No church (except for the free meals), no marriage (except for the married people they run with), no education, no job, no need for any of that because somebody else will NOT let the child do without. Again, the child is innocent. Nothing is going to change until the Lord makes his return visit; it's just going to get worse. Sorry.

This happened within the last 48 hours. And I repeat that addiction to screwing and having babies caused it. Maybe you will see nothing wrong with it. Maybe you will say so what? Maybe you do it, how would I know? Maybe you don't? Maybe. I get off work at 6 p.m. and stop by the drug/grocery store on my way home. A guy and his children are in the store and when I walk in, he tells them, "If you don't behave, that policeman is going to get you." Wonderful, on 13 levels. If that child is ever a victim of a crime, he will run if he sees a policeman coming because his father has instructed him "he will get you"... So I smile and say to the child, "No we won't, we are here to help you." The kid doesn't speak, he just stares and looks afraid. I go on about my shopping.

A few minutes later on another aisle, I hear dad say, "Put that up goddamnit, I'm gonna beat your ass if you touch that again." No idea which child he was talking to. One looked about 5 and the other about 7. I shook my head and went on about my business. Here it comes, me and about five other people hear someone say, "Mother f*&^%$, I told you about that, get your goddamn ass in the car. I'm gonna beat your ass." I put the two or three things I was carrying down and walked out the door. I don't really deep down in my soul care if you believe this story or not. The guy probably grew up in a world that talked to him like that when he was a child and now, the circle will be unbroken. The children were in a drugstore where there are hundreds of things a child will touch and look at and want to play with. What did he expect? If the dad didn't want to take the time to teach his sons that a police officer will help you and you can (about 99 percent of the time) trust them, what should we expect when they are 17 or 18? Remember, we aren't all Wyatt Earp. And the circle continues to be unbroken.

When dad was getting his groove on, did he think about "I am going to have to teach this child about God and life and forgiveness and health and education and sacrifices and respect, and it is going to cost about $250,000 before he gets out of high school?" Did he wonder if he was going to stay with this child's mother for eternity? Did he love the child's mother? Are they even his children? Who knows? The children were born, they are here on this earth, and they are literally doomed if they are going to be talked to and dealt with like they were. And the circle will be unbroken... they will have children and "you do what you know"... you tell me the answer, I don't have one. Not one time did I say Chinese or white or black or German or Hispanic or Hawaiian or Greek or anything else. It doesn't matter who dad was, it was so much more about who he wasn't. He was NOT capable in his present frame of mind and value system to be a dad.

Not much new to report on the gambling front. We still have 48 ways to scratch off a ticket from $1 to $20... there are so many daily 3 and 4 and fantasy 5 and money for life and on and on that I don't bother to count them. I think it would be a safe bet to say there are 50 ways to leave your lover... I mean leave your money at the lottery counters or machines every day.

I still believe going to Vegas is one of the most exciting trips I have taken in my life... it was wonderful. I also went to Philadelphia, MS to a casino to do a Body-*for*-LIFE presentation. That was a pretty nice place also. The cruise with Jerry Braam was wonderful, and I gambled away almost $13. But, nothing compares to Vegas! The Chamber of Commerce hasn't asked me to endorse Vegas, and I am not getting a penny discount from anybody there (they don't need my money, they've got everybody else's), but if you haven't been, go. What a place...

Wonder what Atlantic City is like? I hear good things but on a policeman's salary, it won't happen any time soon. I'm going somewhere else on my vacation. All that said, if I ever go, I will take exactly what I can afford to leave there. I will continue to buy 1 Mega Million and 1 Powerball ticket each week and keep my fingers crossed they come in. I hope you buy a ticket now and then and I hope you are a winner. Keep in mind that in every race there is one winner and the rest aren't... don't put all your money on the good chance of being an "AREN'T." Gambling is fun and exciting if you take exactly what you can live without and QUIT when it's gone. Please don't stay underwater week after week hoping to win a ride on the Queen Mary when all that's coming by is the Titanic.

More news this week about shark attacks. Some guy in Australia was bitten in half by a shark and his buddy saw it happen. God, that's got to be awful. I think of my friends: Eric and Bill and Tommy, Kelly, Duke, and Jim and a few others and the thought of seeing them cut in half by anything is too much to bare. I feel safe in saying, they might get shot by a jealous girlfriend or maybe an insane wife or some other bad behavior, but they won't be eaten by a shark. The sharks were here first and my friends respect their territory.

When I watched the news about the shark attack, the Australian government was hunting the shark to kill it. Think about that for a minute... we go into the only place the shark can live and survive and when it does exactly what nature has taught it to do for a million years, we kill it. BRAVO, GOOD SHOW, MATE... kill them all. Makes me think about the American Indian... we came here and took and took and when the Indians stood their ground (or land) we slaughtered them. BRAVO, GOOD SHOW... we taught them a lesson, yes sir. And it was everybody, white, black buffalo soldiers, Germans, Irish, all the men in the Army took pride in their military history. So, I trust the Aussie shore patrol will catch and kill several dozen of those renegade sharks that had no business swimming that close to shore. The nerve of those fish... maybe they should put "No Swimming" signs 100 yards off the beach in the ocean so the sharks will read it.

No more than I want to be eaten by a bear when I snow shoe and no more than I want to be bitten by a rattlesnake when I bike and no more than I want to be blown up by a suicide bomber when I fly, it can and sometime might happen. Go back and read the chapter on sharks again... what were they thinking? I am so honestly sorry for that guy and his family, but he loved to surf... a healthy activity that will always be conducted in a very dangerous environment.

This is a review, so let's review: You are walking through life and you have no addictions. You try something by choice or by accident (falling in love with the wrong person) and slowly, but quickly because you don't see it happening, you have to have the thing that you wanted so much but is now hurting you. Suddenly it hurts more to be without whatever is hurting you than to break away from it. What a mess we find ourselves in... the good news is we can GET OUT... no more expected pain. No more lying to ourselves and others. We know the truth and usually they do too.

I have a friend who is getting off methadone... he had some horrible surgeries and had to have morphine and all kinds of pain drugs. After a couple of weeks in the hospital and pounds of drugs, the doctors are easing him off of drugs; they can't just stop them cold. Mentioning cold, he lives in Florida and the temperature has been around 100, but he tells me he is freezing. As he comes off this drug, he stays cold and his teeth actually chatter during the day. He wears sweaters and sweatpants but is still cold. The good news is, he is getting better and better and soon will be completely off this medication, thank God. Do you see why Dianne didn't want to take any?

Now, think if you are sick and cold and the only thing that will hold you over is another dose of some street drug. Don't sit back and say, well, all you have to do is quit. It isn't that easy. This is a strong guy who was hurt terribly and had massive surgeries. A team of doctors are monitoring his ever-decreasing level of drugs and he is still sick as a dog. For the sake of argument, imagine he was someone who was being fed the drug as a control agent and had to find some relief from the pain somewhere. Addiction to relief is easy; addiction to pain beyond normal people's concept is too hard to explain. You can draw the line on addiction with people you love and care about, but please offer them some other form of help when you do. I tell you here and now, I could not have gotten out of my addiction without Eric and Joey's help. I could not have done it alone.

Go back and read the dog chapter again... I can't add anything to that. Well, hold on a minute, maybe I can. The only thing I thought of that would make it worse is if you were in love with the dog.

Good old food addiction... really nothing has changed there. Have you been to New York City? What a place. It's bigger and more alive than I can explain. I went there and had a blast, and.... I went there a few weeks after 9-11. The guys at the PAPD made it possible, and I wrote my best effort to explain what I saw and felt. It was 100 percent horror. But, NYC came back with both barrels. It is alive and jumping and as exciting as ever. Let me take a minute and thank Dan Rather. Regardless of his career after 9-11, I stayed glued to the TV and radio listening to his reports for the next 10 days. Thank you, Dan. By the way, on 9-11 I was in the Detroit Airport, in the holding room getting on a plane when the first plane hit. They got us off the plane before the second one hit.

Back to food addiction and NYC. They have the best food ever. You can get ethnic food and cheap food and expensive food and you can eat Italian, walk across the street and eat Chinese. And the Delis... OMG! They have Jewish food and Arab food and Greek food and you could eat from here to next Thursday. So here is my question... did their mayor really make it against the law to have a soda over 16 ounces? You have got to be kidding. That has got to be part of a comedy routine from a Broadway play. Let me get this straight. A 12-year-old child can walk in a donut store and buy two dozen cream-filled, double-glazed, chocolate-drenched donuts and buy a peppermint-white-chocolate-caramel-dripped-ice-cream-whipped milkshake to wash the donuts down with, but she better not put it in a 17-ounce cup. Brilliant! This guy is a genius!

By God, you can order and eat six cheese, double-deep, heavy-on-the-pepperonis-and-pork-sausage, 18-inch pizza pies, but if you get an 18-ounce soda to wash it down with, you're gonna get whacked by the mayor's Food Police. That's like spending your last dollar on a wallet and then you have nothing to put in it. I don't get it? Maybe I don't understand how it works. I'm not as bright as the mayor of Salley, South Carolina, much less the mayor of New York City, but it sounds like a money-making scheme to me. What's he going to do, go to every wedding in NYC and have the Food Police measure the brides and tell them how much wedding cake they can eat? Enough about the mayor and New York, you like his ideas, reelect him.

Seem to remember a program on television about really obese people who were getting to the "can't move" stage. There was this one lady who could pack it away. I don't remember if she smoked or drank, but she could get serious with a knife and a fork. Anyway, I think the producers did it on purpose to film her reaction when they placed a plate of fresh-baked chocolate chip cookies on a table behind her. Do you remember this program? Regardless, she had eaten all morning long and had to be full, but in addiction, you never get full. As the interview proceeded, she smelled and became acutely aware of the cookies. Everything changed. Her attention quickly went from the interview to the cookies. She couldn't really move to face them (they were behind her), but she could strain her 22-inch neck to look at them, and she did, constantly. She began talking about them and finally she broke free and went to get one... two...

three… all of them. You could have put a pound of cocaine up there, nothing. You could have set a bottle of booze or a carton of cigarettes up there, nothing. But buddy, like a duck watching a June bug, she couldn't take her eyes or mouth off those cookies.

You don't have to drink booze, you don't have to smoke, you don't have to reproduce, but you got to eat. What the hell, for a few days why not try and eat clean? You can go back to lard and sugar and fat, it isn't going anywhere, but why not at least try? If you can't make it a week, try for a day or two. If you can't do it and you refuse professional help, I don't know what to tell you. I wish I did, but I don't. There is help available and I urge you to go get it before you can't go get it. You do not have to be 100 pounds overweight. Remember that, if nothing else, you do not have to be… there is no rule that says you do. You are 100 pounds overweight because you "want" what is causing it more than you "want" to be fit and healthy.

OK… my addiction was alcohol and the wrong lady. I drank professionally. I worked in bars and was around booze 16 hours a day, week in and week out. Plus, I liked to drink. I liked it a lot. I still do. If you are not an alcoholic, I cannot explain the draw of a drink at the end of a day or with your buddies or for no reason at all. You blow into some new and strange town and don't know anybody, there are two places you can go and meet people and usually feel welcome: church and a bar. There are chain restaurants that include that "you are never alone" message in their commercials. It works.

Have you seen the beer commercial where the two drunks are passed out in an alley and are surrounded by 48 empty beer cans? Have you seen the vodka advertisement in that men's magazine where the lady is in a straight jacket because of the DT's… I remember that one guy who broke his car key off in the kitchen door so he couldn't get in the house and he couldn't open his car with the house key so he slept in his drawers on the hood of his car. What an idiot! By the way, there are no such commercials or advertisements, but you are reading the words written by the idiot on the car right this second. Never again, I swear.

The thought of an ice-cold beer in a frosty, cold mug is inviting. The idea of a glass or two of wine before dinner is great. The idea of a shot of liquor over a couple of ice cubes and a splash is calling my name right now. It all sounds so inviting except there is a little more to it. It can, not always does, but it can lead to addiction. I don't think alcohol is the end game; it's just the avenue to the end game. If you don't like where you are, and you can't leave, alcohol will make you think and feel as if you are somewhere else. It can kill you while it is taking you to the land of "no pain." I have thought about this so much and don't know how to explain the draw it has on some people (including me). Let's try this explanation:

It is perfectly legal for a parent or grandparent or legal guardian to let a 16-year-old child who has a "LEGAL DRIVERS LICENSE" drive the parent's car. From experience, every police officer in the USA has probably stopped a car for some infraction and the driver was 16 or 17 years old. It is perfectly legal. The state says if you go down and pay the fee and take the test and pass it, you get a license to drive. Some places you can get a learner's permit at 14 years of age. Don't believe me, look it up. You can't go out and start driving a cab at 14, but you can get a learner's permit, and each state is different but you can legally drive. At 16 in almost every state, you can drive by yourself (no adult in the car) as long as there are no more than three other people in the car and it isn't between midnight and 6 a.m. Regardless, you get my drift on all this... it's legal for a 16 year old to drive a car. I don't think they can own one but they can drive a car. OK.

Here's where I am slowly going with this: There are about ten 2012 model cars that come with 500 and 600 horsepower motors. These cars can go from zero to 60 mph somewhere between 3 ½ seconds and 6 seconds give or take a half-second either way. They have a listed top speed of between 130 and over 200 mph, give or take a few MPHs. Some of you already see it coming, don't you?

It is perfectly LEGAL to let a 16- or 17-year-old child who has taken the courses and passed the test, drive any one of these above-listed cars (or any other street-legal car) on a public street in America. And it happens and you and I know it. All they have to have is the little piece of paper in their pocket saying they have shown the MINIMUM ability to control an automobile. What we all hope is that parents and grown-ups have enough brains to not give a child a 3,000-pound car that is built to go 150 mph. The old station wagon in the garage will probably do 90 mph flat out. We have to assume someone will think it through before they give a 16 year old a land rocket.

317

Now apply that to alcohol. Let's say a 21-year-old guy walks into a liquor store and as he stands there, he remembers all the pretty girls in all the advertisements in all the guy magazines. Let's suppose he remembers all the fun everybody was having at the parties in those commercials at the "club" and the ball games with the in-crowd. Do you think a little voice in the back of his head is going to say "drink responsibly"? Do you think the first time some cute girl shucked her drawers and told me to "slip on down to the oasis" that my mother's voice and warnings danced through the front of my head? I had something else on my mind... same thing with the alcohol. You ain't thinking about the end result. Yet it is absolutely 100 percent stone cold legal.

Did you take a course in school about alcohol? Did you get a learner's permit to start sipping booze at 17? Did anybody sit down and explain all the ramifications of abusing alcohol? Some places can't teach sex education because so-and-so's parents don't want their child to ever touch pee-pees. Brilliant! Do schools today teach anything outside of Driver's Ed about drinking? I have no idea. Nobody taught me that three or four beers will make you laugh and dance with a lampshade on your head and six or seven will make you mad and fall down. You learn that on your own. A lot of my friends thought if three is fun, 10 must be nirvana. I had so much algebra shoved down my throat between the and grade that I quit dreaming about girls and started dreaming about fractions and square roots. But not one word about alcohol. I have used algebra one time since 1968. I admit I needed it and it worked. I took my algebra 1 book and put it under the broken leg of a table. Leveled it right out. That algebra works!

I guess the thing is, we need to teach people that alcohol works. One or two, no problem. Keep drinking and problems come with the territory, and if you like to drink, if you have an addictive personality and if buying gallons of booze is legal, you can get in a hell of a lot of trouble quick. I should know. Teach your children about alcohol. It's a must!

What a sad day yesterday was. Some dude goes into a movie theater and starts shooting people for absolutely no reason. It doesn't matter one iota if the innocent people were black, white, Chinese, Latino, young, old, babies, or where they went to school—it all didn't matter, and their sexual identity was of no importance. They were just innocent people going to watch a movie. Because I am trying to be a better Christian, I, like so many Americans, said a prayer for them and their families. I sincerely hope they are at peace with whatever God they believed in.

I don't know if gun control is the answer. I wish this morning that somebody, anybody, would have had a concealed weapons permit and had it with them in that theater. If just one person had been armed besides the shooter, maybe things would be different this morning. I lived in Colorado when Columbine happened and wrote about it in another book. I mean, a public theater, maybe something bad will happen. A mall, maybe something bad will happen. I remember in Killeen, Texas, in 1991, a shooting happened at a restaurant called Luby's. Anybody remember that? Remember those three or four police officers sitting at that table doing paperwork and the shooter walked in and started blasting... but a high school? How can you prevent these horrible events from happening? I don't think you can, so you better be prepared one way or the other. If you don't like guns and you are not willing to train and learn and get a license to carry one, you better be sure and attend church on a regular basis! If you are getting shot at and you can't shoot back, you are going to need the Lord more than you know. Like abortion and capital punishment and freedom for all religions, people are going to be split on gun issues forever. I'm not trying to talk you into one or out of one... that is your decision.

Day before yesterday, I watched a video about a 71-year-old guy sitting in a computer café in Ocala, Florida. That's a neat little town about 50-or-so miles northwest of Orlando and Sanford. Anyway, the cafe is busy and all of the sudden these two charming young men burst through the front door with a baseball bat and a gun. They are wearing hoodies and although I got no audio, I could pretty much make out they were robbing the place. It was an old-fashioned stick-up! Well, 71-year-old grandpa eases his .380 pistol out of his shorts (the report tells he had a PERMIT), and he changes the circumstances around a little bit. He starts shooting back! Guess what? They skedaddle right on out of there. Were they going to start killing people? Were they on a little league team and the bat was for fastball practice? I looked at the video three or four times and never saw a home plate. Maybe they were just lost. Maybe, just maybe, that 71-year-old man PREVENTED another mass slaying by some deranged piles of $#@& that wanted to rob and "maybe" kill people instead of working for a living. I guess I am politically incorrect to view this as I did. Remember, it's better to have a gun and not need it than to need a gun and not have it. Amen. Probably

319

this is a good time to either address hate or religion. They both seem like they would flow with the tempo of things. I'll go with religion...

Neither you nor I know what is in a person's heart. In truth, the only person who knows is the person themselves. I do not know if I would have the character of a Todd Beamer or any of the other people in Flight 93 on 9-11. I don't ever want to find out. They were put to the true test and at the cost of their lives, they passed with 100 percent. They knew they were going to die, but they were not going to let the hijackers kill any other innocent people. I can't think about that and not get a little emotional. They and the people who ran into the burning towers have proven with their lives who they really were. God bless them all.

A friend of mine was nominated for the Silver Star for actions in combat. He was on a helicopter and landed in a "hot" LZ in order to extract a squad of guys who were catching hell. I believe he was a door gunner and jumped off the ship to help the ground unit get on board. He was telling me this story over quite a few beers in one of the joints I used to run, so I might be a little fuzzy with the details, but let's keep going. I did later read the citation, so I think I got it about right. Anyway, he is getting guys on the chopper and bullets are flying all over the place. The ship is getting shot up and the pilot radios to get on board; we have to get out of here, now. Well, my pal looks up and sees a wounded grunt lying on the ground about 40 or 50 yards in front of him. There is nothing between the ship and the grunt except my pal and behind the grunt is about a hundred bullets a minute coming at the soldier, the door gunner, and the helicopter. It was a bad situation for everybody except the ones in the trees.

My pal starts on a dead run for the wounded guy. No questions asked. He runs like Jesse Owens in Berlin. My pal gets to the wounded guy and does the old fireman's carry and starts running back to the chopper. They both make it. He has a ribbon to prove they made it. I asked him if he could remember what he was thinking when it happened. He said he was scared to death but if it had been him out there, he would have appreciated somebody coming to get him. My pal showed what was in his heart. No question about it.

There are thousands and thousands of examples of people who "show" their true colors... missionaries come to mind. Young Christians who go to help starving people in places you won't find on a map. Not cramming it down anyone's throat, but they're working to improve a life... as are soldiers and military of all branches that step into harm's way damn near on a daily basis. Cops and firefighters and first responders who, when called upon, are willing to give their all for innocent people. At 63 and with everything on me hurting, I'm not much of a policeman, but I think if I had to, I would try my best to do what was necessary. Hope I never get tested.

If you drive by a hospital today, walk in and say thank you to all the medical personnel in the emergency room. They see it all and sometimes you never see them. By the time we wake up and get discharged, we are on a ward and never go back to the ER. I could not do what they do. I could not deal with what they deal with for 8 and 10 and 12 hours at a time. Thank you to everybody in every ER in America. Lord knows we need you! By their fruits, ye shall know them.

Now, tell me what is in the hearts of the Money and It's All Going To Be All Right preachers? I can't stand them. They have every right to do what they do. You have every right to believe them and send your cash, if you wish. One day somewhere here or in eternity, the truth will be known. I want to ask God what it was about those men and women that he chose them instead of my grandfather. If the examples I mentioned above are people who show their hearts and intention day in and day out, what are these television preachers (male and female) showing us? They all have houses that could be on the cover of Better Homes and Gardens, most all have chauffeurs and some have jets and homes with runways and yachts. Damn, God has been good to them, hasn't he? Remember Reverend Moon? All those followers were out day and night, rain, sleet, or snow, selling flowers. I never saw the reverend himself out there, did you?

How do you learn the anointing thing? How do you learn to make people you never heard of come up to you and give you the 30, 40, 50,000 dollars they won last night in the lottery? Is it their cologne? What breath mints do they use? Please, somebody get them to share the secret of their divine healing powers. Here is the deal. For the life of me, I cannot understand why they don't go to the VA hospitals and heal the sick and hurt veterans who are returning from Iraq and Afghanistan. Aren't those folks Christians also? Why aren't the Holy Ghost preachers like Benny Hinn and Mike Murdock and Todd Bentley and Prophet Manasseh Jordan and Todd Coontz and Creflo Dollar and many more sharing their wisdom with all the people on welfare? Maybe they are. I don't follow them around to see where they go and what they do when they are not on television. Maybe they are in the mission fields of Brazil with my brother-in-law. He hasn't reported seeing them there, but he's building hospitals and schools in pretty remote places. Why don't they go into the wards with the AIDS patients in Africa and heal them? I don't know... call me crazy, but one lady had water in the ear and she was cured in front of me. Water in the EAR? What the hell... one man and his wife couldn't have children... I don't know how that one turned out. Maybe they got a private healing. These people use more wigs and hair dye than the Spit and Curl over on Broad Street! Probably the television folks ask them to.

Now remember, this is about addiction, and if you are addicted to these men and their wives and the few female money preachers, you are in an addiction I don't know anything about. I can't argue with the Lord and his chosen few. I can't see their hearts. I admit, they know the Bible and can spit out chapter and verse. Here a couple of verses I want to share with you: Matthew 6:19-21. Try Jeremiah 23:17... again, just light reading. Try all of Revelations (especially Rev. 19:20) the Kings James Version, beginning to end. I'm not sure if it was written by the Apostle John or Stephen King. Just be careful, if you start reading it, you can't put it down. It gets down to the real nitty-gritty.

Wait, wait a minute, I am getting an anointing right this second. Something is happening here tonight. This is amazing. I have been having a problem in and around my groin. No doctor has been able to cure it. I am not sure what it is but at times it bothers me a great deal. I am getting a name, it's coming to me with an anointing, hold on a second... yes, I am getting it. It's the name Mary. Yes, that's it, Mary. Is there a Mary reading this? Wait, hold on, I am getting the name Betty or Elizabeth. I am also getting the name Sally and Joy and Wendy. That's correct, Sally and Joy and Wendy and wait, there is an anointing here happening right this minute. The name Chris and Jessie and Tasheka, and I don't know where this is coming from, but I am getting the name Tammy and is there someone out there named Candy? The name Candy is really coming through loud and clear. Wait, there are only a few more. I am getting the name Kimberly from Virginia and Kim from somewhere else. Yes, is there a Bonnie and an Amber and any ladies with the letter "A" in their name (first or last), either one. Wait, I am getting Instruction... yes, it's all clear now. We are to meet at a predetermined spot and there will be a laying on of hands to help me with my problem area and an all-night prayer session may be in order. It just came over me and if I can't question the TV money preachers and if they refuse to work their "on stage" miracles in the VA Hospital and in the poor parts of town, then they cannot question my getting an anointing and a special Instruction and Wisdom from the same place they do. Hold on, I just got the name Paula and Sherri and Teresa and Monique and Thelma. If I missed your name, please contact me and we will work something out. We want everybody anointed as fast as I can get to you.

Now, I beg you to look again around your neighborhood and your town and your community and find the sick and shut-in and helpless and those in need and consider spending your money right there where you live. You will see your few dollars at work, and you will know the person or people who are receiving your gifts. Give to the blind or the Red Cross or the American Cancer Society or the Disabled Veterans at a VA Center near you. Give to the Salvation Army; give to the Denver Children's Hospital or the St. Jude Hospital in Tennessee. Try the Arnold Palmer Children's Hospital in Florida. Try the Shiners Hospital. Then you can SEE your money working. One more time, I do not know what is in those preachers' hearts; I am not God and I can't see in their soul. If you want to buy them a new jet, have at it. Want to get them another Rolex, buy them one. Want to believe they can cure rabies, take them a sick dog and see what happens. Hell, Bruce Lee couldn't touch you with one finger and knock you out, but these people can knock down row after row after row. Annette, yes it is Annette!

Hold on a minute, I just got the anointing message for Jessie and Tina or Teena, either one. Is there a Linda reading this? I am also getting a Phyllis.

I give up, do what you want to do. Religion is a belief and a set of boundaries and a way of life and maybe an existence after death. It is not bought with cash or coin. It doesn't matter the size of the church or who is in the pulpit or behind the alter. Hairstyles won't matter and jets won't matter and expensive watches won't matter and being a fashion trendsetter won't make a bit of difference. It is a personal walk with the God of your choice, not man. I don't care how big the check you write, it can't buy a ticket to heaven.

Please pray for me, I am a sinner and will sin again. I am trying to do better but I am weak. We all are. I will pray for you.

Have you seen Jesus? Have you met God? What if on that day God is Japanese or an American Indian? If you believe the Bible, then isn't it written that God created man in his own image? Well, Aborigines are man and God created them, so isn't it possible he looks like an Aborigine? Something to think about, ain't it?

We are almost at the end of this book. Thank the Lord. It has been a real test of character and patience for me. What I thought was going to take a year has turned into four. That is the Lord or fate or life or something reminding me who is in charge. I'm not. I can control the things I can control... but have no say-so in the unexpected or little surprises that life deals us. Only one or two major events set me back on this book (maybe three), yet I couldn't quit. Don Wilson wouldn't have. I wanted you to meet some of the major players in this offering and see that they came through as rough a time as you might be going through right now and you can do it just like they did. I want to thank everybody that added one thing to this book. They probably don't think like I do and are probably going to buy up all the copies so no one will see they associated with me... don't hold them responsible for all my ranting, they are innocent.

I believe I will close with a review of the "hate chapter." The more I am around Kim, the more impressed I am with the woman she has become. She has been through the pain that the parents of the Aurora shooting victims are going through. She understands. I know her heart is with each and every one of them. Christians believe we will all see each other again someday soon. Sooner than we think. I still hate the guy that cut my dad's face and head. I really hate him. He has no idea how much. I guess I am not a good Christian. But I am a good son.

I hate bullies. They make people's lives miserable with threats and with intimidation. I love that television program "Bully Beatdown"... This is America and nobody, I mean nobody, who is minding their own business has to be threatened or yelled at or made a coward. If you are in somebody's business where you shouldn't be, well that's another subject. But just to prey on the weak is wrong on every level. I am sorta beginning to hate Jerry Springer. He makes his fortune by offering people a big visit in the city so the audience and viewers at home can laugh and make fun of them. You don't have to tune in, and the pitiful people don't have to go on there, but they don't know any better so they do. At the end of the program when all the laughter and fist fights are over, he says "can't we all just get along" and take care of each other? How very kind of

324

him. I just don't like him but he doesn't give a damn about me... he's laughing all the way to the bank. I doubt he reads this book and I thank the Lord for the remote control.

If you have been watching the news, CBS Evening News did a program where they stopped people on the street and asked them if their clothes and jewelry and shoes were made in America? It seems to me that they (or some other news) had gone to the gift shop in Washington, D.C. and found a lot of trinkets were made in China. I feel sure Diane Sawyer was the reporter who reported how much stuff we as Americans buy that is made in some other country. It was a great piece and very eye-opening. There is just one little thing. Did CBS do a survey of their offices and auditoriums and buildings to see how many Chinese and Japanese television monitors they were using? Did they look to see where the microphones came from? Where was the cable made that feeds all that tape and video to the airwaves? Did CBS do an honest review of their own backyard before they pointed out other people's foreign products? Did Mrs. Sawyer show her labels and did she show the labels from the Italian suits the executives wear up on the top floor? Wouldn't anything made in England be imported? Wouldn't any clothes from Savile Row be "not made in America"? Just wondering... Hey Diane, go through CBS and do a report on that. Ha-ha, just kidding, I know they won't do it.

In about a week I plan to fly to the Far East and get lost for a couple of weeks and not think about work or this book or anything... we will see how that turns out. I guess I should write what I think is coming to pass now just in case I don't come home. I might meet Miss. Right in Singapore!

I believe there is another conflict coming, a major conflict. I'm afraid we may have gone too far to turn back. I hope I am wrong but I don't think so. The civil conflict will be divided into about six categories. Here comes the 600-pound gorilla... act like you don't think it's real. There is going to be much more overt trouble between the races, mostly black and white but some minorities will be in there with both sides. That's what I think and because it is America, I have as much right to think that as you do not to. I cannot UN-teach what some children are being taught at whatever home they live in from birth. Some people will only live in a same race community. You know it's happening, and I know it's happening, and there is nothing to be done about it. Often time someone gets a parking ticket or a speeding ticket or a late fee or any type of correction, it's always blamed on "race, or religion" Some people have been taught to yell "race" or at the very least yell "because I'm Arabic" during any traffic stop. It doesn't happen every time, but it damn sure happens, that is the God's honest truth. We are having a Sheriff's election here in Richmond County, and everybody is smiling and shaking hands and all the black citizens sit on one side of the meet and greets and all the whites sit on the other side. I'm not talking about deputies, I mean the public. Tell me it's not so... tell me these meetings are all mixed up like a checker board, and I will tell you you're wrong. Because you are. The division and tension is so thick you can taste and smell it. What a shame. Our county commissioners are worse. Again, what a shame. By all, you know I mean most.

There is a black guy running for sheriff and a white guy running for sheriff. Whichever one gets elected, he should hire the other one as undersheriff... I have no idea what to suggest to the commissioners.

This war isn't just going to be race, forget race... it's going to have the really poor and the really rich at each other's throat. The guy who worked his ass off for 40 years and built a company and did exactly what he was supposed to has just about had it with giving a third of his efforts to people who sit on their ass all day and do nothing. They get free lunches that he/she pays for and they get a free education that he/she pays for and they get more and more and more that he/she pays for. And he/she is beginning to hate them. On the other hand, the poor say that they have nothing; they were born into poverty and can't get out. They get hungry and sick and they want the same things the guy has that worked 40 years, but they have no way to ever get it and they hate him for it. Can't they have a little something from the rich to at least get by? The only way they can make ends meet is to have more babies and more permanent injuries so they can't work and that equates to a bigger check each month, race doesn't come into it. So... include in the civil conflict the two sides from worked and have something vs. don't work because I never had the opportunity you did and never will.

There are two more groups that will be in this conflict. They are the average run-of-the-mill Americans who get up and go to work and pay their taxes and mind their business and never bother anybody. The reason they are going to get caught up in this is because of their parents and their political party and the fact they are going to be forced to pick a side. They are neither rich nor poor, they just are. But the day is coming like college football where you are going to

326

have to declare where you stand, and it's roaring toward us. Can't you hear it coming? I can. It is all based on hate. Hate is something taught and learned. Look at the Middle East. Children are taught hate at an early age and it festers for life. Look at some religions... hate is taught from the cradle to the grave and it never goes away.

Go back and read Animal Farm, one of my all-time favorites. The dogs are growing fast and their teeth are getting sharper and the other animals are fed up. I hope I am wrong, but from experience, I don't think so. Too many people have nothing and too many people have too much. Too many people hold on to the past and too many people have learned to yell race (black and white) at the drop of a hat. You know it's true, I know it's true, and it's getting worse. What a shame to see this country go up in flames, but it might. Too much greed and too many handouts have created a country of "owe me" and a country of "I don't owe you jack."

I hate you, you hate me, we hate them, they hate us, I honestly believe it gives some people an identity. Alone, these people can't function in society, but if they belong to a hate group, they find like people who accept them. Here's an idea, if you hate a group of people for whatever reason, try and speak to them tomorrow just for the hell of it. Just for no other reason but I asked you to; just say hello to someone you see or work with and find out if they are really the devil you think they are. Maybe they are but you know what, maybe they aren't and you just never gave them a chance. You hated them without knowing what they had done or who they were or anything about them. I don't hate all preachers, just the crooked ones. You can speak for yourself, but somebody has to earn my hate. I don't just give it freely or on a buffet. I do hate that guy that stabbed my dad, but I would hate him if he were a 70-year-old Eskimo grandmother from Mars.

There are some Democrats who hate Republicans and vice-versa. You don't want to know anything about the person, you just know they are not your party and that's all you need to know. They are the opposite party and you hate them. Brilliant!

I will try and close with this. Do you think when Roy was freezing to death in a Korean Prison Camp he hated any American regardless of color or political affiliation? He did not. Do you think he shared his food with South

Koreans who were fighting on his side, just like he did with the Americans? He did. Do you think when my pal Duke Dearing was running to save his fellow Marine in Vietnam that he gave a hooters damn what color the Marine was? He did not. Do you think that anybody in the life-saving business gives a damn what color or what nationality or what your level of income is? We do not. It seems to me the people advocating this war and a huge portion of the problems coming are not activists, they are agitators. You figure it out for yourself.

A friend of mine signs all his correspondence with BMA... buy more ammo. Another friend of mine owns a gun store and sales are through the roof. Not just on pistols and rifles, but on everything! Watch animals along the Atlantic coast before a rocket launch from Cape Kennedy... they begin to get nervous long before the lift off. They know something is going to happen. I can't explain it, it just is. All six sides are gearing up. How sad. We should stop before we can't.

I was so very fortunate to get to go to Washington, D.C. on several occasions. I saw some amazing things. A few of the things I know for sure are as follows: Washington swallows up whoever comes there. It's like a big snake that swallows its own tail. I believe the movie was Mr. Smith goes to Washington. You might shake a thousand hands and you might have a good, honest heart, but when you get to Washington, you either play ball with the people in power, or you go down in flames. I hear all the candidates telling us what they are going to do when they get to D.C. if we elect them... horse$#%&. They are going to do exactly what they are told if they want to get anything done, or stay there for any time.

I remember in Florida a candidate coming by Rosie's and grinning like the Cheshire cat when he was running. He chatted with me for 20 minutes, "How many employees do you have, I would really appreciate your vote, how can I help you?" He came back twice... he did get elected and when he came back the first time, he expected us to pay for his lunch (I wouldn't do it), and the second time he came he wouldn't speak to me. He got what he wanted, he got elected. He didn't need me or Rosie O'Grady's anymore.

There are two times in this life when everybody is equal: underneath the sheets and behind the curtain. If you get naked and the person with you is naked, you are equal. I don't mean physically, I mean you are both exposed and in the same bed together. Look at that person because for the next 20 minutes or hour or day or whatever time period, you and them are even. The second time is when you vote. You get one vote, the president gets one vote, the richest person in America gets one vote, and the poorest in America gets one vote. All equal. Trust me, I have seen it all my life... things change when the bottom candidate gets on top, and they change again when he or she goes back on bottom. I think that's why I think people sent to Washington vote for lifetime benefits for themselves... they know they won't be there forever, but the benefits will be.

I couldn't help but laugh recently when Cher was texting or tweeting or screeching or whatever she was doing to say she didn't care for such and such and her political choice was so and so. That carried a lot of weight with me. This is just my opinion, but the only thing she might be an expert in is 60's music and really, really interesting children. You have just as much insight on political issues as she does. You get a vote, she gets a vote. You and your opinion are every bit as important as hers or Clint Eastwoods's or Brad Pitt's or mine or anybody else's. Don't forget it.

Back in May of 2011, four young men went up to an 81-years-old man's house and the old man was shot through the living room window. According to reports, the old man was watching television that night. Excuse me, it is alleged four young men went up to a house and shot the guy through the window. One of the four has already admitted to doing it. To make a horrible story short, the three who went into the house (one stayed in the car keeping it running) robbed the 81-year-old man and took a couple of boxes from the house. Before they left, the old man was not quite dead so the shooter let him have it again. That did it, now he was dead.

According to the report, the four young men were 19, 18, 16 and 15 years old. Together, that doesn't total 70 years on this earth. But, they knew enough to shoot the 81-year-old gentleman through the window and then again as they were leaving. He couldn't identify them if he was dead. Within 40 minutes, the police had stopped a car and had a confession from one of the four. They got NOTHING for that 81-years-old man's life. Did they need more playgrounds for afterschool fun and games? Did they need more government money for clothes and cars to make them feel good about themselves? What did they need from the community to make them love each other and love all of their brothers of all races? Some people will say they were underprivileged and if they had an iPod and a decent car, they wouldn't have had to rob and kill. It's society's fault and they were all underprivileged. Bull$%#&. They were and are thugs. They live in Thugville and they graduated from Thug High with honors. Now they are on their way to Thug University... unless of course, a slick lawyer can prove it was mine and your fault and they were forced to do the crime because of us. Good luck.

Other than the terrible loss of an innocent man's life, the most horrible report from the local paper was this: Thug #1 reported he had aspirations to become a doctor or a lawyer. I could see him being a lawyer but not too sure about the doctor, unless it was a pathologist. Thug #2 was accepted to a couple of colleges and wanted to be an officer in the military. Maybe he was practicing Night Recon. Thug#3 was working for a welfare and family recreation group. Here's my question: Where was Al and Jesse? If a drunk stripper in North Carolina can get Al and Jesse and the Black Panthers to run to her rescue (incidentally, she is up on a Class C felony for stabbing her boyfriend in the chest) when she was a damn liar, where were they when this 81-year-old man died? Where were they when Roy got stabbed? And you don't think there is trouble coming? Be real quiet and listen closer, get closer, closer. We better stop and think it through before it gets too close... there is enough trouble aimed at the United States without us fighting among ourselves. Two boxers get in the ring and start hitting each other, and then one of the boxers starts hitting himself. He is going to lose. That's what America is headed for, fighting the people that hate us and fighting ourselves all at the same time. We better quit hating each other real soon.

I think I am done writing books. If I write another book, I have decided to cover one of two topics: he/she transgender people from Asia; I think the title should be: "Third and Long" or a book about "Goat Farming for the Beginner"... I'm sure I will have to do a lot of research for either of them. Nothing I wrote or think will have any effect on anybody. If you are in an addiction, just like me and Joey and Carl and everybody else, you and you alone decide how long you stay and at what price. If you decide to stay, at the very least talk to a few people about how to get out so you will always know there is a way out. You have read about a few people in this book who didn't think there was a way out. There was... they either didn't know it or chose not to take it.

330

There are classes that teach Rules for Survival. I learned these two from a U.S. Marshal a long time ago... 1) Know your enemy; and 2) Plan your escape. Better advice was never given when it comes to addiction.

A special Thank You to First Sgt. Ken Young, USMC. Ken is headed to Afghanistan in a month or two, be safe, come home, and bring each and every American home with you.

Chapter 24
John 5:5-6

John 5:5-6: When Jesus saw him lying there and learned he had been in that condition for a long time, he asked him, "Do You Want to Get Well"?

To me, that is as powerful as anything in the Bible... Do YOU WANT to get well? Do you? Some of us do... some think it's too hard, and others don't want to get well. Where are you? Where am I?

All over the world, there are people just like you and I who build our own Addictions Prison. We go out and buy the material, we may or may not read the blueprints, but somehow (and sometimes with help from our "friends"), we build a jail cell and then we step in it, we close the door, and stay there until we WANT to get well. It ain't the Roach Motel and it ain't a hotel in California. We can leave anytime we WANT to. It's our prison... we built it and we can tear it down. I figured out that we have to take the money and effort and buy a key instead of putting more bars on the window.

LUKE 23:34: At the Crucifixion, Jesus said, "Father, forgive them, for they know not what they do." I think we all know what the Crucifixion was, and I cannot imagine forgiving a group of people who would do that to me or to someone I loved. It's too much to think about. That's why we are human and not God.

You don't need preaching to and if you could see all my sins, the line would be from here to Oklahoma City. The point being, Joey, myself, and a couple of others have tried to change. We asked for forgiveness and are making an honest attempt at getting out of the Addiction Prison we each built for ourselves. It's everyday work; addiction doesn't take a day off and we can't either. As a matter of fact, I noticed addiction works overtime during the holidays. We are with friends and family, we are laughing, we are peaceful... I asked a lot of folks when did they relapse, when did they slide backwards, where were they? Most often the answer was when they were at a party or having fun with their friends, or when they were completely alone and couldn't stand being alone.

The good news is; you can be forgiven. Sometimes you have to pay a price to the people you hurt along the way, but you can be forgiven. First, I think the Lord will forgive us if we are sincere. Then I think we must forgive ourselves. That's often harder to do than you think. When we realize who we have hurt and how much, it is a pain that does not go away quickly. There is more good news, it will go away. And then we have to ask the people who we lied to and stole from and cheated and deceived for forgiveness. If they refuse, (they have that right) all we can do is live a different life and continue showing the world that we are no longer sick and we are trying to stay well.

I have a dear friend who was sick. He was sick in his addiction to drugs and paid a horrible price. Thank God, he finally realized he needed help and he got it. Years passed and he stayed clean and sober. I may have already told you this, but it's like your favorite song, it's worth repeating. One night he told me if he did "one" bump of cocaine, just one little taste, he would spend the rest of the night looking for enough dope to take him back to where he had quit years ago. We were all proud of him for being well for so many years, and he was proud of himself.

Then he slipped. He slipped and it took him about one second to be right back where he was when he stopped using years before. There are two problems here: The addiction had not stopped and we all had to either forgive him all over again or not. You may be at that very spot tonight, whether or not to forgive someone and how many times? Unfortunately, I do not have the answer. I so well remember Joey telling me the addiction doesn't quit, it keeps right on growing. It matures and gets stronger and trains and gains power. When you go back to it, it has become so much stronger than before.

Every time an addict relapses, they shorten the patients with the rest of us. One mistake, we should help them back up. Two times, really need to look at some outside help. Three times, at this point it becomes whether or not they want help and how much are you willing to suffer for them? Four times, five times, now we are at the point where we hide our money from them, we never believe what they say, and we begin to set up boundaries. We have to quit lending them money; we don't allow them into our homes or around what is valuable to us. We have to distance ourselves from them in order for us to survive. But, when they are ready to get well, I think we have to begin forgiving them. If the tables were turned, I would hope they forgave us.

Maybe you can find it in your heart to forgive me for some of the stuff in this book. I have become addicted to telling the truth, and it's becoming more and more politically incorrect. Here is some last truth. I have screwed up as much as I was capable at times. To quote another of my favorite philosophers The Blues Brothers, I've made some mistakes, had some bad breaks, now my mind don't work and my whole body aches... I have flat-out messed my life up at times.

That said, I have also cleaned up my life and will work constantly at keeping it between the ditches. So can you. We are forgiven. From this day forward we can do better. Let's don't make the same mistakes again. Let's try not to find fault with everybody else. Let's clean up our own back porch and set a good example. We just have to want it. You have character and the addiction has character, I guess it boils down to who has the most.

The End

Nobody and I mean "Nobody" is always right. That man or woman has not been born. I don't care if he or she is a Supreme Court Justice or the President or a Senator or Congressperson. I don't care if they are head of the church or on 250 television stations or get messages from God or Buddha or Muhammad or if they speak to George Washington in unknown tongues. Not me, not you, not your boss, not the CEO of anything.......nobody born had all the perfect answers.

There are however, some damn smart people. There are a lot of educated people who are absolute experts in their field. Sometimes they disagree with each other and both parties have degrees and advanced degrees and years and years of hands on training. The best examples that come to mind are Lawyers and Forensic Chemist. They all have the same evidence, they all question the same people, they all get to look at the same lab reports and yet they see completely different results. That's why 12 other good people listen and pay attention and form their opinion. Even Doctors tell you to get a second opinion.

That's where I am going with this. You have a right to your opinion. It is not for me to say or anyone else to say what is right for you. Why do you think there are a thousand types of cars on the road? Probably because everyone doesn't want to drive a 4 door, 6 cylinder, cloth seat, flat black, basic family car. Some people want a 2 door, bright red, 300 horsepower, 4 speed, European Sports car. And both people are right, they are entitled to their opinion.

Here's mine: I wish each and every teacher at that elementary school had had a pistol in his or her locked desk. Would it have saved one child, maybe. Would it have saved two or three or four children, maybe. In hind sight do you think anyone wishes at least one or two of those teachers had had a gun? Is there anyone reading this that thinks the teachers should have only tried to talk and reason the shooter out of his weapon? You are certainly entitled to your opinion as I am to mine. Remember this: the shooter didn't stop and he could not have been stopped with what was available to those teachers. He finally stopped himself. What if he hadn't?

An old cowboy named Dunaway told me "the place to have a gun when the shooting starts, is in your hand".

I am so very sorry that shooting happened. I honestly wish I could have been there locked and loaded and so many of my friends, Firefighters and Law enforcement and Military would have been with me.......to have put an early end to it all. God Bless and Keep the children and the Teachers and the Families. God bless the First Responders and hospitals for what they tried to do. God please bless them all....amen.

"What your lungs had for dinner"

It could be a picture of empty liquor or beer bottles, a picture of crumpled up candy wrappers, a picture of credit card receipts, of torn lottery tickets, or a picture of the wrong person or wrong memories, of the wrong preacher or wrong church, of fast food wrappers, a picture of porn videos, of plastic surgery, of steroids, of wardrobes, of endless lovers, of street drugs and especially prescription drugs. It could be a picture of an anchor that you assign a name to. It didn't have to be cigarette butts. It could have been any one of a thousand hooks that we swallow and then refuse to spit out...ask any fish flopping around in the boat "was that worm worth it"?

Joey, from right. Recognize any other fighters?

"Mr. Excitement" in action.

Vincent Wins Title On TKO In Third

By LOUIS SAPSIS
Herald Correspondent

ORLANDO — Emmett Atlas' reign as Southern middleweight champion ended unceremoniously Tuesday night at the Orlando Sports Stadium when he was unable to answer the bell for round four of his pulsating brawl with Joey Vincent.

The loss ended his brief reign which began last September when he upset the world's No. 1 ranked middleweight, Gene Wells.

Vincent's win didn't come easily.

Worried about a cut over his left eye, and expecting it to break open, Vincent stormed out of his corner at the opening bell and made war on Atlas at every possible moment.

Atlas fought back, meeting Vincent's clubbing blows, as the pair of gladiators smashed each other around the ring for the first two sessions.

"The guy is tough," Vincent beamed after the bout had terminated. "I hit him with everything I had in those first two rounds and he kept coming back.

"In fact, he did hurt me in the second but I was able to clear my head by just walking forward, throwing punches.

"After two rounds, I thought it couldn't get any tougher out there, but I was wrong, the third was a living hell."

In that stanza, Vincent staggered Atlas with a crushing left-right combination that spun the champion completely around.

Vincent stuns Atlas with right cross to head

Quick to seize the opportunity, Vincent was all over Atlas with a volley of lefts and rights to his head and body. But the champ refused to go down, and instead stood toe-to-toe with Vincent and exchanged bone rattling shots.

With the large crowd in near hysterics, the two battlers went after each other, taking turns. First Vincent would crash blow after blow on Atlas, only to watch the beleaguered champion roar back with his own counter attack.

Despite the pounding both men were taking, it was obvious that Vincent's superior power was taking a toll on Atlas.

By the time the bell sounded to end the most exciting round ever fought in this area, Vincent had Atlas out on his feet.

The champion was staggering around, not knowing where he was, but still trying to throw punches until the end.

Between rounds, Atlas's manager, Clarence Cook, tried to get his fighter ready for the fourth. But the champion was through, and Joey Vincent had brought the Southern title back to Florida.

The win was Joey's 25, 26 by KO, as compared to four losses and two draws.

It also brought him all the way back from the ashes Taco Perez left him on last year. In that fight, for the Southern junior middleweight title, Vincent was stopped in four rounds by the Sanford fighter.

"It has taken me 15 months and almost 20 fights, but I think I proved to everyone just who Joey Vincent is. A lot of people think I have a big mouth. And they think that I am cocky. Be that as it may, after tonight, they can think what ever they want. But they all have to admit that I can fight and when it comes to guts, I don't have to take a back seat to anyone."

Vincent's sensational win overshadowed Edgar "Mad Dog" Ross' four round KO over Texas' Rolando Garcia. But, not by much.

Ross was clearly in control of his junior middleweight title defense from the outset, but Garcia never stopped trying.

Overpowering Garcia with snapping left jabs and hooks, Ross brought Garcia down in the fourth with a solid, straight right hand.

The right had dropped Garcia in the third, but the gamester was able to get back to his feet and battle back. In the fourth, he also got up but Ross drove him back down with a series of blows to the head.

The Texan took the fatal 10 count on his back, while the crowd cheered both, his and Ross', gutty battle.

In six round action, of a card that saw every fight end in a KO, Milton Owens remained undefeated by stopping Miami's Bobby Niles in just 1:42 of the first round.

Slick Mitchell, of Brunswick, Georgia, opened the show with a KO over Zellwood's Willie Vasser in 2:06 of the fourth.

The next card will be a charity affair, with the proceeds going to the Central Florida Children's Home. It is set for Dec. 7th, and is expected to feature Vincent, Ross, Owens, Scott Clark, Frankie Santore, and a host of others. Also included in the last card of 1976 at the Sports Stadium, will be an amateur card of seven to ten important bouts.

Joey winning one of several titles…

Dianne Weeks, a Southern Beauty.

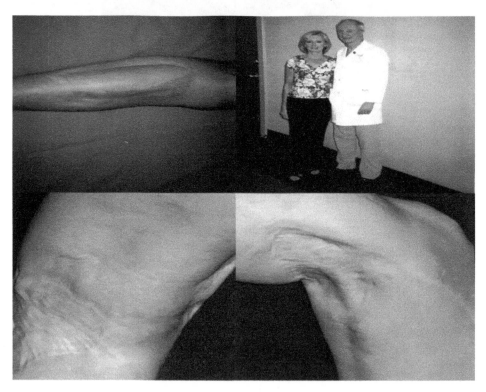

Dianne's shattered leg and Dr. Feliciano who helped save it.

Roy Broussard, 19 years old, headed to Korea.

SFC. Roy Broussard, Vietnam. A true American…

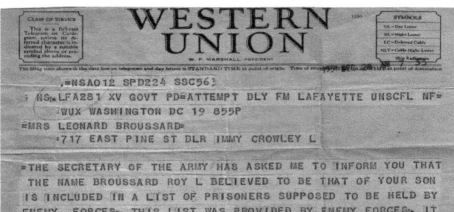

Western Union: "Bad News".

ROY L. BROUSSARD, 19, son of Mrs. Leona Broussard of 717 E. Pine street, Crowley, reported missing in action in Korea by the adjutant general of the army, was carried as injured on casualty lists Monday. Young Broussard joined the armed forces on Aug. 9, 1949 and went overseas in July of last year. His father, Leo Broussard, lives in Rayne. He has five sisters and three brothers.

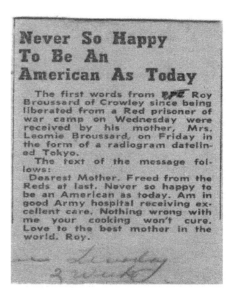

Never So Happy To Be An American As Today

The first words from Pfc Roy Broussard of Crowley since being liberated from a Red prisoner of war camp on Wednesday were received by his mother, Mrs. Leomie Broussard, on Friday in the form of a radiogram datelined Tokyo.

The text of the message follows:

Dearest Mother. Freed from the Reds at last. Never so happy to be an American as today. Am in good Army hospital receiving excellent care. Nothing wrong with me your cooking won't cure. Love to the best mother in the world. Roy.

Dec. 1950 – Aug. 1953. He finally wrote his mom that he was free.

Freed POWs Tell Of Beatings, Burnings, Death Marches And Starvation At Hands Of Reds

FREEDOM VILLAGE, Korea —Americans and South Koreans freed by the Communists today told of beatings, burnings, death marches and starvation at the hands of their Red captors—horrors which they said killed countless fellow prisoners.

Lt. Col. Thomas D. Harrison, highest ranking American officer set returned in the two-day prisoner exchange, arrived on crutches with one leg missing. He said the Communists starved him seven days, then repeatedly smothered him with a wet towel and revived him with jabs from a lighted cigarette. It was a fruitless attempt to get military information, he said.

He said he knew of "at least 60 officers who were so ill they should have been returned" last April during the exchange of disabled prisoners. He said the Reds told him he was held back "because I was a bad boy—I used my rank and eloquence to influence other prisoners."

Harrison, a 22-year-old fighter-bomber pilot from Clovis, N. M. is the second cousin of Lt. Gen. William K. Harrison, senior Allied truce negotiator. He is one of 70 Americans freed today at Panmunjom.

Today's accounts, if not as sweepingly lurid as ordeals described by sick and wounded POWs freed last April, were all the more intense and personal. A new Army censorship rule allows a liberated prisoner to tell only of atrocities he saw.

In April, the POWs told and retold horror stories which circulated in the camps.

The accounts were grimly accented by the sight of pitiful, broken wrecks of men who made up part of today's 392 returnees. Some could hardly walk. Others were terribly emaciated. One, a South Korean, was delivered dead.

Some of the returning Americans were in excellent condition. But in general, they were worse than the British, though not in as desperate shape as the South Koreans. U. S. and other airmen appeared

to be special targets of Red brutality, probably a reprisal for deadly Allied bombings and strafings, Allied officers said.

A Negro B26 co-pilot, Lt. Samuel E. Massinberg of Detroit, said he got four days of continuous torture and starvation from the North Koreans, followed by a special effort to woo him to communism "because of my race."

"I understand communism better now, I hate it more," he said. "They butted me around, they slugged me, they gave me no food for four days. When they saw I would not give them the information they wanted, they turned me over to the Chinese to fatten me up."

Massinberg's hands were frostbitten after he bailed out over Pyongyang when a Red MIG jet shot down his B26 last Jan. 11. The Reds bound them tightly, he said. "They hurt terribly all the time and I lost part of the left one."

The returning prisoners presented grim evidence that some of the thousands of missing Americans never will return.

Shung Keum Shoon, a 28-year-old emaciated South Korean, told of seeing North Korean Reds beat seven Americans so severely with rifle butts that five died within a few hours.

Cpl. Russell P. James of Auburn, Wash., told of grisly burial details in the bitter winter of 1950-51 in the notorious mining camp that prisoners called "Death Valley."

"We buried 25 to 35 men practically every day. We had no medical treatment at all and all we got to eat then was a little bit of millet every day."

Later things improved and James added, sarcastically, "Then we got beans and rice on weekdays and chicken and photographs on holidays. The photographers took pictures of us eating chicken."

With tears of emotion in his eyes, S. Sgt. Robert M. Wilkins of Detroit, an airman shot down in a B26 last January, told of being thrown into a "black hole" and

Felt Being—

(Continued From Page One) of the study of English by much reading as he could. He started a diary, said he lost interest in it, and then wryly remarked, "They would have kept it anyhow."

The type of reading allowed was that which would "poke fun" at wealthy people or the capitalists, Roy said.

He pointed out that Charles Dickens wrote humorously of the "upper classes" and so his works were allowed to be read.

The Reds have their own version of everything. Usually they simply take the opposite view of us.

Roy said that some seven or eight prisoners appeared to have gone over to the theory of Communism, but Roy described them as "persons of a narrow mind."

On June 10, 1953, the prisoners on the Yalu first heard of the proposed POW exchange. "Then," said Roy, "came that Syngman Rhee deal."

He continued, "We knew we were going home on July 27. At that time the propaganda was stepped up and we were told it was only because of the great Chinese desire for peace that the truce was brought about."

"The night before we left for Freedom Village we were told we were being released. They had to tell us then because we had to prepare our own food for the trip," Roy explained.

Roy saw no killings while in camp.

He said you could tell how the battle was going or how the truce was going by the Chinese attitude. He explained that after violating the Geneva Convention agreement at will, they suddenly began shouting "Geneva Convention, Geneva Convention" and accused the UN of violating it. Roy said the prisoners pointed out the Reds never accepted it or lived up to it before.

Roy got a real homecoming last night. As he pulled up in front of his uncle's home, relatives and neighbors almost mobbed him. Although bone-tired, the youth was highly excited and the excitement kept him going through the night. Friends and neighbors kissed him and said simply, "Oh, Roy." Obvious happiness on the faces of assembled people it unnecessary to say more.

Roy was teased and asked if he forgot how to speak French and he immediately lashed back in the French tongue. From the kitchen came a mouth-watering smell of French cooking.

Said one lady, "Roy, we have roast duck."

In the many months t h a t had passed, the youngsters grew up and changed and for a little while there had to be introductions followed by

exclamations of wonder and surprise at the passage of time.

Today, the tired young man could give no account to plans of tomorrow.

"I'm considering reenlistment, but I might run into complications with Dot on that. We'll see."

At any rate, today was holes apart from the long prison wait where each day was looked upon in the soldierly expression of "This is it."

Tomorrows, explained Roy, just didn't exist.

It wasn't the Ritz Carlton.   (Continued)

'Felt Being Torn Apart Inside"

"I felt I was being torn apart inside. I don't know how else to say it. The feeling of being free comes all of a sudden. I couldn't wait to get down from the truck. I jumped. No one can describe the feeling."

Red-eyed from long travel and lack of sleep, Pfc. Roy Broussard, repatriated prisoner of war, dragged heavily on a cigarette as he spoke these words slowly to describe his arrival at Freedom Village in Korea on his long trip home from 36 months of misery and despair in a Chinese Communist prison camp perched on the bleak waters of the Yalu River.

The youthful repatriate, still under military command, arrived in Crowley late Tuesday evening with his mother, Mrs. Leonide Broussard, and other relatives after a long auto trip from San Francisco, Calif. After a visit in Crowley he will report to the Camp hospital for further examination and orders.

Freedom was Roy's great thrill. Close on its heels came unexpected and surprise reunion with his family and fiancee in San Francisco.

As the young corporal tells it "It was at the end of the ship and as it came to dock, I was walking down and I waved back. I guess I was the first to start to tell the plank. Others waved and I waved

automatically. Then I recognized my sister, I didn't expect to see anybody there I knew. Then I saw my mother. The girl that had waved at me was Dot. When she smiled I knew who she was."

But it was Sergeant Patlow of Longview, Wash., Roy's fiancee, said the soldier, "Please tell all the people who helped my mother get to San Francisco to meet my boys I am most thankful to and their fortures indebted to them."

But before the successions of joys and happiness, there were months of grim living.

South of a geographical location known as Kunu-ri Roy was captured early one morning while the 2nd Infantry Division was battling its way to the rear from an encirclement by the enemy.

Roy's unit fought a day and a night in an effort to break the encirclement. With the enemy cutting off unit after unit from the division, the Crowley soldier found himself with a musical outfit. During the next few days he headed south, the unit kept losing men.

"The jets tried to protect us the whole time," Roy said.

"They kept up a continuous strafing of the Chinese as long as there was daylight left."

The soldier said he became so

tired during the retreat that he sought sleep in some rice stalks by his unit. When he awoke he headed for a railroad, hiding in huts along the way. He was removed from one of them, he heard firing and saw bullets kicking up the dust near him. A matter of seconds he was a prisoner of the Reds.

Roy was thoroughly searched. Anything of value was taken. Because he was wearing an Air Force parka, he was at first mistaken for an officer. But finally the Chinese understood his rank.

The soldier was marched to a valley where about 400 other Americans were being kept in captivity. According to Roy, the Reds kept circling the valley trying to pick off the Chinese and to let the men escape.

Two groups eventually wound up in the prison camp at Pukdung on the border of Manchuria.

Said Roy, "I swam to the Yalu." He continued, "It was half of first. There was a manner supply of food. We slept on hard floors. We constantly complained and put up corruption from breathing the black dust of the huts in which we lived. We had no wood for fires. The soldier of 1950 in Korea was one of the coldest on record, yet we provided for cooking fires only

and we had only two meals a day, some millet and cracked corn, a scroll bowl in the morning and at night.

In the winter of 1950, Roy went down with pneumonia. He said the Chinese provided no medical care. His only help came from soldiers of medical units who were prisoners and Roy was embittered in the praise of their efforts.

Said the soldier, "I just recovered. Before I did, I went down to about 75 pounds.

Like others, young Broussard received his share of ignominious treatment. On Pen. it he was put in a hut that he described as a prison vault with ice on the floor. He was allowed to take a single blanket with him. "It was like opening the door of a refrigerator," Roy said.

Roy's offense, according to the Chinese, was attempt to sabotage and show actions the Chinese. Everything was compulsory, according to the youth, the propaganda lectures and other activity.

He smiled and pointed out, "The food got better in 1953 when the lectures started.

Mail was sent up all the time, according to Roy. He got his first letter from home in 1952.

During his prison days, Roy about lost as much as possible, the stress

(Continued On Page 5)

Felt like he was being torn apart. (Continued, above right)

344

Crowley Prisoner Of War Released From Red Camp

ROY BROUSSARD
—Before Capture—

BROUSSARD IN POW CAMP NO. 5
—Tomorrow Now Healthier—

MRS. LEOMIE BROUSSARD
—All Is Now Well—

"Mrs. Leomie Broussard, Deliver immediately, 1016 S. Ave. J, Crowley, La. The Secretary of the Army has asked me to inform you that your son Pfc Broussard, Roy L. was returned to military control in Korea and will be returned to the United States by surface transportation at an early date. Signed, Wm. E. Bergin, Major General USA The Adjutant General of the Army."

This telegram, delivered at 8:30 a. m. today to Mrs. Broussard, meant the end of almost four years of waiting for the son she last saw on Dec. 15, 1949, his last visit at home. She cooked a good Christmas dinner for him that day, never dreaming that he would have to somehow survive long months of starvation before they met again.

Mrs. Broussard's last news of her son came direct from a fellow prisoner of war, Raymond Smith of Lake Charles, who was among the sick and wounded exchanged some time ago and who visited her on June 21. Smith reported that Roy was well and that during the past year or so, the man in the camp had fared not so badly.

In fact, Roy weighs 130 pounds, he said. Smith worked in the kitchen and whenever he could slip some food, he made certain that Roy got his share.

Pfc Roy Broussard's name was contained on the official list of prisoners of war who were transferred from the Chinese to the U.S. command last night.

Mrs. Broussard couldn't sleep last night thinking that at last her son "had a real bed to sleep in and was not worrying." "He always used to be so spoiled. Everything he wanted, I would go through everything to get it for him. He was such a sweet child. When he said 'Mama' he said everything," Mrs. Broussard said.

Wondering what he will ask for first when he comes home, Mrs. Broussard thought of his guitar. "He likes best to play his guitar, to get together with the boys and play the guitar," she said. "We have three here waiting for him."

Nothing could be sent to him except what could go in an envelope and Mrs. Broussard sent him gum, candy and cigarettes. In his last letter to his mother, dated May 19, 1953, Roy told his mother that he received more letters than anyone else in the camp.

It was the first letter in quite some time and he explained that he had been so optimistic about coming home that he hadn't written lately because he expected to "be home before my letters would have time to reach you."

The letter was typical of the others received from Roy, who was gifted at writing letters. It follows:

"I realize it has been quite some time since I have written you last. I certainly hope this has not caused any unnecessary worries.

"It was not because of illness I didn't write, the main reason was perhaps due to the stimulating effects of repatriating all sick and wounded. I was terrifically in high spirits upon hearing this wonderful news, because through this, everyone of us here began to have faith in the success of the peace negotiations, which would invariably mean reunion with the ones nearest and dearest to our hearts.

"But judging from the present news we received, the peace talks have back tracked a step, instead of advancing one, this of course has caused my morale to descend back to reality, and face life here the same as before this news was made known. To be frank, Mom, I became so optimistic that I actually was of the opinion that I would be home before my letters would have time to reach you, and this is why I didn't write, because of being over-optimistic.

"However, Mother, though my morale has been lowered once again, I have not completely lost all of it, for thanks to you, Mother, and my friends, who are devoting much time in writing me, and who help immensely to build my morale back up.

"Only a few days ago I received 40 letters and 29 the time before that. I actually think I receive all your mail. Besides the photographs, cigarettes and chewing gum. As of the present, I've received more letters and photos than anyone else in this camp.

"By the way, Mother, I have received three copies of Gentlemen's Journal the Crowley High paper. Well, I have already written the Student Council a letter for their kindness such a rare issue of reading material. But I still feel as though I should do more than this to show my gratitude, therefore, Mom, I would appreciate it very much if you or Eunice would donate something to the Council for me and I shall compensate you with the same amount upon my return home. Or shall you do as the bank, and charge me interest? Smile - - if so it is still perfectly all right.

"Tell the children, I am very pleased to receive such excellent reports about them, and that I wish very much for them to continue having this good attitude towards school, or shall I say education.

"Please tell Patsy that I've received and replied to her letter. Also, tell her to send photos of expenses. I shall repay...the only object is to keep them coming in frequently.

"Love to the entire family, Roy."

Roy went overseas on July 17, 1950 and went immediately to the battlefront. He was captured Dec. 1, 1950, and it was a long year before any definite news was received that he was still alive. On Dec. 10, 1951, Mrs. Broussard heard his name read among those who were listed as prisoners of war. Then came two letters from him, and she recognized his handwriting and had faith to believe that he was still alive.

Since then news of him has come regularly but the best news of all came today. "Roy is on his way..."

Roy is Mrs. Broussard's third oldest of her nine children. The others are Rufus Lapointe, Beaumont, Tex.; Mrs. Lovinia Haley, Port Arthur, Tex.; Mrs. Harry Lee Spell, Lake Jackson, Tex.; and Miss Eunice LeBlanc, Overton, Belle, Wilton and Betty Jean LeBlanc, of Crowley.

Roy's father is Leo Broussard of Rayne. He has three half-brothers and two half-sisters on his father's side. They are Clarence of Esther, wood, Irene and Nelson of Crowley, Malsie of Rayne and J. C. of Midland.

"Crawley Prisoner Released" "FREEDOM"

Jessica smiling, she was Alive.   A recent photo

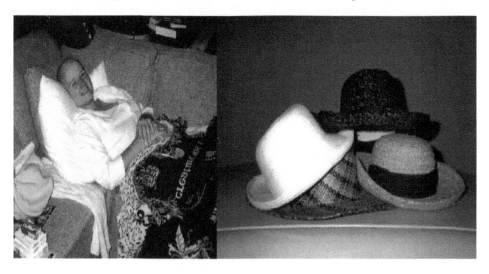

So very sick and a few of the 45 hats.

All her hair came back.

Wade Cobar with hat and cane. He is joined by several other Wounded Warriors and our host from NEX. Bill Marx

Navy Captain Jan Wynn standing on sacred ground: Mt. Suribachi, Iwo Jima.

Being sworn in as a Richmond County Deputy Marshal with Chief Deputy Teresa Russell.

Honored to be Deputy Marshal of the Year. See the black ribbons on our badges, in a few months we had lost three police officers in our area. They were the real Officers of the Year.

Nelson Reyes. I am Honored to call him my friend.

Col. Ron Reid-Daly founder of Selous Scouts.

Myself, Jim Schneeberger and seated is Willie van der Riet.

Cheryl Thomas, Johne Fletcher, some foreigner, Phee Fletcher and Tom Thomas at a Selous Scout meeting somewhere in Africa. That's all I know.

Selous Scout President Tom Thomas.

Some drunk standing on his head in a bar trying to drink a bottle of beer.

Selous Scout "Wingnuts" laughing at the idiot who tried to drink upside down!

Don Wilson's "Star Search"

My pals, Donnie Hair and World Champion Don "The Dragon" Wilson.

LIVE FIT

NYPD Detective Miguel Rivera, Roy L. Broussard and PAPD Lt. Steve Grossi. I cannot find the words to tell them how much they each mean to me.